Digital
computer
fundamentals

Digital
computer
fundamentals

SECOND EDITION

Thomas C. Bartee   *Harvard University*

McGraw-Hill Book Company

New York

St. Louis

San Francisco

Toronto

London

Sydney

Digital computer fundamentals

Preface

The purpose of this book is to present, in as clear and readable a manner as possible, the principles of modern digital computers. The only prerequisites are some knowledge of elementary algebra and electricity. Questions are included at the end of each chapter, and answers to most of the odd-numbered questions are given at the end of the book.

This is the second edition of the book. Since the digital computer industry is now the largest part of the electronics industry, in dollar volume as well as number of circuits and components used, the competition among manufacturers as well as the many sponsored projects has led to a considerable amount of research and development. As a result, new circuits and new machine organizations continually appear, and older devices and machines disappear. This has led to a substantial amount of rewriting as well as an increase in the size of the book.

In addition, and perhaps more important, this book has been widely used as a text, and as a result I have received many suggestions as to how to improve the presentation of the material from teachers using the book. I would like to express my appreciation to those who have contributed, and freely admit that any improvements are probably due to these suggestions. It is my hope that users of the book will continue to forward their suggestions. I will certainly incorporate reasonable recommendations wherever possible.

The block diagram symbols used in this book are those which have been adopted by the American Standards Association and also as Military Standards by the Armed Services. Although other systems are still in existence, these symbols are the most used at present, and their future use seems assured. Also, other systems are easily understood using these as a base. The programming language introduced is PL/I, the new language devised by IBM for all its new computers and used as well as by many other manufacturers. Most other programming languages are similar. FORTRAN and MADTRAN, for example, are almost identical in those details presented here.

The book may be divided into three major sections. The first section consists of two chapters which describe the uses of digital machines in business, industrial, and scientific organizations, ending with an introduction to computer programming. The second section of the book consists of three chapters which treat computer number systems, primarily binary and binary-coded-decimal

(Chap. 3); computer circuitry, with emphasis on transistor and diode switching circuits (Chap. 4); and the fundamentals of logical design, with an introduction to Boolean algebra and the use of block diagrams (Chap. 5).

The third section of the book consists of four chapters, each covering one of the major divisions of a digital computer. The chapters describe the arithmetic element (Chap. 6); the memory element (Chap. 7); input-output devices (Chap. 8); and the control element (Chap. 9). The basic functions performed by each section of the machine are covered, as are the characteristics of such components as magnetic cores, drums and tape, punched cards and paper tape, and other components common to the computer industry. Each section of the machine is described from both a systems and components viewpoint.

Professor W. W. Peterson has contributed improvements to both editions. I would especially like to thank Prof. Glenn Goff for his careful reading of the text for the new edition and for his many helpful suggestions, as well as Robert Carroll of Lincoln Laboratory of M.I.T. for his comments on the programming sections.

I would also like to thank the following members of the M.I.T. Lincoln Laboratory staff for their helpful criticisms during the preparation of this book. The statements are my own, but comments from the experts have been greatly appreciated. I have listed the contributors under the titles of the chapters on which they gave assistance.

Computer Operations—W. J. Canty, S. H. Dodd, R. W. Sittler, W. I. Wells, B. Widrow.
Programming—S. H. Dodd, R. W. Sittler, W. I. Wells, B. Widrow.
Number Systems—W. J. Canty, H. J. Kushner, R. W. Sittler, W. I. Wells.
Basic Logical Circuits—R. H. Baker, W. J. Canty, V. J. Sferrino, W. I. Wells.
Logical Design—C. R. Burgess, D. Keren, I. L. Lebow, F. L. McNamara, R. W. Sittler.
The Arithmetic Element—I. L. Lebow, R. C. Norris.
The Memory Element—F. L. McNamara, V. J. Sferrino, B. Widrow.
Input-Output Devices—F. L. McNamara, R. W. Sittler, B. Widrow.
The Control Element—I. L. Lebow, R. W. Sittler.

I would especially like to thank Mrs. E. M. Vadeboncoeur for her painstaking and accurate work in the preparation of both editions.

Thomas C. Bartee

Contents

5 Logical design   120

Digital computer fundamentals

1

Computer
operations

The growth of the digital computer industry scarcely requires documentation. Digital computers now route our long-distance telephone calls, process and issue the checks in our banks, schedule our trains and planes, and make our weather forecasts. The glamorous computers which direct space vehicles during flight are brothers—and not necessarily bigger brothers—to the computers which control the billing, shipping, warehousing, and writing of checks in our factories.

Having made its initial impact as an accepted worker in the areas of banking, bookkeeping, and scientific calculations, the digital computer quickly infiltrated many other areas. About one-sixth of our total yearly defense expenditures now go into the purchase of data-processing equipment. It is difficult to obtain current figures,[1] but in 1962 a little over 1.3 billion dollars of an 8-billion-dollar defense budget was allocated to computer purchases, and the expenditures in this area have exceeded 1 billion dollars each year since that time. This is only a part of the total market, however. In 1964, *Time* magazine estimated that over 650,000 people were employed in the manufacturing and selling of computers and that total machine sales were on the order of 5 billion dollars.

As might be expected, the growth of the computer industry has been attended by a shortage of skilled people at all levels. In 1964, the backlog of machines ordered but not delivered exceeded the total number of machines delivered in the period 1951 through 1960.

The computer business has also grown to occupy the largest share

[1]It is not just difficult but virtually impossible to obtain current figures on the size of the computer industry. Manufacturers guard their figures very closely until several years have passed.

of the electronics industry (communications runs second). In *Spectrum*, the official journal of the Institute of Electrical and Electronics Engineers, Leonard C. Maier of General Electric estimated that in 1963 over 1 billion signal-level active and passive components, such as transistors and resistors, were consumed by the computer industry, making it the largest user of electronics circuitry.

All estimates are that the computer industry will continue to expand. Most estimates place the yearly growth rate at about 10 to 12 percent. The Industrial Securities Committee of the Investment Bankers Committee of America estimates that in 1970 the total sales of data-processing equipment should be on the order of 20 billion dollars and the total employment in computer construction and sales should be more than 1 million people.

1 · 1   A brief history

From the time man first started using arithmetic, he has been inventing devices to aid him in handling numbers. One of the earliest and most ingenious examples of an aid to computation is the abacus. This primitive (4000 to 3000 B.C.) predecessor of modern computers consists of a rectangular frame carrying several parallel wires. Each wire supports a number of beads which are free to slide along the length of the wire. The Romans called these beads *calculi*, the plural of *calculus*, meaning pebble. This Latin root gave rise to our word "calculate." By manipulating the beads, a skillful operator can add, subtract, multiply, and divide with amazing speed. In a contest between a Japanese proponent of this ancient invention and the trained operator of a modern manually operated calculating machine, the abacus won easily. Science will have the last word, however, as the computers described in this book perform operations at least a million times faster than the best of the abacus experts.

Calculating machines, including such familiar devices as adding machines, desk calculators, and cash registers, were invented more recently. The first successful mechanical calculator was constructed by Blaise Pascal in the seventeenth century. It was completed in 1642 and authentic models are still in existence. The primary conception which this machine introduced was the mechanization of the carry. The machine consists of a series of numbered wheels or dials, each numbered from 0 to 9 and arranged to be read from left to right. When one of the dials passes from 9 to 0, a ratchet causes the wheel on its left to be moved one unit forward. The machine adds and subtracts directly, but multiplication and division are accomplished by repeated additions and subtractions.

In 1671, Leibniz constructed a calculating machine which could not only add and subtract but also multiply. Addition and subtraction were accomplished in the same manner as in Pascal's machine, but additional gears were included which enabled the machine to multiply directly.

Leibniz commented that although the device was not completely automatic, the slight effort involved in using it was certainly far better than the tedious and often erroneous procedures required in manual arithmetic. The calculator designed by Leibniz was the model for most later machines and embodied almost all of the principles now used in the design of calculators.

As business techniques and science progressed, the need for the mechanization of simple arithmetic operations increased. The amount of arithmetic done by business concerns increased vastly and became far more complex, and bookkeepers increased in number as did all types of white-collar workers. The paper work required to manage government functions efficiently also reached staggering proportions. For instance, it took so long to process the data gathered during the United States government census that the information was not available in a convenient summary form until after it had lost its timeliness.

In the fields of science and engineering, many problems were being reduced to mathematical expressions which were so complex that it took a prohibitive amount of time to perform the arithmetic necessary to evaluate them for the various sets of parameters. For example, when the mathematical formulas describing the flight of an artillery shell along a ballistics trajectory were first known with considerable accuracy, the solution of these formulas (involving many different gun-elevation angles, distances, etc.) required the services of a large staff of human computers for long periods of time. Further, the tables had to be recalculated for new types of shells and weapons. This often introduced a lag from the time weapons became available until they could be accurately used.

Fortunately, the calculating machine was progressing also. Improvements in design and construction increased the speed and the number and variety of operations which could be performed by these devices, and at the same time improved manufacturing techniques made them more readily available. The machines had been even more automatic in operation. Hand cranks were replaced by electric motors and the speed of calculation was increased. Numerous aids to the operator had been introduced, thus increasing the speed of computation and decreasing the chances of error. Various types of desk calculating machines were common, and most business arithmetic was performed by these devices.

The speed with which desk calculators may be used to solve problems is limited in one main respect: the desk calculator must be manually operated, step-by-step. No matter how ingenious the design or carefully planned the problem, each arithmetic operation which is performed must be manually initiated. The numbers to be manipulated must be inserted by the operator, and great care must be taken to avoid errors. Experience in this field indicates that a good operator with a good machine can accurately perform about five hundred operations a day. If the problems are very complex or if the operator must make many decisions, this number will decrease significantly. Since almost all of the time is taken by the operator, an increase in machine speed will have little effect on the overall speed of computation. The next step would seem to be increasing the skill of the operator rather than the speed of the machine. At any rate, it can be clearly seen that there is a definite limit to the speed which may be attained using calculators and that this limitation is due to the fact that a human being is in the system and is holding things up.

A solution to this problem was actually proposed in the nineteenth century by Charles Babbage, an English scientist and mathematician. Babbage attempted to mechanize the entire process, eliminating the operator and designing the machine so that it would perform all the necessary operations in a predetermined sequence. The machine designed by Babbage used cardboard cards with holes punched in them to introduce both instructions and the necessary data (numbers) into the machine. The machine was to perform the instructions dictated by the cards automatically, not stopping until an entire sequence of instructions had been completed. The punched cards used to control the machine had already been used to control the operation of weaving machines. Surprisingly enough, Babbage obtained some money for his project from the English government and started construction. Although he was severely limited by the technology of his time and the machine was never completed, Babbage succeeded in establishing the basic principles upon which modern computers are constructed. There is even some speculation that Babbage, if he had not run short of money, might have constructed a successful machine. Although Babbage died without realizing his dream, he had established the fundamental concepts which were used to construct machines elaborated beyond even his expectations.

1 · 2 Differences between desk calculators and computers

The basic difference between the automatic digital computer and the desk calculator is that the computer performs long sequences of computations without human intervention. The computer can also make certain logical decisions and even alter its future actions as a result of these decisions. The sequence of instructions which tells the computer how to solve a particular problem is called a *program*. The program tells the machine what to do, step by step, including all decisions which are to be made. It is apparent from this that the computer does not plan for itself, but that all planning must be done in advance. The growth of the computer industry created the need for trained personnel who do nothing but prepare the programs, or sequences of instructions, which direct the computer. The preparation of the list of instructions to the computer is called *programming*, and the personnel who perform this function are called *programmers*.

1 · 3   Application of computer to problems

Large office forces have for many years been employed in the accounting departments of business firms. The clerks employed by these businesses spend most of their time performing arithmetic computations and then entering their results into company books and on pay checks, invoices, order forms, etc. Most of the arithmetic consists of repetitious sequences of simple calculations which the clerks perform over and over on different sets of figures. Few decisions are required, as rules have usually been defined which cover almost all problems which might arise.

A typical task in a payroll office is the processing of pay checks for company employees who work at an hourly rate.[2] This job involves calculating total earnings by multiplying each employee's hourly wage rate by the number of hours worked, taking into consideration any overtime; figuring and then deducting taxes, insurance, contributions to charity, etc.; then making out the necessary check and entering a record of all figures. Figure 1 · 1 is a flow diagram of a possible procedure. Flow diagrams such as this are standard tools of business and are often used by the computing industry. Such diagrams are very useful when reducing problems to the necessary steps required and are an invaluable aid in the field of programming. The example given deliberately omits overtime rates, irregular taxes such as F.I.C.A., and other such complicating features. The procedure followed by a clerk in performing this sequence of computations might be as follows:

1   First, the clerk looks up the employee's daily work record. He adds the number of hours worked each day, obtaining the total number of hours worked during the week.

[2]It is interesting to note that 95 percent of the checks issued by the Federal government are made out by computers.

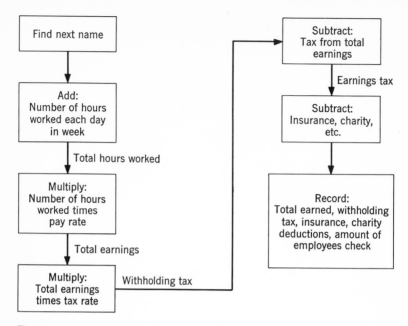

Fig. 1 · 1   Flow diagram of pay-check calculation.

2   He multiplies the total number of hours worked by the pay rate, obtaining the total earnings for the week.

3   He multiplies the total earnings by tax rate for the employee, finding the amount of withholding tax.

4   Withholding tax is subtracted from the total earnings.

5   Any regular deductions such as insurance are subtracted.

6   A record of each of the above operations is entered in the company books and a check is made out for the correct amount.

It can be seen that almost all of the above procedures can be mechanized by a machine which can be caused to add, multiply, and subtract in the correct sequence. The machine must also have the following less obvious features:

1   The ability to remember the intermediate results which have been obtained. For instance, the total amount earned must be remembered while the tax is being figured. It is also convenient to keep the employee's pay rate, rate of withholding tax, insurance rates, and the amount regularly given to charity, in the machine.

2   The ability to accept information. The records of time worked, changes in pay rates, deduction amounts, etc., must be entered into the machine.

3   The ability to print out the results obtained.

The widespread acceptance of digital computing machines in payroll offices is largely due to the simple, repetitious type of work which is normally done in such offices. Mechanization of such tasks is straightforward, although often complicated; but the additional accuracy and speed as well as the lower operating costs which electronic business machines make possible have made their use especially popular in this field. Many large companies now use special time clocks which enter the time each employee arrives and leaves by punching holes in time cards. The time cards are "read into" a computer which interprets the holes in the cards, then automatically performs all the necessary arithmetic operations and prints a record of all totals, subtotals, etc., for the company books. The computer also keeps a record of the total amount paid each week and each year to the employee, as well as a record of the various deductions, such as withholding tax. The computer can detemine the total number of hours worked by all employees during any given week, the average pay for all workers during any selected period, the number of people contributing to various charities, and practically any other type of payroll information.

1 · 4   Applications of computers in business

It can be readily seen that the use of computers is not restricted to the area of scientific calculation. In fact, far more machines are produced for business than for laboratory use. The main difference between the use of digital machines in business and their use in scientific work lies in the ratio of operations performed to total data processed. While the business machine performs only a few calculations using each datum, a great volume of data must be processed. The scientific problem generally starts with fewer data, but a great many calculations are performed using each datum. Both types of machines still fall under the heading of automatic digital computers, and either type of work may be done on all computers, although some machines may be better adapted to one or the other type of problem.

One of the first uses for the digital computer has been in the mechanizing of the more routine and clerical aspects of management. The description of the use of a computer in figuring payrolls (Sec. 1 · 3) is an example of a business application and illustrates the similarity in programming the operation of a computer and figuring out employee office procedures. First, the problem to be solved is reduced to a series of simple operations: finding the name of the next employee whose wages are to be computed, figuring how many hours he has worked, and multiplying this figure by his hourly rate of pay. After the procedure to be used has been worked out and explained to the clerk, he is provided with the necessary numerical information such as pay rates, insurance rates, etc. If the operations are further simplified, each step in Fig. 1 · 1 may be performed by a different clerk. For instance, the first clerk may find the employee's record and send it to the second clerk, who computes the total number of hours worked and presents this to the next clerk, who multiplies by the wage rate; and so on until all the operations have been performed. It may be seen from this that the breaking down of business procedures into basic steps is a very old practice indeed.

The procedure for preparing a list of instructions for a digital computer is basically the same. All the operations the computer is to perform are written in flow-diagram form (Fig. 1 · 1). The problem is then broken down into a list of instructions to the machine, which specify exactly how the solution is to be obtained. After the problem has been programmed, the list of instructions is transferred onto some medium which the machine can "read" (punched cards, for instance) and read into the machine. The machine then automatically performs the required steps. Notice that once the procedure has been established and the programmed steps have been read in, the programming is finished until a change in procedure is desired. Changes in rates, for instance, can be inserted by simply reading the new pay rates into the machine. This does not affect the procedure.

1 · 5 Scientific applications

Modern science and engineering use mathematics as a language for expressing physical laws in precise terms. The electronic computer is a valuable tool for studying the consequences of these laws. In some cases the exact procedures for solving problems have been found, but the time required to perform the necessary calculations manually has been prohibitive. In many cases it is necessary to solve the same problem many times using different sets of parameters, and the computer is especially useful for solving problems of this type. The computer is not only able to evaluate types of mathematical expressions at high speeds, but if a set of calculations is performed repeatedly on different sets of numerical values, the computer is able to compare the results and determine the optimum values which were used.

An algebraic formula is an expression of a mathematical relationship. Many of the laws of physics, electronics, chemistry, etc., are expressed in this form in which case digital computers may be used, because algebraic formulas may easily be changed to the basic steps they represent. Figure 1 · 2 is a flow diagram illustrating the steps necessary to evaluate the expression $ax^3 + bx^2 + cx + d$, given

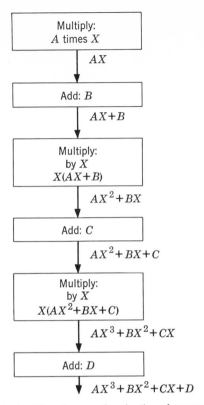

Fig. 1 · 2   Flow diagram of evaluation of expression.

numerical values for a, b, c, d, and x. The required steps are as follows:

1 Multiply a times x, yielding ax.
2 Add b, yielding $ax + b$.
3 Multiply this by x, forming $ax^2 + bx$.
4 Add c, yielding $ax^2 + bx + c$.
5 Multiply this by x: $x(ax^2 + bx + c)$ or $ax^3 + bx^2 + cx$.
6 Add d, obtaining $ax^3 + bx^2 + cx + d$.

While it would take several minutes to perform the calculations necessary to evaluate this algebraic expression for a single set of values using manually operated calculators, practically any of our larger computers could perform this series of operations several thousand times per second. While the algebraic expression shown is certainly much simpler than most formulas encountered by members of the engineering and scientific professions, the value of using a computer for certain types of problems may be readily seen.

1 · 6 The use of digital computers in control systems

The ability of digital computers to make precise calculations and decisions at high speeds has made it possible to use them as parts of control systems. A prime example of the use of a computer in a large control system may be found in the SAGE Air Defense System. In this system, data from a network of radar stations, which are used to detect the positions of all aircraft in the area, are fed via communication links into a high-speed computer. The computer stores all the incoming positional information from the radar stations, and from this calculates the future positions of the aircraft, their speed, altitude, and all other pertinent information. A number of other types of information are also relayed into the computer, including information from picket ships, AEW aircraft, Ground Observer Corps aircraft spotters, flight plans for both military and civilian aircraft, and weather information.

A single computer receives all of this information and from it calculates a composite picture of the complete air situation. The computer then generates displays on special oscilloscopes which are used by members of the military services to make tactical decisions. The computer further aids these operators by calculating the most effective use of the interceptor aircraft, anti-aircraft guns, and also anti-aircraft missiles. By means of radio links, the computer automatically guides both interceptor aircraft and missiles to their targets.

It may be seen that the computer in this system is truly a high-speed data-processing machine. The computer receives data from many sources, processes this data, and then "controls" the defending air power.

A system of this sort is called a *real-time control system* because information must be processed and decisions must be made in real time. When a computer is used to process business data or to perform regular scientific calculations, time is not as critical a factor. In real-time systems, the computer must "keep up," processing all data at high speeds in order to be effective.[3]

Other examples of real-time control applications include the use of computers in oil refineries and other manufacturing areas where the computer is used to control the manufacturing processes automatically. Digital computers are also used to guide machine tools which are performing precision-machining operations automatically. Further, both manned and unmanned space vehicles carry digital

[3]An interesting example of a real-time control system is the American Airlines SABRE computer, a 30.5-million-dollar computer which handles all reservations for the company automatically. This processing of data must be performed as reservations are made; delays cannot be tolerated.

computers which perform the necessary guidance functions, while a network of computers on the ground monitor and direct the progress of the flight.

Most real-time control systems require an important device known as an *analog-to-digital converter*. The inputs to these systems in many cases are in the form of *analog quantities* such as mechanical displacements (for instance, shaft positions) or temperatures, voltages, pressures, etc. Since the digital computer operates on digital data rather than analog data, a fundamental "language" problem arises which requires the conversion of the analog quantities into digital representations. The analog-to-digital converter does this.

The same problem occurs at the computer output, where it is often necessary to convert numerical output data from the computer into mechanical displacements or analog-type electrical signals. For instance, a "number" output from the computer might be used to rotate a shaft through the number of revolutions indicated by the output number. A device which converts digital-type information into analog quantities is called a *digital-to-analog converter*. A description of both analog-to-digital and digital-to-analog converters will be found in Chap. 8.

The basic elements of a control system using a digital computer consist of (1) the data-gathering devices which perform measurements on the external environment and, if necessary, also perform analog-to-digital conversion on the data from the system which is to be controlled; (2) the digital computer itself, which performs calculations on the data supplied and makes the necessary decisions; and, (3) the means of communication with, or control over, certain of the elements in the external environment. If no person aids the computer in its calculations or decisions, the system is considered to be fully automatic; if a human being also enters the control loop, the system is defined as semiautomatic.

1 · 7 Special-purpose and general-purpose computers

In general, there are two types of digital computers. The first is the *special-purpose digital computer*, which has the sequence of calculations it performs permanently wired in. This type of computer may be constructed more efficiently in that it can be lighter, smaller, and may consume less power, etc., than the general-purpose computer. On the other hand, since the sequence of calculations which is performed is fixed, it is necessary to change the actual construction of the machine in order to change its operation. Because of the advantages in construction, small special-purpose computers are used where such factors as weight, power consumption, etc., are critical, such as in aircraft control systems, missile guidance systems, special checkout equipment for military devices used in the field, etc.

The second type of computer is defined as a *general-purpose digital computer*. The sequence of instructions which the machine follows is generally read into this type of machine and stored in the memory of the machine. The machine can be made to follow another sequence of instructions by simply reading in the desired set of instructions. Since the sequence of operations performed by the general-purpose digital computer may be easily changed, the machine possesses great flexibility, and this is the type of machine generally used in business and for scientific computations. The general-purpose computer can process a stack of payroll cards, and then, after another program has been read into it, can perform an inventory of a company's stock. In scientific applications, a general-purpose computer can calculate the orbit of a satellite and then, after a new program has been read in, design a set of lenses for a movie projector. The general-purpose computer may be used to solve a wide variety of problems, the details of which may have been unknown when the machine was designed. The special-purpose computer is generally only capable of solving a special type of problem.

1 · 8   Time-shared computer systems

A good bit of work has been done on computer systems which are specifically designed to aid research workers, businessmen, and military decision makers. The purpose of these systems is to provide the user with a large file of information and a computational facility with which he can communicate in a direct manner. The user of the system is able to introduce his instructions to the computer by utilizing some device such as a teletype keyboard or a set of push buttons at a console. The computer responds by either printing the results or displaying them on an oscilloscope. The interaction between the user and the computer is direct; the computer is made to respond immediately. In general, the time elapsing from when a program is given to a computer to when results are obtained is called *turn-around* time. The designer of a time-shared system tries to minimize turn-around time.

These systems are used in many ways. Computer-aided design systems have consoles and displays such that a designer can work out the details of a design by using the computer to perform all calculations and to display the effects of changes in the design. The designer then attempts to optimize his design by changing the parameters and noting the effects of those changes in the design.

The businessman or military leader uses large digital systems in a manner which relies heavily on the enormous number of records which can be stored in the memory of a digital machine. Military systems called *Command and Control Systems* store the military information required by officers to make critical decisions. This information is continually updated using communications facilities. When a category of data is requested, the computer locates it in its memory and provides selected features upon request. For instance, the computer might store the types of aircraft available at each airport in the world, along with the range and ability of each aircraft to carry bombs. If aircraft were flown from one place to another, or if they were in the air or had been lost, this information would be entered into the computer. If Air Force personnel then wanted to design a bombing raid, they would ask the computer for this data and then try to use aircraft which were favorably placed and suited for their tasks. The computer could also supply data concerning the fuel and ammunition available at each place in order to further facilitate decision-making.

In the above systems, the control-processing unit or computer is liable to be *time-shared*. This means that the machine has many input and output information channels and that those channels share the main computational devices. In addition, time-shared systems generally communicate directly with people rather than processing punched-cards or other physical media. The time-shared system responds directly to the user and is shared among a number of users.

The main reason for sharing a computational facility concerns efficiency. If a number of people can use a computer system jointly, this, of course, reduces the price per user.

2

Programming

Business and scientific organizations spend much of their time processing enormous quantities of numerical data. This processing consists of performing, over and over, basic arithmetic operations, and then, at various points during the calculations, making some decisions based on the results obtained. A modern digital computer can not only perform the necessary calculations, but can also make many of the necessary decisions, performing all operations with fantastic accuracy. Various figures are given on the speeds and reliabilities of present-day machines. Large commercial machines can generally add two numbers at rates of from 500,000 to 2,000,000 additions per second, and most manufacturers would hope for at least 10^{12} operations between failures for their control processing units.

Despite their obvious data-handling abilities, it is erroneous to think that the machines offer a cure-all for any problem which may arise. Present-day machines cannot be used to solve a problem until each step of the procedure to be followed has been worked out.

A procedure for accomplishing some particular task involving calculations is often called an _algorithm_. As soon as we have developed a procedure or algorithm for our problem, we can program the problem and use a digital machine to obtain the solution, providing that the algorithm or procedure does not require too many steps. "Too many steps" is a difficult phrase to pin down, however. The logician or pure mathematician may feel that too many steps is an infinite number of steps; the businessman may feel that too many steps is simply more steps than he can afford to have performed; and the designer of a guidance system may feel that too many steps is more steps than can be performed in time to correctly change the inputs to the control system of a computer-guided space vehicle.

Fortunately, for modern computers "too many" is quite a few. An addition or a multiplication costs only a fraction of a penny, and at a rate of 500,000 operations per second the guidance system engineer is reasonably well off. As a result, the usage of modern computers has risen, is rising, and will continue to rise at a fantastic rate. The main limitations on the rate of growth of computer usage are doubtless the general lack of knowledge of how to use digital machines, the time required to program a problem, and the lack of technical personnel able to design, construct, and maintain the machines.

2 · 1   Computer programs

Decision

It has been mentioned that the machines can make simple logical decisions. Most of these decisions are based on numbers and are therefore quantitative decisions rather than qualitative ones. The sort of decision the computer might make is whether one number is larger than another or whether the result of some series of calculations is positive or negative. However, most of the decisions made by clerical workers and scientists are also based on figures. For instance, once physical phenomena have been expressed in formulas, the solutions to specific problems are expressed by means of numbers. Perhaps the following remark, made by Lord Kelvin, is relevant: "When you can measure what you are speaking about, and express it in numbers, you know something about it. But when you cannot measure it or express it in numbers, your knowledge is of a meagre and unsatisfactory kind."

The digital computer does not figure out its own solution to problems but must be told exactly how to solve any given problem, as well as how to make all decisions. As mentioned in Chap. 1, preparing a list of instructions which tells the computer how to perform its calculations is called programming. The procedure for programming a problem is generally broken into two separate steps. The first step, planning the program, consists in determining the sequence of operations required to solve the problem. This step consists, generally, in breaking the problem down into flow diagrams such as those illustrated in the preceding chapter. Once the problem has been reduced to this form it is ready to be *coded;* this is the second step. Coding consists in writing the steps outlined in the flow diagram in a special language which can be interpreted by the machine. The final coded program consists of a list of instructions to the computer written in a special format, which details the operations the computer is to perform.

2 · 2 Basic components of a digital computer

The block diagram in Fig. 2 · 1 illustrates the five major operational divisions of the electronic digital computer. Although presently available machines vary greatly in the construction details of various components, the overall system concepts remain roughly the same. It is interesting to note that present-day machines are basically designed according to the precepts which Charles Babbage proposed for his "analytic engine." Although Babbage's machine was of mechanical construction whereas present day computers are electronic, the functions which the various sections of the machines perform are much the same.

Perhaps the outstanding conceptual difference lies in the ability of the modern computer's memory to store either instructions or the data to be used in the same location. This permits more efficient use of the memory and also enables the computer to alter the instructions which comprise the program while the computer is operating.

The following are the fundamental units into which a digital computer may be divided:

1 *Input*. The input devices read the necessary data into the machine. In most general-purpose computers, the instructions which constitute the program must be read into the machine along with all the data to be used in the computations. Some of the more common input devices are punched-card and punched paper-tape readers, magnetic tape readers, and various manual input devices such as toggle switches and push buttons. Another class of input devices are the analog-to-digital converters which were described in Chap. 1.

2 *Control*. The control section of a computer sequences the operation of the computer, controlling the actions of all other units. The control circuitry interprets the instructions which comprise the program and then directs the rest of the machine in its operation.

3 *Storage*. The storage or memory section of the computer consists of

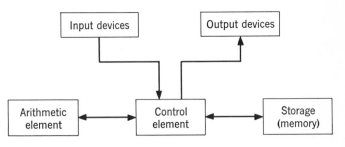

Fig. 2 · 1   Block diagram of typical digital computer.

the devices which are used to store the information which will be used during the computations. The storage section of the computer is also used to hold both intermediate and final results as the computer proceeds through the program. The principal storage devices for a computer are divided into pieces of equal size, each of which is then identified with what is called an *address* or *location in memory*. If the control unit is looking for a specific piece of information or an instruction located in the memory section, it calls for it by means of its address. Storage devices are constructed so that it is possible for control to obtain the information contained at any address. The length of time required to obtain information may vary somewhat, however, and is determined by the type of device used to store the information. Common storage devices are magnetic cores, magnetic drums, magnetic tape, magnetic disks, and various types of delay lines.

4 *Arithmetic Element.* The arithmetic elements of most of the newer computers are capable of performing the operations of addition, subtraction, division, and multiplication as well as some "logical operations" which will be described. The control unit tells the arithmetic element which of these operations to perform and then sees that the necessary numbers are supplied. The arithmetic element can be compared to the calculating machines described previously, in that the numbers to be used are inserted and it is then directed to perform the necessary operation.

5 *Output.* The output devices are used to record the results obtained by the computer and present them to the "outside world." Most output devices are directed by the control element, which also causes the necessary information to be supplied to them. Common output devices are card-punching machines, magnetic-tape machines, special electromechanical typewriters, oscilloscopes, and high-speed printing devices. There are also many unusual types of output devices such as lights, buzzers, and loudspeakers. A class of output devices found in the computers which are used in control systems are the digital-to-analog converters described in Chap. 1.

2 · 3   Construction of storage

It has been mentioned that storage is broken into a number of addresses or locations. At each of these addresses a group of digits is stored and is handled by the computer as a unit. The group of digits stored at each address in memory is generally referred to as a "word."[1]

[1]There are actually two ways of organizing a memory now in general use. One way is to store a *character* at each address (a character is a 1 or 2, an A or B, etc.). These systems are called *character addressable* systems. The second way is to store a complete

Each address in memory is assigned a number and the address is then referred to by that number. We say that address 100 contains the number 300, or that address 50 contains an instruction word. Notice that the memory stores both "number words" and "instruction words." In most machines instruction words may be stored in the same locations as number words, which makes the memory more flexible. Notice also that instruction words consist of a group of digits when stored in the computer.

The time it takes to obtain a word from a storage device is called the _access time_. The access time of the storage devices used in a machine has a profound effect on the speed of the computer. One of the factors which for a long time impeded the construction of high-speed computers was the lack of reliable storage devices with short access times. The development of storage devices (such as magnetic cores) with very short access times plus the ability to store information for an indefinite time was a great step forward.

2 · 4   Instructions

The instruction words which direct the computer are stored in the machine in numerical form. The programmer rarely writes his instructions in numerical form, however; instead, each instruction to the computer is written using a letter code to designate the operation to be performed, plus the address in memory of the number to be used in this step of the calculation.[2] Later, the alphabetical section of the instruction word is converted to numerical form by a technique which will be described. An instruction word as written by the programmer therefore consists of two parts: (1) the "operation-code" part which designates the operation (addition, subtraction, multiplication, etc.)

operand at each address (an operand can be a number such as 99059 or 573452 or perhaps the name BARNES). These systems are called _word addressable_ systems. As might be guessed, character addressable systems have smaller amounts of information at each address than word addressable systems. There are, quite naturally, pros and cons for each type of system, but almost all large systems are word addressable while most small systems are character addressable.

The programmer does not worry about this because character addressable memories deliver a complete word when an address is given, taking the characters in the word from successive addresses. We shall simplify the description by assuming that each successive address contains a word as in word addressable systems.

[2]The instructions described are typical instructions for a _single-address computer_. Computers are also constructed which use two, three, and four addresses in each computer instruction word. These computers are called _multiple-address computers_, and will be described in Chap. 9. The single-address type of instruction is very straightforward, and will be used in the illustrations in this chapter. The two-address computer is equally popular, equally easy to learn, and will be discussed later in the book. Learning two-address coding after single-address coding has been mastered is very simple indeed.

to be performed, and (2) the address of the number to be used. A typical instruction word as written by the programmer is:

ADD 535

This instruction word is divided into two main parts: first, the *operation-code* part, consisting of the letters ADD, which directs the computer to perform the arithmetic operation of addition; and second, the *address part*, which tells the computer the address in storage of the number to be used.

It is important to notice that the second section of the instruction word gives only the location (address) in storage of the number to be added. The number 535 in the instruction shown is not the actual number to be added, but only tells the computer where to find the desired number. To what is the number at address 535 added? It is to be added to the number which is already in the arithmetic element. If the arithmetic element contains zero before the instruction is executed, the arithmetic element will contain the number which is stored at address 535 after the instruction has been performed. If the arithmetic element contains the number 500 before the instruction is performed, and the number stored at address 535 is 200, the number stored in the arithmetic element after the ADD operation will be 700. In order to illustrate this principle more fully, several more instructions are explained in Table 2 · 1.

A short program which adds three numbers together using these instructions is shown in Table 2 · 2.

The program operates as follows: the control section starts with the instruction word at address 1, which clears the arithmetic element and then adds the number at address 6 into it. The instruction at address 2 adds the number at address 7 to the number already in the arithmetic element. This produces the sum of 200 + 300, or 500. The third instruction adds the contents of address 8 to this sum, giving 900 in the arithmetic element. This number is then stored in memory at location 9 in the memory. The machine is then ordered to halt. Notice that the machine is stopped before it reaches the data. This is to prevent the control element from picking up the data, for instance the number 200 which is at address 6, and trying to use it as an instruction.

There is no difference between a number and an instruction as far as storage is concerned. Both are stored in the same basic form. From this it can be seen that the instructions are generally written in a different section of the program than the data to be used. The computer progresses through the instructions and is stopped before it reaches the data. The fact that either instructions or data may be stored at all

TABLE 2·1

INSTRUCTION WORD		FUNCTION PERFORMED BY INSTRUCTION
OPERATION CODE	ADDRESS PART	
CLA	430	The arithmetic element is emptied of all previous numbers and the number at address 430 is added into it. After the instruction is performed the arithmetic element contains the number in storage at address 430. CLA is a mnemonic code for "clear and add."
ADD	530	The number located at address 530 is added to any number which may be in the arithmetic element. After the instruction, the arithmetic element contains the sum of the number it previously contained and the number in address 530.
STO	433	The number in the arithmetic element is stored at address 433. Any information previously in this address is destroyed. The number which was in the arithmetic element before the instruction was performed remains in the arithmetic element. This is generally referred to as a STORE instruction.
HLT	000	The machine is ordered to stop. The number in the arithmetic element remains.

TABLE 2·2

ADDRESS IN MEMORY	INSTRUCTION WORD		CONTENTS OF ARITHMETIC ELEMENT AFTER INSTRUCTION IS PERFORMED
	OPERATION CODE	ADDRESS PART	
1	CLA	6	200
2	ADD	7	500
3	ADD	8	900
4	STO	9	900
5	HLT	0	900

6 contains the number 200
7 contains the number 300
8 contains the number 400

addresses makes the machine more flexible. It may be seen that either a large amount of data and a few instructions, or many instructions and little data, can be used as long as the total amount of storage available is not exceeded.

2 · 5 Multiplication instruction

By adding another instruction, that of multiplication, it will be possible to write more sophisticated programs (see Table 2 · 3).

The program in Table 2 · 4 evaluates the expression $ax^3 + bx^2 + cx + d$. The actual quantities for a, b, c, d, and x are stored in memory at locations 22, 23, 24, 25, and 26, respectively. It is important to notice that the following program evaluates the expression for any values which might be read into these locations. The expression could be evaluated for any number of values for x by running the program for one value of x, then substituting the succeeding values of x into register 26 and rerunning the program for each value. In actual practice it is possible to have the program automatically repeat itself by means of special instructions. All the various desired values for x can then be stored and the equation solved for each x without stopping the computer.

It can be seen from Table 2 · 4 that very complicated algebraic functions can be evaluated using only a very few instructions. The program shown can be performed by a high-speed computer in less than $\frac{1}{1000}$ sec. The value of such speed in the solution of the more complex problems encountered in engineering and science may readily be seen. Computers are making possible engineering techniques which were previously unusable because of the high costs in time and money of lengthy computations.

2 · 6 BRANCH instructions

All the instructions explained so far have been used to perform problems in simple arithmetic. It has been pointed out, however, that the

TABLE 2 · 3

INSTRUCTION WORD		FUNCTION
OPERATION CODE	ADDRESS PART	
MUL	400	The number at address 400 is multiplied by the number already in the arithmetic element.

TABLE 2·4

ADDRESS IN MEMORY	INSTRUCTION WORD		CONTENTS OF ARITHMETIC ELEMENT AFTER INSTRUCTION IS PERFORMED
	OPERATION CODE	ADDRESS PART	
1	CLA	22	a
2	MUL	26	ax
3	ADD	23	$ax + b$
4	MUL	26	$x(ax + b)$ or $ax^2 + bx$
5	ADD	24	$ax^2 + bx + c$
6	MUL	26	$x(ax^2 + bx + c)$ or $ax^2 + bx^2 + cx$
7	ADD	25	$ax^3 + bx^2 + cx + d$
8	STO	27	$ax^3 + bx^2 + cx + d$
9	HLT	000	$ax^3 + bx^2 + cx + d$

22 contains a
23 contains b
24 contains c
25 contains d
26 contains x
27 contains 0

computer is able to repeat the same sequence of instructions without being stopped and restarted. This facility is provided by a group of instructions referred to as *branch, skip,* or *jump* instructions. These instructions tell the computer not to perform the instruction at the address following that of the instruction being performed, but to skip to some other instruction. Some branch instructions are *unconditional* in nature and cause the computer to skip regardless of what the conditions may be. Other branch instructions are *conditional* and tell the computer to skip only if certain things are true. Branch instructions enable the computer to make logical choices which alter its future actions.

Two typical instructions are shown in Table 2·5.

The short program shown in Table 2·6 illustrates several very important principles. The purpose of the program is to add all the even integers from 2 to 100. The program is of the repetitious sort where a few short orders are used to generate a program which runs for some time by repeating the same sequence of instructions. The program illustrates how the ability to branch on a negative number can be used to form a counter which will determine how many times a part of a program is repeated.

The number stored in location 39 increases by 2 each time the

TABLE 2·5

OPERATION CODE	ADDRESS PART	FUNCTION
BRA	420	This instruction tells the computer to perform the instruction at address 420 next. The computer will skip or branch from the instruction it would have performed and perform instruction 420 instead. The computer will then perform instruction 421, followed by 422, etc.
BRM	420	The computer will branch to instruction 420 only if the number in the arithmetic element is negative. If the number is positive, the computer will not branch, but will perform the instruction stored at the next address in memory. BRM is a mnemonic code for "branch on minus."

TABLE 2·6

ADDRESS	INSTRUCTION WORD		CONTENTS OF ARITHMETIC ELEMENT		
	OPERATION CODE	ADDRESS PART	1ST TIME	2D TIME	LAST TIME
1	CLA	39	0	2	98
2	ADD	41	2	4	100
3	STO	39	2	4	100
4	ADD	43	2	6	$2 + 4 + 6 + \cdots + 100$
5	STO	43	2	6	$2 + 4 + 6 + \cdots + 100$
6	CLA	40	-50	-49	-1
7	ADD	42	-49	-48	$+0$
8	STO	40	-49	-48	$+0$
9	BRM	1	-49	-48	$+0$
10	HLT	000			

39 contains 000
40 contains -50
41 contains 2
42 contains 1
43 contains 0

program runs through. The total of these numbers is stored in address 43 which, after the program has halted, contains the total of all the numbers which have been in location 39. The number stored at address 40 decreases in magnitude by 1 each time the program runs through, until the number stored at 40 is no longer negative. When the program "falls through" the BRANCH-WHEN-MINUS (BRM) instruction, it then performs the next instruction in sequence, which is a "HALT instruction." Zero is considered to be a positive number, although this varies with different machines. Notice that the first section of the program will cycle a number of times equal to the negative number stored in register 40. A simulated counter is formed by the -50 stored at address 40, the 1 stored in location 41, and the instructions at addresses 6 through 9. Any sequence of instructions which precedes a counter of this sort will be run through the number of times determined by the counter. This is an especially useful device for iterative schemes when the number of iterations required is known.

2 · 7   Reading the program into the computer

After the programmer has written the list of instructions which the computer is to perform, another step must be taken before the written program can be read into the machine. This consists in recording the program in some medium, such as punched cards or punched paper tape, which the computer's input devices can read. If the input medium is perforated paper tape, the written program will be given to an operator of a paper-tape punching machine. The tape punching machine has a keyboard resembling a typewriter which contains both alphabetic and numeric characters. A long strip of paper tape is fed through the punching section of the machine as the operator of the machine operates the keyboard. Each time the operator depresses a key of the keyboard, several holes are punched into the paper tape. The holes are coded so that a different combination of holes is punched into the tape for each key which is depressed. The operator of the tape punching machine types the program just as a secretary types a letter. The result is a strip of paper tape which has been perforated with coded groups of holes.

A paper-tape reader connected to the digital computer is used to read this tape into the computer. The paper-tape reader "senses" the holes perforated into the tape and delivers the locations of these holes in the tape to the computer in the form of electrical signals. The computer then stores this information. A description of paper-tape readers, punches, and the way the paper tape is coded will be presented in Chap. 8.

The preceding description of the steps in preparing a program should make it apparent that it is not economical to use a large digital computer to perform very simple sequences of calculations which need be performed only once or twice. The computer is valuable when very repetitious sets of calculations must be performed.

Consider the payroll accounting procedure described in Chap. 1. Once a program has been written which will calculate the weekly gross earnings, taxes, deductions, etc., for the employees of a large manufacturer, the same program can be used to compute each of thousands of employees' checks. If a combined clock and card-punching device is used to punch the time an employee enters a factory and the time he leaves into a time card which also records, in punched form, an identifying number for the employee, the entire operation can be made automatic. The time cards can then be "read" by the computer which will compute the amount of time worked, total weekly earnings, etc., and will actually print the paycheck, and then record in printed form all the data required by the bookkeeping system.

2 · 8   Programming systems

The preceding discussion showed the basic procedure for writing a program and introducing it into the computer. There are, however, various types of programming languages which greatly facilitate the actual writing of programs. One of the first things the programming profession discovered was that the greatest aid to programming was the computer itself; it was found to be capable of translating written programs from a language which was straightforward and natural for the programmer into computer or machine language.

As a result, programs were written whose purpose was to read other programs written in a language natural for the programmer and translate them into the machine's language. The program systems now in use are primarily of two types: _assemblers_ and _compilers._ The assembler and the compiler are intended for the same basic purpose; each is a program designed to read a program written in a programming language and translate it into a machine language. The assembler or compiler is read into the machine first, and is then followed by the program to be translated. After translation, the assembler or compiler stores the machine language program on punched cards or on magnetic or paper tape, so that it can be performed when desired.

The purpose of this procedure is to enable the programmer to write the operations he wants the computer to perform in a manner which is simpler than machine language. The language in which the programmer may write is called a *programming language*, and a program written in such a language is called a *source program*. The translated program in machine language is called an *object program*.

To return to the subject of the translator programs, the assembly program differs from the compiler program in that its language closely resembles machine language, because each instruction to the computer in assembly language is translated into a single computer word. In compiler systems, a single instruction to the computer may be converted into many computer words.

2·9 Assembly languages

Each instruction to the computer in an artificial programming language is called a *statement*. The basic characteristic which most distinguishes an assembly language is that each statement is translated by the assembly program into a single machine instruction word.[3] As a result, an assembly language somewhat resembles machine language. The facilities offered the programmer are substantial, however, and generally include the following:

1 *Mnemonic Operation Codes.* The programmer can write his instructions to the computer using letters instead of binary numbers and the letters which designate a given operation are arranged into a mnemonic code which conveys the "sense" of the instruction. In our preceding example of coding, the mnemonic codes ADD, MUL, CLA, etc., were used. The assembler would translate these mnemonic codes into the correct machine binary or binary-coded-decimal numbers and "package" these into the instruction words comprising the object program.

2 *Symbolic Referencing of Storage Addresses.* One of the greatest facilities offered the programmer is the ability to name the different pieces of data used in his program and to have the assembler automatically assign addresses to each name.

For instance, if we wish to evaluate the algebraic expression $y = ax^3 + bx^2 + cx + d$ as in Sec. 2·5, the program can appear as follows in Table 2·7.

Notice that the address of the first instruction was simply given a name FST consisting of three letters and that no further addresses in memory were specified. If we tell the assembler that FST = 1, the assembler then will see that the instructions are placed in memory as in the program in Sec. 2·5. Notice also that the operands were simply given the variable names X, A, B, C, and D as in the equation,

---

[3]This is not, of course, strictly the case (sometimes a single statement may be translated into several words) but is generally true.

TABLE 2·7

ADDRESS IN MEMORY	INSTRUCTION WORD	
	OPERATION	OPERAND
FST	CLA	A
	MUL	X
	ADD	B
	MUL	X
	ADD	C
	MUL	X
	ADD	D
	STO	Y
	HLT	

instead of assigning addresses in memory to them. The assembly program will assign addresses to these names of variables, and if it assigns A to 22, B to 23, C to 24, etc., the final program will look as in Sec. 2·5.

The assembler will also see that the actual arithmetic values for X, A, B, C, and D are placed in the correct locations in memory when the data are read into the computer.

3 *Convenient Data Representation.* This simply means that the programmer can write his input data as, for instance, decimal numbers or letters, or perhaps in some form specific to his problem, and that the assembly program will convert the data from this form into the form required for machine computation.

4 *Program Listings.* An important feature of most assemblers is their ability to print for the programmer a listing of the source program and also a listing of the object program, which is in machine language. A study of these listings will greatly help the programmer in finding any errors he has made in writing the program and also in modifying the program when this is required.

5 *Error Detection.* An assembly program will also notify the programmer if he has made an error in the usage of the assembly language. For example, the programmer may use the same variable name, for instance X, twice and then give X two different values, or he may write illegal operation codes, etc. This sort of diagnosis of a program's errors is very useful during the checking out of a new program.

Assemblers provide many other facilities which help the programmer, such as the ability to use programs which have already been written as part of a new program and the ability to use routines from these programs as part of a new program. Often, programmers have

TABLE 2 · 8

ADDRESS	INSTRUCTION WORDS		COMMENTS
	OPERATION	OPERAND	
A	DEC	0	
B	DEC	− 50	
C	DEC	2	
D	DEC	1	
E	DEC	0	
N	CLA	A	last value of integer
	ADD	C	
	STO	A	stores sum for next time
	ADD	E	
	STO	E	
	CLA	B	
	ADD	D	
	STO	B	
	BRM	N	
	HLT		

a set of different programs which they will run together in different combinations. This is made possible by simply specifying to the assembler the variable names in the different programs which are to be the same variable, the entry and exit points for the programs, etc. This means that programs written in an assembly language can be linked together in various ways.

Let us consider the short program in Table 2 · 6 which sums the even integers from 0 to 100. This will illustrate the use of symbolic names for addresses when a branch instruction is used. The assembly language program is shown in Table 2 · 8.

Notice that the values of the variables were specified before the program was begun; the DEC's indicate the values given for A, B, C, D, and E are in decimal. This enables the assembler to locate the variables in the memory and assign values to them.[4] Also, note that the transfer instruction BRM was to the symbolic address N.

If the assembler was told to start the program at address 1 in the memory, conversion into object or machine language would make it look similar to the one in Sec. 2 · 6, provided the assembler decided to store A, B, C, D, and E in locations 39 through 43. Also, the operation codes of CLA, MUL, etc., would be converted to numerical or machine form, if this were necessary.

[4]In a sense, the operation code DEC says "assign the decimal value in the operational column to the variable name in the address column."

2 · 10   Compiler languages

The most advanced type of programming languages are the compiler languages. These are the simplest languages to use for most problems and are also the simplest to learn. Compiler languages reveal very little about the digital machines on which they are run, however. The designer of the compiler language generally concentrates on specifying a programming language which is simple enough for the casual user of a digital computer and yet which has enough facilities to make the language and its associated compiler valuable to professional programmers. In fact, many compiler languages are almost completely computer-independent, and programs written in one of these languages may be run on any computer which has this type of compiler in its program library.

Certain compiler languages have been very successful and have found extremely wide usage in the computer industry. The most famous compiler language is FORTRAN, which is the earliest of the languages and has been regularly updated. A program written in FORTRAN can be run on most commercial computers which have a memory size large enough to accommodate a FORTRAN compiler, because most manufacturers will prepare a FORTRAN compiler for their computer.

There are a number of other languages in active use. ALGOL, a compiler language which was designed for international use, is widely used in describing algorithms in technical journals and has had moderate success in actual practice; COBOL is a language especially for business systems; MAD and several other languages have been developed by universities for educational purposes; FORMAC does symbolic manipulation; JOVIAL is a language for real-time systems, etc. About all that can be said is that there is no truly universal programming language but that there are several good languages. Fortunately, there is no staggering difference in these languages from a conceptual viewpoint, and when one of the languages has been learned well, learning another presents no great problem.

A compiler language which was originally developed for the IBM 360 series of computers is called Programming Language One (abbreviated PL/I). Some of the features of this language will suffice for illustrating the general appearance of compiler languages. PL/I has been chosen because of its simplicity for algebraic equations and because of the very elementary format for reading in data and printing results. Also, PL/I at this level looks almost like FORTRAN except that we need not worry about mixing real variables with integer variables, nor about format statements for printing or reading, provided we are willing to use the standard PL/I format.

2 · 11   A short introduction to PL/I

As has been mentioned, the distinguishing feature of compilers and their programming languages is that a single statement which the programmer writes may be converted by the compiler into a number of machine language instructions. Instructions to the computer of this type are often called macro-instructions. In PL/I, for instance, a single statement to the computer can generate quite a number of instructions in object or machine language. As a result, the language is not particularly dependent on the structure of the computer on which the program is run, and the following programs may be run on any computer with a PL/I compiler.

The PL/I compiler is written in machine language, of course, and a PL/I program is ultimately run in machine language. For this reason, knowledge of the machine and its organization can be of great use to those writing and checking out programs. Further, for the systems programmers (those who maintain, modify, and prepare the compilers, assemblers, load programs, etc.) a knowledge of the machine on which the program is operated is indispensable. The fact that compilers are backed up by an army of technical personnel, from systems programmers through design and maintenance engineers, technicians and computer operators, is often overlooked by the user of the machine whose program is miraculously debugged and operated by professionals in the computer field. Like most electronic devices, digital computers are not as independent and self-supporting as they may appear to casual users.

Thus forewarned, let us examine the structure of PL/I in a little detail, leaving a more complete exposition to one of the references at the end of this chapter.

The first thing to be learned in writing statements for most compilers is the use of the $=$ symbol. This is treated somewhat as a command to the computer, for when we write $Y = A + B$, what is meant is "replace the current value of Y with that of $A + B$." So therefore, if we write

A = 50;

B = 20;

Y = A + B;

END;

we find that after this is run, A will be equal to 50, B to 20, and Y to 70. Notice that each statement is followed by a semicolon. As a further example, we can increase, decrease, or otherwise change the current value of Y by adding or subtracting from it. Thus,

Y = 30;

A = 40;

Y = Y + A;

END;

After these four instructions are operated, Y will have the value of 70; that is, the location in memory which has been used to store Y will have the value 70 in it. Notice that the statements above took the form of algebraic equations. Here is one further example:

Y = 20;

Z = 50;

W = Y + Z;

M = W − 30;

END;

After this is run, W will have the value 70 and M the value 40.

In PL/I, the addition symbol is the familiar + and the subtraction symbol is the usual −, but multiplication is indicated by an asterisk (∗), and exponentiation (raising to a power) by two asterisks. Thus, A ∗ B means "multiply A by B" and A ∗∗ B means A^B or "raise A to the Bth power." Therefore, the program statements

A = 20;

B = 30;

C = A ∗ B;

END;

give a value of 600 for C, and the program

A = 20;

B = 2;

C = A ∗∗ B;

END;

gives a value of 400 to C.

Division is indicated by a / symbol. Thus

A = 20;
B = 2;
Y = 20/2;
END;

will place the value 10 in the location in memory delegated to Y.

Let us examine one simple way to form a loop in the program, that is, to repeat a sequence of instructions until we desire to stop. Here are two PL/I statements:

LOOP. DO WHILE X LE Y;

and

END LOOP;

The first of these says "do the following set of statements up to the END LOOP, while X is less than or equal to Y." Or, in other words, "repeat the following instructions until Y is greater than X." If we write the following statements

T = 0;
M = 4;
N = 2;
P = 6;
LOOP. DO WHILE N LE M;
S = P * N;
T = T + S;
N = N + 1;
END LOOP;
Y = T * 2;
END;

then the statements between the LOOP and END LOOP will be repeated until N is greater than M. Since N starts with the value 2 (and a 1 is added each time) while M starts with the value 4, N will take the values 2, 3, 4, 5. But, when N equals 5, it will be greater than M and the program will proceed with the instruction $Y = T * 2$; and then END. The loop statements will therefore be repeated three times. The first time, S will equal P times N or 12, T will be equal to $0 + S$ or 12, and N will then be increased from 2 to 3. The second time, S will equal P times N or 6 times 3 which is 18, T will be equal to $12 + 18$ or 30, and N will be increased to 4. The third and last time through the loop, S will equal 6 times 4 or 24, T will take the value $30 + 24$ or 54, and N will be increased to 5. N will then be greater than M, and the END LOOP statement will be operated. T, which has the value 54, will then be multiplied by 2 giving 108 and the program will stop with Y equal to 108.

Let us examine two other features. In order to read data we simply write

READ (X, Y, Z);

and this will tell the compiler to read the value of X, Y, and Z from cards and continue with the values read as the current values of X, Y, and Z. We must therefore supply values of X, Y, and Z on punched cards. The advantage of this is that we can change the values of X, Y, and Z by simply replacing our data cards with cards containing new values. If we write

READ (X, Y, Z);

M = X + (Y * Z);

END;

and attach cards with the values $X = 20$, $Y = 30$, and $Z = 2$, we shall have $M = 80$. If we change our data cards to read $X = 5$, $Y = 3$, and $Z = 4$, we shall then have $M = 17$ after we run the program.

In order to print out data, we write the statement

WRITE (X, Y, Z, A);

and the computer will print out the current values of X, Y, Z, and A.

It should be noted that the READ and WRITE statements assume that the programmer will be satisfied with the standard format for the input data and print statements. Assuming that this is the case, we can write the following program which will first evaluate the equation $y = ax^3 + bx^2 + cx + d$ for values of a, b, d, and x which are read in on data cards or tape and for $c = 1$. If the value of y for these particular values is greater than 2,000, the program will print the value of y as calculated and also the value $c = 1$. If, however, y is less than or equal to 2,000, the program will calculate the smallest positive integer which when substituted into c will make $ax^3 + bx^2 + cx + d$ greater than 2,000. The program will then print this value of c and the value of $ax^3 + bx^2 + cx + d$ associated with the value of c.

```
READ (A, B, D, X);

    C = 0;

    Y = 0;

LOOP. DO WHILE Y LE 2000;

    C = C + 1;

    Y = A * X ** 3 + B * X ** 2 + C * X + D;

END LOOP;

PRINT (C, Y);

END;
```

We have only touched on the power of this language. It is not possible in a short exposition to do more than show several statements and give a general idea of how such a language operates. Nevertheless, a clever programmer could do quite a lot with the limited vocabulary we have introduced.[5]

One thing which should become apparent from this brief introduction is that once the statement types and details of the language are learned, the job of programming a given problem is greatly facilitated. As a result, the majority of programs today are written in some compiler language.

QUESTIONS

1 Draw a flow diagram for the program in Sec. 2 · 6.

2 Draw a flow chart showing how to find the largest number in a set of five numbers stored at locations 20, 21, 22, 23, and 24 in memory.

3 Values for X, Y, and Z are stored at memory addresses 40, 41, and 42, respectively. Using the instructions for the generalized single-address computer described in Secs. 2 · 4 through 2 · 6 of this chapter,

[5]Given a few more statement types, subscripted or array variables, and a few well-chosen functions, most engineers would have enough of a language to satisfy their needs.

write a program which will form the sum $X + Y + Z$ and store it at memory address 43.

4 Given that values for X, Y, and Z are stored in locations 20, 21, and 22, respectively, use the instructions for the computer given in Secs. $2 \cdot 4$ through $2 \cdot 6$ to write a program which will form $X^2 + Y^2 + Z^2$ and store this at memory address 40.

5 A value for X is stored at address 40; write a program which will form X^3 and store it at address 41 using the assembly language in Secs. $2 \cdot 4$ through $2 \cdot 6$.

6 Write a program that will store $X^5 + X$ in register 40, using the assembly language in Secs. $2 \cdot 4$ through $2 \cdot 6$, given that X is in register 20. Use less than 20 instructions. Now rewrite this program using the assembly language in Sec. $2 \cdot 9$.

7 Values for X and Y are stored at addresses 30 and 31. Write a program which will store the larger of the two values at address 40 using the assembly language in Secs. $2 \cdot 4$ through $2 \cdot 6$.

8 Given three different numbers, determine whether they are in ascending or descending order. Draw a flow chart for the problem, and write a program using the assembly language in Secs. $2 \cdot 4$ through $2 \cdot 6$. Assume that the numbers are stored in memory locations 30, 31, and 32.

9 A value for X is stored at address 40. Write a program which will store X^9 at address 45, using less than 10 instruction words.

10 Write a program for each of the following:

   a. Using the assembly language described in Secs. $2 \cdot 4$ through $2 \cdot 6$, write a program which will branch to location 300 if the number stored in memory register 25 is greater than the number stored in register 26, and which will transfer or branch to location 400 if the number at address 26 is equal to or greater than the number at address 25.

   b. Write a program in both the assembly language in Secs. $2 \cdot 4$ through $2 \cdot 6$ and the compiler language in Sec. $2 \cdot 11$ which will produce the value $X - Y$ or X, whichever is larger. Store this value in location 200 for the assembly program and assign the variable B to this value for the program written in the compiler language. For the assembly program, assume that X is in location 100 and Y in 101.

   c. Calculate the largest of the three numbers A, B, and C and assign the largest of the numbers to the variable X, using the assembly language in Sec. $2 \cdot 9$ to write the program.

   d. Using the compiler language in Sec. $2 \cdot 11$, write a program which will determine which of $X - Y$ or $Y - X$ is positive or equal to 0 and which will print the value of this positive number 0, assigning the variable Z to this number.

11 Modify the program in Sec. 2 · 6 so that it will sum all the odd numbers from 1 through 99.

12 We have 30 numbers stored in successive registers in our memory, starting at location 300. Write a program which will convert any negative numbers in the 30 to positive form. That is, write a program which will take the 30 numbers, convert each number to its positive value without changing its magnitude, and restore it in the same location. Use assembly language.

13 Write a program using the assembly language in Secs. 2 · 4 to 2 · 6 which will rearrange five numbers stored in addresses 300 through 304 so that they are in descending order (for example, 10, 3, 0, −5, −7).

14 In a given statement, the PL/I language, like FORTRAN and ALGOL, first performs exponentiation or raising to a power, then multiplication and division, and then addition and subtraction. Within this hierarchy, statements are evaluated from left to right. Thus, the statement $A = ((B/C) - (D * E))/(C ** D)$ can be written as $A = (B/C - D * E)/(C ** D)$. The following are four more examples of the way in which the compiler evaluates arithmetic statements:

a. $A^B + C \cdot D + E/F$ can be written $A ** B + C * D + E/F$.

b. $(A \cdot B \cdot C)E^F + (G/H)$ can be written $A * B * C * E ** F + G/H$.

c. $\dfrac{A \cdot B \cdot C}{D \cdot E}$ must be written $(A * B * C)/(D * E)$.

d. $A \cdot B + (C/D) + EF$ is written $A * B + C/D + E * F$.

Find the values of X in the following statements if $A = 5$, $B = 2$, $C = 20$, and $D = 15$:

a. $X = A ** B + C$ b. $X = A * C ** B$

c. $X = C + D * B + A$ d. $X = C + D ** B/A + A$

15 Using the compiler language in Sec. 2 · 11, assume we have read in values for the variables X, Y, and Z. Assign the largest of these values to the variable A, the second largest to the variable B, and the third largest to the variable C. For instance, if X is read in as 29, Y as 31, and Z as 23, after the program operates we would like the value $A = 33$, $B = 29$, and $C = 21$.

16 Write PL/I statements which correspond to the following algebraic formulas written in conventional mathematical notation:

a. a^c/b^d b. $a^2 + b^2 + cd$ c. $(a/b) + (c/d)^e$ d. $(a \cdot b)^c + \dfrac{bd}{e}$

17 There are a class of statements in PL/I which are called *control statements*. These statements make it possible to iterate many times through a given set of instructions, providing indexing facilities during these iterations. The general form of the most important one

of these statements, which is the DO statement, is DO N I $= M_1, M_2$. Here N is the statement number or location of some executable statement, I is a simple variable, and M_1 and M_2 are either constants or non-array variables. A typical DO statement might therefore appear as DO 30 I $= 1, 25$. This statement in a program will cause the instructions or statements following the DO statement up to statement 30 to be repeated with the variable I equal to 1 through 25. That is, the loop from the DO statement to statement 30 in the program is repeated 25 times, the first time with the variable I equal to 1, the second time with the variable I equal to 2, the third time with the variable I equal to 3, etc., until I $= 25$. This time the program will pass through statement 30 to the next statement. If we therefore write:

> X $= 2$
> B(1) $= 5$
> B(2) $= 6$
> B(3) $= 7$
> B(4) $= 8$
> DO 19 I $= 1, 4$
> A(I) $=$ B(I) $+ 6$
> 19 X $= X^2$

After this program has been run, A(1) will equal 11, A(2) will equal 12, A(3) will equal 13, and A(4) will equal 14, while X $= 65,536$.

Using the DO statement in PL/I, write a program which will rearrange a set of 20 numbers which are stored in successive registers. These variables are A(1) through A(20), where each value is assumed to be positive. Assign these values to a set of variables B(1) through B(20) so that B(1) is equal to the smallest of the values of A, B(2) is equal to the second smallest of the values of A, and finally B(20) is equal to the largest value of the A variables.

18 In PL/I it is possible to write mathematical statements with subscripted variables, which are called array variables. That is, if we have a set of variables x_1, x_2, x_3, and x_4, we can write these as in PL/I as X(1), X(2), X(3), and X(4). Notice that the parentheses do not indicate multiplication, but rather the fact that the variable is an array variable or a subscripted variable. Now, if we write in a program X(1), whether this indicates X(1) or X(2) or X(3) or X(4), for instance, depends upon the value of the variable I at that particular time. What are the values of X in each of the following statements, if A(1) $= 3$, A(2) $= 4$, A(3) $= 5$, and I $= 1$:

a. X $=$ A(1) $+$ A(2)
b. Y $=$ A(2) $**$ A(1) $+$ A(3)
c. X $=$ A(I) $+$ A(2) $*$ A(3)
d. Y $=$ A(I $+ 2$) $+$ A(I)

19 Using the DO statement explained in Question 18, write a program which will examine and form an average of the values of a set of variables A(1) through A(10), where A(1) through A(10) are assumed to be already stored in the memory of the computer when the program begins. Call this average of the 10 values the *mean* of these values, and give a variable named M this value when the program has operated.

3

Number

systems

It is India that gave us the ingenious method of expressing all numbers by means of ten symbols, each symbol receiving a value of position as well as an absolute value; a profound and important idea which appears so simple to us now that we ignore its true merit.

MARQUIS DE LAPLACE

As a mathematician, Laplace could well appreciate the decimal number system. He was fully aware of the centuries of hard mental effort and sheer good luck which had gone into the development of the number system we use, and was in a position to appreciate its advantages. Our present number system provides modern mathematicians and scientists with a great advantage over those of previous civilizations and is an important factor in our rapid advancement.

Since hands are the most convenient tools nature has provided, man has always tended to use them in his counting. It is both natural and fortunate that our number system is based on the number of digits we possess. It was quite some time after man learned to count, however, that he attempted to represent numbers graphically. The earliest numerals which have been found consist of either vertical or horizontal marks. Our 1 is an example of this sort of symbol and it is interesting to note that the symbol for 2 consists of two horizontal marks with a connecting line, and 3 consists of three horizontal lines with connections. Roman numerals are good examples of lines used as the basis for numerals.

The decimal system for counting has been so widely adopted throughout our present civilization that we rarely consider the possibilities of other number systems. Nevertheless, it is not reasonable to expect a system based on the number of fingers we possess to be the most efficient number system for machine construction. The fact is that a little-used but very simple system, the binary number system, has proved the most natural and efficient system for machine use.

3 · 1   The decimal system

Our present system of numbers has 10 separate symbols: 0, 1, 2, 3, . . . , 9, which are called Arabic numerals. We would be forced to stop at 9 or to invent more symbols if it were not for the use of *positional notation*. An example of earlier types of notation can be found in Roman numerals, which are essentially additive: III = I + I + I, XXV = X + X + V. New symbols (X, C, M, etc.) were used as the numbers increased in value. Thus V rather than IIIII = 5. The only importance of position in Roman numerals lies in whether a symbol precedes or follows another symbol (IV = 4, while VI = 6). The clumsiness of this system can easily be seen if we try to multiply XII by XIV. Calculating with Roman numerals was so difficult that early mathematicians were forced to perform arithmetic operations almost entirely on abaci or counting boards, translating their results back into Roman-number form. Pencil and paper computations are unbelievably intricate and difficult in such systems. In fact, the ability to perform such operations as addition and multiplication was considered a great accomplishment in earlier civilizations.

The great beauty and simplicity of our number system can now be seen. It is only necessary to learn the 10 basic numerals and the *positional notation system* in order to count to any desired figure. After memorizing the addition and multiplication tables and learning a few simple rules, it is possible to perform all arithmetic operations. Notice the simplicity of multiplying 12 × 14 using the present system:

$$
\begin{array}{r}
1\,4 \\
1\,2 \\
\hline
2\,8 \\
1\,4 \\
\hline
1\,6\,8
\end{array}
$$

The actual meaning of the number 168 can be seen more clearly if we notice that it is spoken as "one hundred and sixty-eight." Basically, the number is a contraction of $(1 \times 100) + (6 \times 10) + 8$. The important point is that the value of each digit is determined by its position. The 2 in 2000 has a different value than the 2 in 20. We show this verbally by saying "two thousand" and "twenty." Different verbal representations have been invented for numbers from 10 to 20 (eleven, twelve . . .), but from 20 upward we break only at powers of 10 (hundreds, thousands, millions, billions). Written numbers are always contracted, however, and only the basic 10 numerals are used regardless of the size of the integer written. The general rule for representing numbers in the decimal system using positional notation is as follows: $a_1 10^{n-1} + a_2 10^{n-2} + \cdots + a_n$ . . . is expressed as $a_1 a_2 \ldots a_n$, where n is the number of digits to the left of the decimal point.

The *base* or *radix* of a number system is defined as the number of different digits which can occur in each position in the number system. The decimal number system has a base or radix of 10. This means that the system has 10 different digits $(0, 1, 2, \ldots, 9)$ any one of which may be used in each position in a number. History records the use of several other number systems. The quinary system, which has 5 for its base, was prevalent among Eskimos and North American Indians. Examples of the duo-decimal system (base 12) may be seen in clocks, inches and feet, and in dozens or grosses.

3 · 2   The binary system

A seventeenth century German mathematician, Gottfried Wilhelm von Leibniz, was an advocate of the binary number system which has 2 for a base, using only the symbols 0 and 1. If it seems strange for such an eminent mathematician to advocate such a simple number system, it should be noted that he was also a philosopher. Leibniz's reasons for advocating the binary system seem to have been mystical. He felt there was great beauty in the analogy between zero, representing the void, and one, representing the Deity. The binary system is actually used by some African tribes, but it should be added that these tribes cannot count beyond six.

Regardless of how good Leibniz's reasons for advocating it were, the binary system has become very popular in the last decade. Present-day digital computers are constructed to operate in binary or binary-coded number systems, and present indications are that future machines will also be constructed to operate in these systems.

The basic elements in early computers were relays and switches. The operation of a switch or relay can be seen to be essentially binary in nature. That is, the switch is either on (1) or off (0). The principal circuit elements in more modern computers are transistors similar to those used in radios and television sets. The desire for reliability led designers to use these devices so that they were essentially in one of two states, fully conducting or nonconducting. A simple analogy may be made between this type of circuit and an electric light. At any given time the light (or transistor) is either on (conducting) or off (not conducting). Even after a bulb is old and weak, it is generally easy to tell if it is on or off. The same sort of thing may be seen in radios. As a radio ages the volume generally decreases and we compensate by turning the volume control up. Even when the radio becomes very weak, however, it is still possible to tell easily whether it is on or off.

Because of the large number of electronic parts used in computers, it is highly desirable to utilize them in such a manner that slight changes in their characteristics will not affect their performance. The best way of accomplishing this seems to be by using circuits which are basically *bistable* (having two possible states).

3 · 3   Counting in the binary system

The same type of positional notation is used in the binary number system as in the decimal system. Table 3 · 1 lists the first 20 binary numbers.

TABLE 3 · 1

DECIMAL		BINARY	DECIMAL		BINARY
1	=	1	11	=	1011
2	=	10	12	=	1100
3	=	11	13	=	1101
4	=	100	14	=	1110
5	=	101	15	=	1111
6	=	110	16	=	10000
7	=	111	17	=	10001
8	=	1000	18	=	10010
9	=	1001	19	=	10011
10	=	1010	20	=	10100

While the same positional notation system is used, the decimal system uses powers of 10, and the binary system powers of 2. As was previously explained, the number 125 actually means $(1 \times 10^2) + (2 \times 10^1) + (5 \times 10^0)$. In the binary system, the same number (125) is represented as 1111101, meaning $(1 \times 2^6) + (1 \times 2^5) + (1 \times 2^4) + (1 \times 2^3) + (1 \times 2^2) + (0 \times 2^1) + (1 \times 2^0)$.

To express the value of a binary number therefore, $a_1 2^{n-1} + a_2 2^{n-2} + \cdots + a_n$ is represented as $a_1 a_2 \ldots a_n$ where a is either 1 or 0, and n is the number of digits to the left of the binary (radix) point.

The following examples illustrates the conversion of binary numbers to the decimal system:

$$101 = (1 \times 2^{3-1}) + (0 \times 2^{3-2}) + (1 \times 2^{3-3}) = (1 \times 2^2)$$
$$+ (0 \times 2^1) + (1 \times 2^0) = 4 + 1 = 5$$
$$1001 = (1 \times 2^{4-1}) + (0 \times 2^{4-2}) + (0 \times 2^{4-3}) + (1 \times 2^{4-4})$$
$$= (1 \times 2^3) + (0 \times 2^2) + (0 \times 2^1) + (1 \times 2^0) = 8 + 1 = 9$$

$$11.011 = (1 \times 2^{2-1}) + (1 \times 2^{2-2}) + (0 \times 2^{2-3})$$
$$+ (1 \times 2^{2-4}) + (1 \times 2^{2-5}) = (1 \times 2^1) + (1 \times 2^0)$$
$$+ (0 \times 2^{-1}) + (1 \times 2^{-2}) + (1 \times 2^{-3})$$
$$= 2 + 1 + \tfrac{1}{4} + \tfrac{1}{8} = 3\tfrac{3}{8}$$

Notice that fractional numbers, or what are generally called decimal fractions, are formed in the same general way as in the decimal system. Just as

$$0.123 = (1 \times 10^{-1}) + (2 \times 10^{-2}) + (3 \times 10^{-3})$$

in the decimal system,

$$0.101 = (1 \times 2^{-1}) + (0 \times 2^{-2}) + (1 \times 2^{-3})$$

in the binary system.

3 · 4 Binary addition and subtraction

Binary addition is performed in the same manner as decimal addition. Actually, binary arithmetic is much simpler to learn, as the complete table for binary addition is as follows:

$$0 + 0 = 0$$
$$0 + 1 = 1$$
$$1 + 1 = 0 \text{ plus a carry-over of 1}$$

"Carry-overs" are performed in the same manner as in decimal arithmetic. Since 1 is the largest digit in the binary system, any sum greater than 1 requires that a digit be carried over. For instance, 100 plus 100 binary requires the addition of the two ones in the third position to the left, with a carry-over. Since $1 + 1 = 0$ plus a carry-over of 1, the sum of 100 and 100 is 1000. Here are three more examples of binary addition:

DECIMAL	BINARY	DECIMAL	BINARY	DECIMAL	BINARY
5	1 0 1	1 5	1 1 1 1	3¼	1 1 . 0 1
6	1 1 0	2 0	1 0 1 0 0	5¾	1 0 1 . 1 1
1 1	1 0 1 1	3 5	1 0 0 0 1 1	9	1 0 0 1 . 0 0

Subtraction is the inverse operation of addition. In order to subtract it is necessary to establish a procedure for subtracting a larger from a smaller digit. The only case in which this occurs using binary numbers is when 1 is subtracted from 0. The remainder is 1, but it is necessary to borrow 1 from the next column to the left. This is the binary subtraction table:

$$0 - 0 = 0$$
$$1 - 0 = 1$$
$$1 - 1 = 0$$
$$0 - 1 = 1 \text{ with a borrow of } 1$$

A few examples will make the procedure for binary subtraction clear.

DECIMAL	BINARY	DECIMAL	BINARY	DECIMAL	BINARY
9	1 0 0 1	1 6	1 0 0 0 0	6¼	1 1 0 . 0 1
− 5	− 1 0 1	− 3	− 1 1	− 4½	− 1 0 0 . 1
4	1 0 0	1 3	1 1 0 1	1¾	1 . 1 1

3 · 5 Binary multiplication and division

The table for binary multiplication is very short, with only four entries instead of the 100 necessary for decimal multiplication. The binary multiplication table is:

$$0 \times 0 = 0$$
$$1 \times 0 = 0$$
$$0 \times 1 = 0$$
$$1 \times 1 = 1$$

The following three examples of binary multiplication illustrate the simplicity of each operation. It is only necessary to copy the multiplicand if the digit in the multiplier is 1, and to copy all 0's if the digit in the multiplier is a 0. The ease with which each step of the operation is performed is apparent.

DECIMAL	BINARY	DECIMAL	BINARY	DECIMAL	BINARY
1 2	1 1 0 0	1 0 2	1 1 0 0 1 1 0	1 . 2 5	1 . 0 1
× 1 0	× 1 0 1 0	× 8	× 1 0 0 0	× 2 . 5	× 1 0 . 1
1 2 0	0 0 0 0	8 1 6	1 1 0 0 1 1 0 0 0 0	6 2 5	1 0 1
	1 1 0 0			2 5 0	1 0 1 0
	0 0 0 0			3 . 1 2 5	1 1 . 0 0 1
	1 1 0 0				
	1 1 1 1 0 0 0				

Binary division is again very simple. As in the decimal system (or in any other) division by zero is meaningless. The complete table is:

$$0 \div 1 = 0$$
$$1 \div 1 = 1$$

Here are two examples of division:

DECIMAL	BINARY

```
      5                  1 0 1
  5) 2 5          1 0 1) 1 1 0 0 1
                        1 0 1
                        1 0 1
                        1 0 1
```

DECIMAL	BINARY

```
      2 . 4 1 6 ...                  1 0 . 0 1 1 0 1 0 1 0 1 ...
  1 2) 2 9 . 0 0 0 0          1 1 0 0) 1 1 1 0 1 . 0 0
      2 4                              1 1 0 0
      5 0                              1 0 1 0 0
      4 8                              1 1 0 0
      2 0                              1 0 0 0 0
      1 2                              1 1 0 0
      8 0                              1 0 0 0 0
      7 2                              1 1 0 0
      8                                . . . . .
```

Converting the quotient obtained in the second example from binary to decimal would proceed as follows:

$$
\begin{aligned}
10.0110101 = 1 \times 2^1 &= 2.0 \\
0 \times 2^0 &= 0.0 \\
0 \times 2^{-1} &= 0.0 \\
1 \times 2^{-2} &= 0.25 \\
1 \times 2^{-3} &= 0.125 \\
0 \times 2^{-4} &= 0.0 \\
1 \times 2^{-5} &= 0.03125 \\
0 \times 2^{-6} &= 0.0 \\
1 \times 2^{-7} &= 0.0078125 \\
0 \times 2^{-8} &= 0.0 \\
1 \times 2^{-9} &= \underline{0.001953125} \\
&\ 2.416015625
\end{aligned}
$$

Therefore 10.0110101 binary equals approximately 2.416 decimal.

3·6 Converting decimal numbers to binary

There are several methods for converting a decimal number to a binary number. The first and most obvious method is simply to subtract the powers of 2 from the decimal number until nothing remains. The highest power of 2 is subtracted first, then the second highest, etc. In order to convert the decimal integer 25 into the binary number system, first the highest power of 2 which can be subtracted from 25 is found. This is $2^4 = 16$. Then $25 - 16 = 9$. The highest power of 2 which can be subtracted from 9 is 2^3 or 8. The remainder after subtraction is 1 or 2^0. The binary representation for 25 is therefore 11001.

This is a tedious and laborious method for converting numbers. It is convenient for small numbers when it can be performed mentally, but is rarely used for larger numbers. Instead, the decimal number is repeatedly divided by 2, and the remainder after each division is used to indicate the coefficients of the binary number to be formed. Notice that the binary number derived is written from the bottom up.

$$125 \div 2 = 62 + \text{remainder of } 1$$
$$62 \div 2 = 31 + \text{remainder of } 0$$
$$31 \div 2 = 15 + \text{remainder of } 1$$
$$15 \div 2 = 7 \ + \text{remainder of } 1$$
$$7 \div 2 = 3 \ + \text{remainder of } 1$$
$$3 \div 2 = 1 \ + \text{remainder of } 1$$
$$1 \div 2 = 0 \ + \text{remainder of } 1$$

The binary representation of 125 is therefore 1111101. Checking this result gives the following:

$$1 \times 2^6 = \quad 6\,4$$
$$1 \times 2^5 = \quad 3\,2$$
$$1 \times 2^4 = \quad 1\,6$$
$$1 \times 2^3 = \quad\quad 8$$
$$1 \times 2^2 = \quad\quad 4$$
$$0 \times 2^1 = \quad\quad 0$$
$$1 \times 2^0 = \quad\underline{\quad 1}$$
$$1\,2\,5$$

This method will not work for mixed numbers. If similar methods are to be used, it is necessary to first divide the number into its whole and fractional parts and then use the technique just described. That is, 102.247 would be divided into 102 and 0.247 and the binary representation for each part found and then the two parts added together.

The conversion of decimal fractions to binary fractions may be accomplished using several techniques. Again the most obvious method is to subtract the highest negative power of 2 which may be subtracted from the decimal fraction. The next highest negative power of 2 is then subtracted from the remainder of the first subtraction, and this process is continued until there is no remainder, or to the desired precision.

$$0.875 - (1 \times 2^{-1}) = 0.875 - 0.5 = 0.375$$
$$0.375 - (1 \times 2^{-2}) = 0.375 - 0.25 = 0.125$$
$$0.125 - (1 \times 2^{-3}) = 0.125 - 0.125 = 0$$

Therefore 0.875 decimal is represented by 0.111 binary. A much simpler method for longer fractions consists of repeatedly "doubling" the decimal fraction. If a 1 appears to the left of the decimal point after a multiplication by 2 is performed, a 1 is added to the right of the binary fraction being formed. If after a multiplication by 2, a 0 remains to the left of the decimal point of the decimal number, a 0 is added to the right of the binary number. The following example illustrates the use of this technique in converting 0.4375 decimal to the binary system:

	BINARY REPRESENTATION
$2 \times 0.4375 = 0.8750$	0.0
$2 \times 0.875 = 1.750$	0.01
$2 \times 0.75 = 1.50$	0.011
$2 \times 0.5 = 1.0$	0.0111

The binary representation of 0.4375 is therefore 0.0111.

3 · 7 Representation of binary numbers

The processing of information in an electronic digital computer is performed by switching and storing electric signals. With computers operating in the binary system, it is necessary for the signals to represent only one of two values: that is, each signal must represent either a 0 or a 1. It is possible, of course, to use two signal lines for this purpose, and a signal on one line would indicate a 0 and a signal on the other line a 1. It may be seen that there is redundancy in this technique as the signal on either line is sufficient to determine the value of the binary digit.

A method for representing a binary digit on a single line by means of d-c levels is illustrated in Fig. 3 · 1a. This technique uses a negative d-c voltage to represent a 0 and a positive d-c voltage to represent a 1.

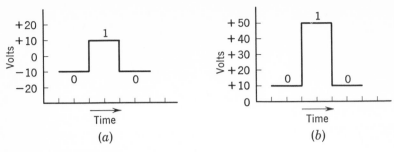

Fig. 3·1   Binary-digit representation in d-c system.

In the illustration, a − 10 volt dc signal is used to represent a 0 and a + 10 volt d-c signal to represent a 1. Any two d-c voltage levels could be chosen, however. A − 50 volt signal could represent a 0 and a + 10 volt signal a 1.

The actual voltages used to represent the binary signals are generally chosen to meet the requirements of the circuits used to transmit and receive the signals. Two positive signals, a + 10 volt dc signal used to represent a 0 and a + 40 volt dc signal used to represent a 1, are illustrated in Fig. 3 · 1b. In all the instances so far, the 1 signal has been relatively positive with respect to the 0 signal. This convention could, of course, be reversed and relatively negative signals used to represent 1's and relatively positive signals to represent 0's. In general, the designer tries to make the signal levels representing 0's and 1's consistent throughout the machine. This simplifies both design and servicing of the machine. It is sometimes necessary, however, to change the meanings of signals in various parts of the machine. These changes in the meaning of the basic signals used must be clearly notated in order to facilitate the maintenance of the machine and also to facilitate changes in the design of the machine.

3 · 8   Representation of binary numbers using pulses

Binary digits can be transmitted by means of a-c as well as d-c signals. The signals used are often signals of very short duration called pulses. Figure 3 · 2a illustrates a system where a positive pulse with a peak amplitude of + 20 volts is used to represent a 1 and a pulse of − 20 volts is used to represent a 0. The signal line remains at ground or 0 volts until a signal is transmitted, and afterward returns to the same zero potential.

Another more common technique is illustrated in Fig. 3 · 2b. A 1 is represented by a pulse with an amplitude of + 20 volts and a 0 by the absence of a pulse. The pulses used may be quite short in duration

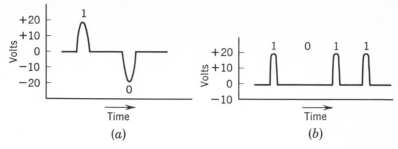

Fig. 3 · 2   Binary-digit representation in a-c system.

(0.1 μsec has been used in several machines). The shapes of the pulses used are generally standardized throughout a machine. Specifications for a given machine will generally include the maximum and minimum acceptable amplitude, the minimum and maximum pulse widths, and the amount of "overshoot," that is, the amount by which the pulse passes the d-c level in one or both directions. Figure 3 · 3 defines some of the important measurements which may be used to specify the limits on pulse shapes.

There are many other ways in which binary values are represented by electric signals in computers. Sometimes sinusoidal a-c signals are used. In this case a given signal in the machine can be compared with a reference source to determine whether it represents a 0 or a 1. If the signal is, for instance, in phase with the reference source, it may represent a 0, and if out of phase, a 1. Sometimes the presence of a sinusoidal a-c signal may represent a 1 and the absence of a signal a 0.

Machines have been constructed which use only the d-c-level technique for the representation of binary digits. Other machines use only a-c signals. There is a tendency at present to use both types of signals in the same machine. In order to differentiate between the two types of signals, a convention will be used (Fig. 3 · 4) in the block diagrams in this book. D-c signals are indicated by means of a hollow diamond on the end of the signal line in a drawing, and a solid arrow will be used to indicate a pulse-type signal.

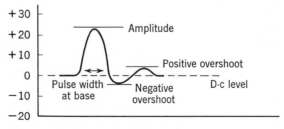

Fig. 3 · 3   Pulse parameter designations.

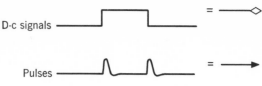

D-c signals $=$ ──────◇

Pulses $=$ ──────→

Fig. 3·4   Pulse and d-c signal symbols.

3·9   Parallel and serial transmission

Several methods of representing a single binary digit have been illustrated, but it is generally necessary to transmit complete binary numbers consisting of several binary bits. An obvious method of doing this, and a frequently used one, is to transmit each of the binary digits (bits) comprising the number on a separate line. This is called *parallel transmission*. Figure 3·5 illustrates a 4-bit binary number being transmitted over four parallel lines. In a system like this, each line is assigned a different weight. The blocks labeled *a*, *b*, *c*, and *d* transmit the binary number 1010; pulses indicating 1's are present on lines *a* and *c*, which have the weights 2^3 and 2^1, while lines *b* and *d*, with weights 2^2 and 2^0, contain no signals, indicating 0's.

The other method of transmitting signals is called *serial transmission* and is also illustrated in Fig. 3·5. When this technique is used, the signals representing the digits of a number are transmitted in sequence over a single line, generally starting with the signal representing the least significant bit of the number. It is apparent that some sort of timing is necessary for the receiving element to distinguish several 0's or 1's which follow each other in a sequence. This could be resolved by always using negative pulses for the 0's and positive pulses for the 1's and returning the line to zero potential between the pulses. A more common technique utilizes timing pulses

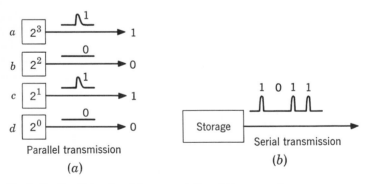

Fig. 3·5   Parallel and serial representation of binary numbers.

(about which more will be said later) which effectively tell the receiving element when to look for each bit.

3 · 10   Negative numbers

A standard convention adopted for writing negative numbers consists of placing a "sign symbol" before a number which is negative. For instance, negative 39 is written as -39. If -39 is to be added to $+70$, we write

$$+70 + (-39) = 31$$

When a negative number is subtracted from a positive number, we write $+70 - (-39) = +70 + 39 = 109$. The rules for handling negative numbers are well known and will not be repeated here, but since negative numbers comprise an important part of our number system, the techniques used to represent negative numbers in digital machines will be described.

In binary machines, numbers are represented by a set of binary storage devices, each of which represents one binary digit. In a set of five switches, any number from 00000 to 11111 may be represented by the switches. For instance, we may define a switch with its contacts closed as representing a 1, and a switch with open contacts as representing a 0. If we desire to increase the total range of numbers which we can represent so that it will include the negative numbers from 00000 to -11111, another bit (or switch) will be required. We then treat this bit as a *sign bit* and place it before the magnitude of the number to be represented.

Generally, the convention is adopted that when the sign bit is a 0 the number represented is positive, and when the sign bit is a 1, the number is negative. If the previous situation where five switches are used to store the magnitude of a number is extended so that both positive and negative numbers may be stored, a sixth switch will be required. When the contacts of this switch are open, the number will be a positive number equal to the magnitude of the number stored in the other five switches, and if the switch for the sign bit is closed, the number represented by the six switches will be a negative number with a magnitude determined by the other five switches. An example is shown in Fig. 3 · 6.

Sets of storage devices which represent a number or are handled as an entity are referred to as *registers*. We then write that register A contains $+12$ and register B contains $+22$. In writing a number, the sign bit is set apart from the magnitude of the number by means of a radix, in this case a binary point, so that 0.0111 represents positive

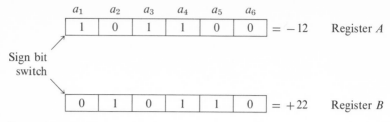

Fig. 3·6 Example of net negative number representation.

0111 or 7 decimal and 1.0111 represents −0111 or negative 7 decimal. If the computer handles numbers in a binary-coded-decimal system, a sign bit will still be used. For instance, −1099 may be stored as 1.1099 and +989 as 0.989.

The confusion which arises from the separating of the sign bit from the magnitude of the number with a radix (binary or decimal) point is compensated for when negative numbers are handled in what is known as the "complemented form," as we shall see in the following section. It should be emphasized that a symbol other than the "period" radix point could be used, such as a hyphen or a star. Then −1011 (negative 11 decimal) could be written 1-1011 or 1 * 1011, and +1100 as 0-1100 or 0 * 1100. There is no particular objection to these conventions, but the use of a period (radix point) to separate the sign bit from the magnitude is fairly well established and will be adhered to in this text.

3·11   The use of complements to represent negative numbers

The convention of using a sign bit to indicate whether a stored number is negative or positive has been described. The magnitude of the number stored is not always represented in normal form, however, but quite often negative numbers are stored in "complemented form." By using this technique, a machine can be made to both add and subtract using only circuitry for adding. The actual circuitry involved will be described in Chaps. 4 and 6.

There are two basic types of complements which are useful in the binary and also the decimal number systems. In the decimal system the two types are referred to as the 10's complement and the 9's complement. A machine will generally use only one of these systems; that is, a machine expressing numbers in a binary-coded-decimal system will use either the 9's complement system or the 10's complement system throughout the machine.

The 10's complement of any number may be formed by subtracting each digit of the number from 9 and then adding 1 to the least significant digit of the number thus formed. For instance, the 10's complement of 87 is 13, and the 10's complement of 23 is 77. Subtraction may be performed by simply adding the 10's complement of the subtrahend to the minuend, and discarding the final carry, if any. For instance:

NORMAL SUBTRACTION   10'S COMPLEMENT SUBTRACTION

$$
\begin{array}{r} 8\,9 \\ -\ 2\,3 \\ \hline 6\,6 \end{array}
\qquad
\begin{array}{r} 8\,9 \\ -\ 2\,3 \end{array} =
\begin{array}{r} 8\,9 \\ +\ 7\,7 \\ \hline 1\ \ 6\,6 \end{array}
$$

└→ the carry is dropped

$$
\begin{array}{r} 9\,8 \\ -\ 8\,7 \\ \hline 1\,1 \end{array}
\qquad
\begin{array}{r} 9\,8 \\ -\ 8\,7 \end{array} =
\begin{array}{r} 9\,8 \\ +\ 1\,3 \\ \hline 1\ \ 1\,1 \end{array}
$$

└→ the carry is dropped

The 9's complement of a decimal number is formed by subtracting each digit of the number from 9. For instance, the 9's complement of 23 is 76, and the 9's complement of 87 is 12. When subtraction is performed using the 9's complement, the complement of the subtrahend is added as before, but any carry generated must be added to the rightmost digit of the result.

NORMAL SUBTRACTION   9'S COMPLEMENT SUBTRACTION

$$
\begin{array}{r} 8\,9 \\ -\ 2\,3 \\ \hline 6\,6 \end{array}
\qquad
\begin{array}{r} 8\,9 \\ -\ 2\,3 \end{array} =
\begin{array}{r} 8\,9 \\ 7\,6 \\ \hline 1\ \ 6\,5 \\ \longrightarrow 1 \\ \hline 6\,6 \end{array}
$$

$$
\begin{array}{r} 9\,8 \\ -\ 8\,7 \\ \hline 1\,1 \end{array}
\qquad
\begin{array}{r} 9\,8 \\ -\ 8\,7 \end{array} =
\begin{array}{r} 9\,8 \\ 1\,2 \\ \hline 1\ \ 1\,0 \\ \longrightarrow 1 \\ \hline 1\,1 \end{array}
$$

The rules for handling signs during the subtraction process and for handling all combinations of positive and negative numbers will be explained in Chap. 6. If this seems, at first, to be an unwieldy technique, it should be noted that the majority of machines now being constructed subtract using a complemented number.

3 · 12   Complements in other number systems

There are two types of complements for each number system. Since only binary and binary-coded-decimal machines are now being constructed in quantity, only these number systems will be explained in any detail. The two types of complements and the rules for obtaining them are:

1   *True Complement.* This is formed by subtracting each digit of the number from the radix-minus-one of the number system and then adding 1 to the least significant digit of the number formed. The true complement of a number in the decimal system is referred to as the 10's complement and in the binary system as the 2's complement.

2   *Radix-minus-one Complement.* The radix-minus-one is 9 for the decimal system and 1 for the binary system. The complement in each system is formed by subtracting each digit of the number from the radix-minus-one. For instance, the radix-minus-one complement of decimal 72 is 27.

3 · 13   Binary-number complements

According to the rule in the previous section, the 2's complement of a binary number is formed by simply subtracting each digit (bit) of the number from the radix-minus-one and adding a 1 to the least significant bit. Since the radix value in the binary number system is 2, each bit of the binary number is subtracted from 1. The application of this rule is actually very simple; every 1 in the number is changed to a 0 and every 0 to a 1. A 1 is then added to the least significant bit of the number formed. For instance, the 2's complement of 10110 is 01010, and the 2's complement of 11010 is 00110. Subtraction using the 2's complement system involves forming the 2's complement of the subtrahend and then adding this "true complement" to the minuend. For instance:

$$
\begin{array}{r} 1\,1\,0\,1\,1 \\ -\,1\,0\,1\,0\,0 \\ \hline 0\,0\,1\,1\,1 \end{array} =
\begin{array}{r} 1\,1\,0\,1\,1 \\ +\,0\,1\,1\,0\,0 \\ \hline \llcorner\!1\ \ 0\,0\,1\,1\,1 \end{array}
\quad \text{and} \quad
\begin{array}{r} 1\,1\,1\,0\,0 \\ -\,0\,0\,1\,0\,0 \\ \hline 1\,1\,0\,0\,0 \end{array} =
\begin{array}{r} 1\,1\,1\,0\,0 \\ 1\,1\,1\,0\,0 \\ \hline \llcorner\!1\ \ 1\,1\,0\,0\,0 \end{array}
$$

└────→the carry is dropped   └────→dropped

Subtraction using the 1's complement system is also straightforward. The 1's complement of a binary number is formed by changing each 1 in the number to a 0 and each 0 in the number to a 1. For instance, the 1's complement of 10111 is 01000, and the 1's complement of 11000 is 00111.

When subtraction is performed in the 1's complement system, any end-around carry is added to the least significant bit. For instance:

$$\begin{array}{r} 1\,1\,0\,0\,1 \\ -\,1\,0\,1\,1\,0 \\ \hline 0\,0\,0\,1\,1 \end{array} = \begin{array}{r} 1\,1\,0\,0\,1 \\ +\,0\,1\,0\,0\,1 \\ \hline 1\quad 0\,0\,0\,1\,0 \\ \hline \llcorner\!\!\longrightarrow 1 \\ \hline 0\,0\,0\,1\,1 \end{array} \quad \text{and} \quad \begin{array}{r} 1\,1\,1\,1\,0 \\ -\,0\,1\,1\,0\,1 \\ \hline 1\,0\,0\,0\,1 \end{array} = \begin{array}{r} 1\,1\,1\,1\,0 \\ 1\,0\,0\,1\,0 \\ \hline 1\,0\,0\,0\,0 \\ \hline \llcorner\!\!\longrightarrow 1 \\ \hline 1\,0\,0\,0\,1 \end{array}$$

3·14 Binary-coded-decimal number representation

Since most of the electronic circuit elements used to construct digital computers are inherently binary in operation, the binary number system is the most natural number system for a computer. Also, computers constructed using the binary number system require a smaller amount of circuitry and are therefore more efficient than machines operating in other number systems. On the other hand, the decimal system has been used for a long time and there is a natural reaction to performing calculations in a binary number system. Also, since checks, bills, tax rates, prices, etc., are all figured in the decimal system, the values of most things must be converted from decimal to binary before computations can begin. For these and other reasons most of the early machines operated in binary-coded-decimal number systems. In such systems a coded group of binary bits is used to represent each of the 10 decimal digits. For instance, an obvious and natural code is a simple "weighted binary code," as shown in Table 3·2.

This is known as a "binary-coded-decimal 8, 4, 2, 1" code. Notice that 4 binary bits are required for each decimal digit, and each bit is assigned a weight; for instance, the rightmost bit has a weight of 1

TABLE 3·2

BINARY CODE	DECIMAL DIGIT
0000	0
0001	1
0010	2
0011	3
0100	4
0101	5
0110	6
0111	7
1000	8
1001	9

and the leftmost bit in each code group has a weight of 8. By adding the weights of the positions in which 1's appear, the decimal digit represented by a code group may be derived. This is somewhat uneconomical as $2^4 = 16$, and therefore the 4 bits could actually represent 15 different values; but the next lesser choice, 3 bits, gives only 2^3 or 8 values, which are insufficient. If the decimal number 214 is to be represented in this type of code, 12 binary bits are required as follows: 0010 0001 0100. For the decimal number 1246 to be represented, 16 bits are required: 0001 0010 0100 0110.

This is a very useful code and has been much used. One difficulty with the code, however, lies in forming the complements of numbers in this system. It is common practice to perform subtraction in a computer by adding the complement of the subtrahend; however, when the binary-coded-decimal 8, 4, 2, 1 system is used, the most natural complement of the number stored is not useful. The most direct way for a computer to complement a number is simply to change each 0 to a 1 and each 1 to a 0. However, the natural complement of 0010 (2 decimal) is 1101, which is 13 and not an acceptable binary-coded-decimal character in this system. In order to get around this difficulty, several other codes have been used. One of the first, a code which was used in the early Mark machines built at Harvard and has been used a good deal since, is known as the "excess 3" code and is formed by adding 3 to the decimal number and then forming the binary-coded number in the normal weighted binary code. For instance, to form the excess 3 representation for 4, first 3 is added, yielding 7, and then the "normal" binary-coded decimal is used, which is 0111. Therefore, 0111 is the excess 3 code for the decimal digit 4. Table 3 · 3 shows all 10 decimal digits and the code for each.

TABLE 3 · 3

EXCESS 3 CODE	
DECIMAL	BINARY CODE
0	0011
1	0100
2	0101
3	0110
4	0111
5	1000
6	1001
7	1010
8	1011
9	1100

TABLE 3 · 4

DECIMAL DIGIT	EXCESS 3 CODE	9'S COMPLEMENT
0	0011	1100
1	0100	1011
2	0101	1010
3	0110	1001
4	0111	1000
5	1000	0111
6	1001	0110
7	1010	0101
8	1011	0100
9	1100	0011

By complementing each digit of the binary code group representing a decimal digit, the 9's complement of that digit may be formed. For instance, the complement of 0100 (1 decimal) is 1011, which is 8 decimal.

The decimal number 243 coded in the excess 3 system would be 0101 0111 0110, and the decimal number 347 would be 0110 0111 1010. The 9's complement of 243 is 756 decimal or 1010 1000 1001 binary. Table 3 · 4 lists the excess 3 code representation for each of the 10 decimal digits along with the 9's complements listed below. It may be seen that the 9's complement of each code group may be formed by changing each 0 to a 1 and each 1 to a 0 in the code group.

There are actually a number of codes in which the 9's complement may be formed by complementing each one of the 4 bits which represent a decimal character.

The excess 3 code is not a weighted code, however, as the sum of the weights of the bits does not equal the number represented. The 8, 4, 2, 1 code previously described is a weighted code, but does not form the 9's complement when the individual bits of a coded character are complemented. It is, however, possible to build circuits which will form the desired complements, and such circuits are described in Chap. 6. A weighted code in which the 9's complement may be formed by complementing each binary digit is the 2, 4, 2, 1 code (see Table 3 · 5).

If each bit of a code group is complemented, the 9's complement of the decimal digit represented is formed. For instance, 0010 (2 decimal) complemented is 1101 (7 decimal), and 1011 (5 decimal) complemented is 0100 (4 decimal). There are several weighted codes which form the 9's complement in this manner.

Since various types of number systems are used in computers, the

TABLE 3 · 5

DECIMAL	2, 4, 2, 1 CODE
	CODED BINARY
	WEIGHT OF BIT
	2 4 2 1
0	0 0 0 0
1	0 0 0 1
2	0 0 1 0
3	0 0 1 1
4	0 1 0 0
5	1 0 1 1
6	1 1 0 0
7	1 1 0 1
8	1 1 1 0
9	1 1 1 1

following convention is generally adopted to distinguish binary from decimal. A binary number is identified by a subscript of 2 placed at the end of the number (00110_2) and a decimal number by the subscript 10 (for instance, decimal 948 may be written 948_{10}). We may then write 0111_2 as 7_{10}. This convention will be used when necessary.

3 · 15   Octal and hexadecimal number systems

There are two other number systems which are immediately useful in the computer industry: the octal number system and the hexadecimal number system.

The octal number system has a base of 8; eight different symbols

TABLE 3 · 6

OCTAL	DECIMAL	OCTAL	DECIMAL
0	0	11	9
1	1	12	10
2	2	13	11
3	3	14	12
4	4	15	13
5	5	16	14
6	6	17	15
7	7	20	16
10	8	21	17

TABLE 3·7

THREE BINARY DIGITS	OCTAL DIGIT
000	0
001	1
010	2
011	3
100	4
101	5
110	6
111	7

are used to represent numbers. These are commonly 0, 1, 2, 3, 4, 5, 6, and 7. Using positional notation, the first few octal numbers and their decimal equivalents are as shown in Table 3·6.

To convert an octal number to a decimal number we use the same sort of polynomial as was used in the binary case, except that we now have a base of 8 instead of 2. Therefore, 1213 in octal is $(1 \times 8^3) + (2 \times 8^2) + (1 \times 8^1) + (3 \times 8^0) = 512 + 128 + 8 + 3 = 651$ in decimal. Also, 1.123 in octal is $(1 \times 8^0) + (1 \times 8^{-1}) + (2 \times 8^{-2}) + (3 \times 8^{-3})$ or $1 + \frac{1}{8} + \frac{2}{64} + \frac{3}{512} = 1\frac{83}{512}$ in decimal.

The primary use of octal is in conveniently recording values stored in binary registers. There is a simple trick for converting a binary number to an octal number. Simply group the binary digits into groups of threes starting at the octal point, and read each set of three binary digits according to Table 3·7.

These are also, of course, the decimal values for each set of three binary digits.

Let us convert the binary number 011101. First we break it into threes (thus 011 101) and then converting each group of three binary digits, we get 35 in octal. Therefore 011101 binary = 35 octal. Here are several more examples:

$$111110111_2 = 767_8$$

$$110110101_2 = 665_8$$

$$11011_2 = 33_8$$

$$1001_2 = 11_8$$

$$10101.11_2 = 25.6_8$$

$$1100.111_2 = 14.7_8$$

$$1011.1111_2 = 13.74_8$$

Conversion from decimal to octal can be performed by repeatedly dividing the decimal number by 8 and using each remainder as a digit in the octal number being formed. For instance, to convert 200_{10} to an octal representation, we divide as follows:

$$200 \div 8 = 25 \qquad \text{remainder is } 0$$
$$25 \div 8 = 3 \qquad \text{remainder is } 1$$
$$3 \div 8 = 0 \qquad \text{remainder is } 3$$

Therefore, $200_{10} = 310_8$.

Notice that when the number to be divided is less than 8, we use 0 as the quotient and the number as the remainder. Let us check this:

$$360_8 = (3_{10} \times 8_{10}^2) + (1_{10} \times 8_{10}^1) + (0_{10} \times 8_{10}^0)$$
$$= 192_{10} + 8_{10} = 200_{10}$$

Here is another example. We wish to convert 3964_{10} to octal.

$$3964 \div 8 = 495 \qquad \text{with a remainder of } 4$$
$$495 \div 8 = 61 \qquad \text{with a remainder of } 7$$
$$61 \div 8 = 7 \qquad \text{with a remainder of } 5$$
$$7 \div 8 = 0 \qquad \text{with a remainder of } 7$$

Therefore, $7574_8 = 3964_{10}$. Checking,

$$7574_8 = (7_{10} \times 8_{10}^3) + (5_{10} \times 8_{10}^2) + (7_{10} \times 8_{10}) + 4_{10}$$
$$= (7_{10} \times 512_{10}) + (5_{10} \times 64_{10}) + (7_{10} \times 8_{10}) + (4_{10} \times 1_{10})$$
$$= 3584_{10} + 320_{10} + 56_{10} + 4_{10}$$
$$= 3964_{10}$$

There are several other tricks for converting octal to decimal and decimal to octal, but they are not used very frequently manually, and tables prove to be of about as much value as anything in this process. Octal-to-decimal and decimal-to-octal tables are readily available in a number of places, including the manuals distributed by manufacturers of binary machines.

An important use for octal is in listings of programs and for memory "dumps" for binary machines, thus making the printouts more compact. Also, in keeping track of the contents of different registers and in orally conveying the contents of a binary register to someone, it is very useful to use octal characters rather than binary. If, for instance, we want to convey the binary number 011101111 over the telephone, it is easier and less conducive to errors to say "three-five-seven in octal" rather than "zero-one-one-one-zero-one-one-one-one in binary."

The hexadecimal number system is useful for a similar reason. All the IBM 360 series of machines and the RCA Spectra 70 have their memories organized into sets of "bytes" (a byte consists of eight binary digits). Each byte either is used as a single entity to represent a single alphanumeric character or is broken into two 4-bit pieces. (We shall examine the coding of alphanumeric characters using bytes in Chap. 8.) When the bytes are handled in two 4-bit pieces, the programmer is given the option of declaring each 4-bit character as a piece of a binary number or as two binary-coded-decimal numbers. For instance, the byte 0001 1000 can be declared a binary number, in which case it is equal to 24 decimal, or as two binary-coded-decimal characters, in which case it represents the decimal number 18.

Another class of machines, including the Minneapolis-Honeywell 120 and 200, have character addressable memories in which each character consists of four binary digits. A given character can be declared either as 4 bits in a binary word or as a binary-coded-decimal character.

When the machine is handling numbers in binary, but in groups of four digits, it is convenient to have a code for representing each of these sets of four digits. Since there are 16 possible different numbers which can be represented, we need a base 16 number system. The digits 0 through 9 will not suffice, so the letters A, B, C, D, E, and F are also used (see Table 3 · 8).

To convert binary to hexadecimal we simply break a binary number into groups of four digits and convert each group of four digits according to the preceding code. Thus, $10111011_2 = BB_{16}$, $10010101_2 = 95_{16}$, $11000111_2 = C7_{16}$, and $10001011_2 = 8B_{16}$. The mixture of letters and decimal digits may seem strange at first, but these are simply convenient symbols, just as decimal digits are.

The conversion of hexadecimal to decimal is straightforward but time-consuming. For instance, BB represents $(B \times 16^1) + (B \times 16^0) = (11 \times 16) + (11 \times 1) = 176 + 11 = 187$. Similarly,

$$AB6_{16} = (10_{10} \times 16_{10}^2) + (11_{10} \times 16_{10}) + 6$$
$$= (10_{10} \times 256_{10}) + 176_{10} + 6_{10}$$
$$= 2560_{10} + 176_{10} + 6_{10}$$
$$= 2742_{10}$$

TABLE 3·8

BINARY	HEXADECIMAL	DECIMAL
0000	0	0
0001	1	1
0010	2	2
0011	3	3
0100	4	4
0101	5	5
0110	6	6
0111	7	7
1000	8	8
1001	9	9
1010	A	10
1011	B	11
1100	C	12
1101	D	13
1110	E	14
1111	F	15

Again, tables are convenient for converting hexadecimal to decimal and decimal to hexadecimal. Table 3·9 is useful for converting in either direction.

In order to convert, for instance, $D3A6_{16}$ to decimal, we notice that $D000_{16} = 53248_{10}$. Then,

TABLE 3·9

HEXADECIMAL	DECIMAL
1000	4096
2000	8192
3000	12288
4000	16384
5000	20484
6000	24576
7000	28672
8000	32768
9000	36864
A000	40960
B000	45056
C000	49152
D000	53248
E000	57344
F000	61440

$$3A6_{16} = (3_{10} \times 16_{10}^2) + (10_{10} \times 16_{10}) + 6_{10}$$
$$= (3_{10} \times 256_{10}) + (10_{10} \times 16_{10}) + 6_{10}$$
$$= 768_{10} + 160_{10} + 6_{10}$$
$$= 934_{10}$$

and

$$D3A6_{16} = D000_{16} + 3A6_{16}$$
$$= 53248_{10} + 934_{10}$$
$$= 54182_{10}$$

The chief use of the hexadecimal system is in connection with character-organized machines. Programmers, technicians, and engineers become amazingly adept at handling the hexadecimal and the octal systems when they use them a great deal.

QUESTIONS

1 Convert the following decimal numbers to equivalent binary numbers:

a. 39　　　　　b. 59　　　　　c. 512
d. 0.4475　　　e. $^{25}\!/_{32}$　　　f. 0.796875
g. 256.75　　　h. 129.5625　　i. 4096.90625

2 Convert the following decimal numbers to equivalent binary numbers:

a. 43　　　　　b. 64　　　　　c. 4096
d. 0.375　　　 e. $^{27}\!/_{32}$　　　f. 0.4375
g. 512.5　　　 h. 131.5625　　i. 2048.0625

3 Convert the following binary numbers to equivalent decimal numbers:

a. 1101　　　　　　b. 11011　　　　　　　c. 10111
d. 0.1011　　　　　e. 0.001101　　　　　　f. 0.001101101
g. 111011.1011　　h. 1011011.001101　　i. 10110.0101011101

4 Convert the following binary numbers to equivalent decimal numbers:

a. 1011　　　　　b. 100100　　　　c. 10011
d. 0.1101　　　　e. 0.1001　　　　f. 0.0101
g. 1011.0011　　h. 1001.1001　　i. 101.011

5 Perform the following additions and check by converting the binary numbers to decimal:

a. 1001.1 + 1011.01　　b. 100101 + 100101
c. 0.1011 + 0.1101　　　d. 1011.01 + 1001.11

6 Perform the following additions and check by converting the binary numbers to decimal:

    a. 1101.1 + 1011.1   *b.* 101101 + 110110
    c. 0.0011 + 0.1110   *d.* 1100.011 + 1011.011

7 Perform the following subtractions in the binary number system:

    a. 64 − 32   *b.* 127 − 63
    c. 93.5 − 42.75   *d.* $84\tfrac{9}{32} - 48\tfrac{5}{16}$

8 Perform the following subtractions in the binary number system:

    a. 37 − 35   *b.* 128 − 64   *c.* 94.5 − 43.75   *d.* 255 − 127

9 Perform the following multiplications and divisions in the binary number system:

    a. 24 × 12   *b.* 18 × 14   *c.* 32 ÷ 8
    d. 27 ÷ 18   *e.* 49.5 × 51.75   *f.* 58.75 ÷ 23.5

10 Perform the following multiplications and divisions in the binary number system:

    a. 15 × 13   *b.* 10 × 15   *c.* 44 ÷ 11
    d. 42 ÷ 12   *e.* 7.75 × 2.5   *f.* 22.5 ÷ 4.75

11 Convert the following decimal numbers into both their 9's and 10's complements:

    a. 5436   *b.* 1932   *c.* 45.15   *d.* 18.293

12 Convert the following decimal numbers into both their 9's and 10's complements:

    a. 3654   *b.* 2122   *c.* 54.19   *d.* 37.263

13 Convert the following binary numbers into both their 1's and 2's complements:

    a. 1011   *b.* 11011   *c.* 1011.01   *d.* 11011.01

14 Convert the following binary numbers into both their 1's and 2's complements:

    a. 10111   *b.* 100100   *c.* 10111.10   *d.* 10011.11

15 Perform the following subtractions using both 9's and 10's complements:

    a. 948 − 234   *b.* 347 − 263   *c.* 349.5 − 245.3   *d.* 412.7 − 409.2

16 Perform the following subtractions using both 9's and 10's complements:

    a. 1024 − 913   *b.* 249 − 137   *c.* 24.1 − 13.4   *d.* 239.3 − 119.4

17 Perform the following subtractions using both 1's and 2's complements:

    a. 1011 − 101   *b.* 11011 − 11001
    c. 10111.1 − 10011.1   *d.* 11011 − 10011.11

18 How many different binary numbers can be stored in a register consisting of six switches?

19 How many different binary-coded-decimal numbers can be stored in a register containing 12 switches using an 8, 4, 2, 1 code? Using an excess 3 code?

20 Write the first 10 numbers in the quaternary number system, which has a base or radix of 4. Use the digits 0, 1, 2, and 3 to express these numbers.

21 Write the first 25 numbers in a base 11 number system using the digits 0, 1, 2, 3, 4, 5, 6, 7, 8, 9, and A to express the 25 numbers that you write. (Decimal 10 = A, for instance.)

22 Using the 1's complement number system, perform the following subtractions:
   a. $0.1001 - 0.0110$ *b.* $0.1110 - 0.0110$
   c. $0.01111 - 0.01001$ *d.* $11011 - 11001$
   e. $1110101 - 1010010$

23 Using the 2's complement number system, perform the following subtractions and also represent the answers as decimal fractions:
   a. $0.101010 - 0.010101$ *b.* $0.11001 - 0.00100$
   c. $0.111000 - 0.000111$ *d.* $0.101100 - 0.010011$

24 Convert the following hexadecimal numbers to decimal:
   a. B6C7   *b.* 64AC   *c.* A492   *d.* D2763

25 Convert the following octal numbers to decimal:
   a. 2376   *b.* 2483   *c.* 386431   *d.* 22632

26 Convert the following binary numbers to octal numbers:
   a. 101101   *b.* 101101110   *c.* 10110111
   d. 110110.011   *e.* 011.1011011

27 Convert the following octal numbers to binary:
   a. 7423   *b.* 3364   *c.* 33962   *d.* 3232.14   *e.* 3146.52

28 Convert the following decimal numbers to octal:
   a. 932   *b.* 332   *c.* 545.375   *d.* 632.97   *e.* 4429.625

29 Convert the following hexadecimal numbers to binary:
   a. CD   *b.* 649   *c.* A13   *d.* AA.1A   *e.* AB2.234

30 Convert the following binary numbers to hexadecimal:
   a. 10110111   *b.* 10011100   *c.* 1011111
   d. 0.01111110   *e.* 0.10110111101

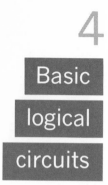

4

Basic
logical
circuits

Although a modern electronic computer is composed of a large number of electronic components, an entire machine will usually contain only a few types of basic circuits. The current theory of computer construction dictates the use of a few basic "blocks" which are used over and over. Construction of this sort greatly simplifies the design of the machines, increases reliability, as only a few well-tested circuits are used, and makes maintenance of the machines simpler and faster. The circuits used in these blocks are simple in principle, simpler, in fact, than most of the circuits used in modern radio and television sets. There are several types of circuits: circuits which perform logical operations on input signals; storage elements, such as flip-flops, which store bits of information; and accessory circuits, such as co-axial line drivers, neon-light indicator circuits, etc.

The circuits described in this chapter have been classified according to the functions they perform. For instance, following the description of transistor characteristics, the first type of circuit to be described is the diode AND gate. The description of the diode AND gate is followed by a diode-and-transistor AND gate, then finally, an all-transistor AND gate. The intent here is therefore to describe the function each circuit performs, why one circuit may be preferable to another and, at the same time, to explain the manner in which the circuits function.

For this reason, the input and output signals will often be described as representing binary values. For instance, a pulse may be referred to as representing a 1 and the absence of a pulse as representing a 0. This is emphasized because the concept of the circuits performing logical operations on the input signals is very important.

No attempt has been made to describe every circuit configuration now in use; only representative circuits of each type are included in the discussion.

Along with the description of the operation of each typical circuit, a block diagram symbol for each circuit will be presented. These symbols will be used in the diagrams illustrating the operation of various sections of digital machines.

4 · 1   The characteristics of transistors used in switching circuits

Before analyzing logical circuits, we shall briefly describe the general characteristics of transistors and diodes when used as switching devices. This does not imply that the characteristics of these devices in switching circuits are radically different from those used in audio or r-f circuitry; however, most general introductions to transistors treat them as linear amplifying devices. When transistors are used in switching circuits, they are generally operated at or near the extremes of their operating points. That is, they are quite often operated either in a "cutoff" or "saturated" condition. Therefore, some of the characteristics which are most important to the computer circuit are of less importance in other fields.

The characteristics of semiconductor diodes will be briefly noted. A semiconductor diode is made of two pieces of semiconductor material of different types jointed together. One type of semiconductor material is called *p-type* material and the other *n-type* material (refer to Fig. 4 · 1a). When two differing types of semiconductor material are joined together, a *semiconductor junction* is formed and a single junction is also called a *diode*. Figure 4 · 1a shows that the *p*-type of material is referred to as the *anode* of the diode (or sometimes the *plate*), and the *n*-type material is called the *cathode* of the diode. Figure 4 · 1a also shows the schematic symbol for the diode.

A study of semiconductor or solid-state devices would explain the physical internal workings of the diode; however, our sole interest here is to view the diode as a component in electronic switching circuits, so we will examine the diode from the viewpoint of its electrical characteristics only. When we apply an electric voltage, possibly through a resistor as in Fig. 4 · 1b, so that the anode of the diode is positive with respect to the cathode, the diode is said to be *forward biased*. A diode which is forward biased will conduct current rather freely. (*Conventional current* will be used in our discussion; conventional current flows from positive to negative.)

Figure 4 · 1c shows a pair of typical characteristic curves for semiconductor diodes. There are two kinds of semiconductor diodes now commonly used in computer circuits; one is the *germanium* diode and the other is the *silicon* diode. The curves for the two types of

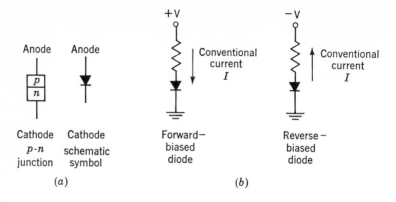

(a)

(b)

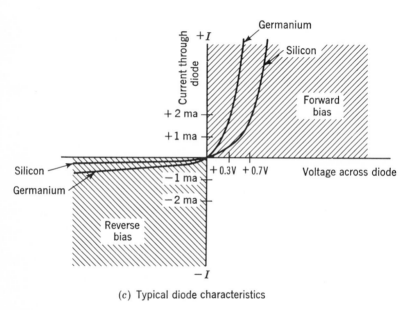

(c) Typical diode characteristics

Fig. 4 · 1   Transistor parameter definitions.

diodes show that for diodes which are forward biased, the germanium diode presents somewhat less resistance to current flow than the silicon diode; the germanium diode has a voltage drop from anode to cathode of about 0.3 volts for reasonable forward currents, while the silicon diode drops on the order of 0.7 volts. Notice that the forward-biased region on the graph lies to the right of the ordinate of the graph.

When the cathode of a diode is positive with respect to the anode, the diode is said to be *reverse biased*, and it will present a very high resistance to current flow (refer to Fig. 4·1b and c). As shown in the graph in Fig. 4·1c, the germanium diode presents less resistance to current flow than the silicon diode.

Most of the transistors now being used in computers are three-terminal junction transistors. There are two general types of junction transistors, the *pnp* transistor illustrated in Fig. 4·2a and the *npn* transistor illustrated in Fig. 4·2b. Each of the currents which flow

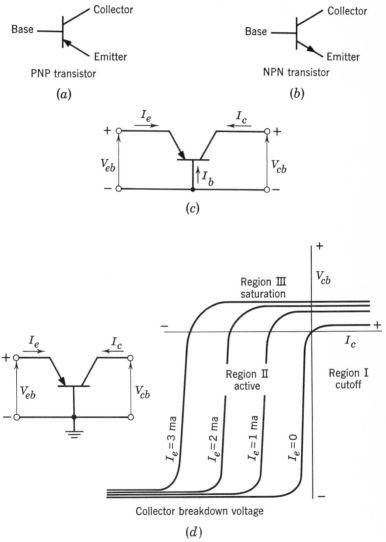

(a)

(b)

(c)

(d)

Fig. 4·2   Typical *pnp* transistor-collector curves.

into the three terminals is identified by a different subscript, for example: I_e in Fig. 4 · 2c refers to the current flowing into the emitter of the transistor, I_b is the current flowing into the base, and I_c identifies the current flowing into the collector. The current referred to is again "conventional" current, which flows from a positive polarity to a negative polarity. (This is in opposition to electron-flow which is from negative to positive.)

The graph in Fig. 4 · 2d shows a family of curves of the collector characteristics for a typical *pnp* switching transistor connected in a grounded-base configuration. Each curve on the graph shows the collector characteristics for a different value of emitter current. The curves are plotted by holding I_e constant, then varying I_c, and measuring and then plotting the collector-to-base voltage (V_{cb}) for each value of I_c.

The graph in Fig. 4 · 2d may be used to define three regions in which a transistor may be operated. Each region is shown separately on the graph. The three regions are:

1 Cutoff: The *pnp* transistor is defined as being "cut off" when the input current flowing into the emitter (I_e) of the transistor is zero, or when current flows *from* the emitter ($I_e \leq 0$), and when the collector potential is negative with respect to the base. The cutoff region in Fig. 4 · 2d lies to the right of the curve plotted for an emitter current equal to 0. This is designated as Region I in Fig. 4 · 2d and extends vertically up to the x axis of the graph. The important thing to note is that the emitter-base junction is reverse biased. For the *pnp* transistor this means that the base is positive with respect to the emitter. (For the *npn* transistor the base would be negative.)

2 Active: In this region the *pnp* transistor has a normal or forward emitter-to-base bias (the emitter is positive with respect to the base), and the collector is negative with respect to the base ($V_c < 0$). The active region is designated as Region II in Fig. 4 · 2d. This is the normal operating region for the transistor and most transistor amplifiers operate in this region.

3 Saturation: When the collector is positive with respect to the base ($V_{cb} \geq 0$), the transistor is said to be saturated. This is Region III in Fig. 4 · 2d.

4 · 2 Characteristics of the three modes of operation

The transistor exhibits different input and output characteristics in each of the three regions. Referring again to Fig. 4 · 2d, the three regions of operation have the following characteristics:

1 When the *pnp* transistor is cut off, the emitter and collector are both

negative with respect to the base. As a result, both the emitter and collector appear as large resistances and little current flows from either the collector or emitter. Some reverse current will flow, however, because of leakage current across the surface and reverse current through the junction[1]. The magnitude of this current varies with the voltage across the junction and the temperature of the transistor, but generally lies somewhere between 0.5 and 200 microamperes (μa) for germanium transistors, and 1 to 100 nanoamperes (namp) for silicon transistors (1 namp is equal to 10^{-9} amp).

2 In the active region, the transistor exhibits all the characteristics common to class A amplifier circuits. The transistor possesses a power gain from input to output in this region, and the current which flows in the collector circuit is a function of the current into the emitter. The current gain from the emitter to the collector is generally designated as α, the ratio of small change in the emitter current to the resulting change in the collector current $\Delta I_c / \Delta I_e$, with the collector voltage held constant. This value generally lies between 0.9 and 0.99 for junction transistors. For a particular transistor the value of α varies somewhat throughout the active region.

If the negative collector voltage is increased beyond a certain point, known as the *breakdown voltage*, the collector current will increase rapidly with virtually no change in collector voltage. This may be caused by either avalanche of the minority carriers or another phenomenon known as *punch through*, which occurs when the collector space charge region extends to the emitter. Care is generally taken to see that transistors are not operated with voltages which will cause breakdown.

3 When the transistor is saturated, both the emitter and collector are positive (forward biased) with respect to the base, and both the emitter-base junction and the collector-base junction present small impedances to current flow.

4 · 3 Response of common-base circuit to pulse input

Figure 4 · 3a illustrates the response of the common-base circuit to a pulse input. The emitter is biased slightly negative with respect to the base by $-V_{ee}$; $-V_{cc}$ is a relatively large negative voltage which holds the collector negative with respect to the base. Since the transistor is biased into the cutoff region (by $-V_{ee}$), only a small leakage current will flow through R_L. When a positive input pulse is applied, the emitter is driven positive with respect to the base and emitter cur-

---

[1]The leakage current is often designated as "cutoff current" and identified with the letter designation I_{co}.

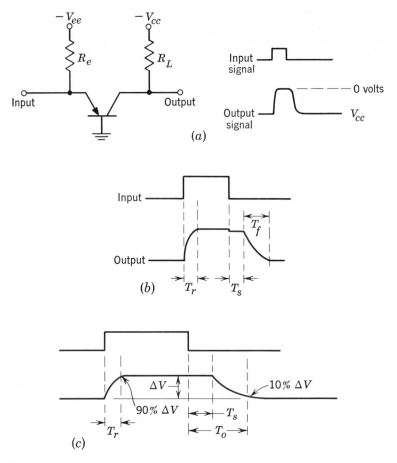

Fig. 4 · 3   Transistor transient-response periods.

rent begins to flow. Because of the transistor effect, the emitter current causes the collector current to increase, and the increase in collector current through R_L causes the collector voltage to become more positive. If the emitter is driven sufficiently positive, the emitter and collector currents will continue to increase until the collector is positive with respect to the base, and the transistor will be saturated.

When the trailing edge of the input pulse is reached, the transistor base-to-emitter junction will again be reverse biased and the collector current will begin to decrease. The transistor will then pass back through the active region and finally into the cutoff region, leaving the circuit in its original cutoff state.

4 · 4   Rise and fall characteristics of the common-base circuit

A more detailed illustration of the rise and fall characteristics of the common-base circuit is presented in Fig. 4 · 3b.[2] As the figure indicates, the response of the circuit to a square-wave input is not instantaneous. The response time of the circuit to the leading edge of the square-wave pulse (designated as T_r in Fig. 4 · 3b) is called the *rise time*. The steepness of the rise time is determined basically by the characteristics of the transistor. Important factors affecting the rise time of the output signal are the frequency response and the gain of the transistor.

If the transistor is saturated during the peak of the pulse, another important response time occurs at the trailing edge of the input pulse. When the transistor is saturated, the base region is flooded with minority carriers. Before the transistor recovers from saturation, these minority carriers must be removed, and the time which elapses during this period is called *saturation delay* or *storage delay*. Notice that in Fig. 4 · 3b the output voltage does not begin to fall instantly after the trailing edge of the input pulse, but instead a delay T_s occurs until the minority carriers which have accumulated are removed.

After the storage delay, the fall time begins. The duration of the *fall time* period (designated as T_f in Fig. 4 · 3b) is a function of the transistor and circuit parameters.

The rise and fall times listed in specifications are generally not the entire period from the time the input pulse is applied or removed until the circuit output rises or falls to its final value. Instead, *turn-on time* may be defined as the time elapsing from the leading edge of a square-input pulse until the output voltage reaches 90 percent of the *steady-state* value (Fig. 4 · 3c), and the *turn-off time* is the time elapsing while the output voltage falls to within 10 percent of the final signal level.

4 · 5   Common-emitter or inverter circuit

The circuit illustrated in Fig. 4 · 4a is connected in a *common-emitter configuration* and is generally referred to as an *inverter*. The input signal to the common-emitter circuit is applied between the base and emitter, and the output is taken across the emitter and collector. In Fig. 4 · 4a, the base is biased slightly positive with respect to the emitter by $+V_{bb}$, and the collector is biased negative with respect to both base and emitter by $-V_{cc}$. With a 0-volt signal input, the circuit

---

[2]The rise and fall sections of the waveforms in Figs. 4 · 3 and 4 · 4 have been expanded to illustrate more clearly the various transistor response times.

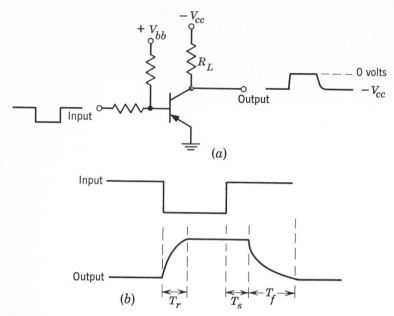

Fig. 4 · 4   Inverter or common-emitter circuit.

is therefore in the cutoff state; little current flows in the emitter and collector circuits, so that the collector will be near $-V_{cc}$. If a negative pulse is applied at the input, the base will be driven negative with respect to the emitter, forward-biasing the emitter-base junction. The increase in emitter current causes an increase in the collector current and a resultant voltage drop across resistor R_L, making the collector voltage increase. If the input signal is of sufficient amplitude, the current flow through resistor R_L will finally increase until the collector voltage is positive with respect to the base and the transistor will be saturated.

If the transistor has been saturated, the delay due to hole storage will again occur when the trailing edge of the input pulse appears, and will be followed by the fall time (Fig. 4 · 4b).

The following are some of the characteristics of the common-emitter circuit:

1   The input voltage is *out of phase* with the output voltage. That is, a negative pulse applied at the input will cause a positive pulse at the output. (The output voltage from a single common-emitter amplifier stage will be 180° out of phase with the input when a sinusoidal waveform is applied at the input.)

2   The common emitter has the largest power gain of the three possible arrangements.
3   The common-emitter configuration provides a voltage gain as well as a current gain. It is the only basic transistor circuit which has both a voltage and current gain from input to output, and for this reason it is often used as an amplifier.

The operation of the common-emitter or inverter circuit can be compared to the operation of a relay. If the base is negative with respect to the emitter, the collector-to-emitter resistance will be very low and the output at the collector will be at approximately the potential of the emitter. In this saturated condition, the transistor may be thought of as representing a closed set of relay points. When the transistor is in the cutoff condition (that is, when the base is positive with respect to the emitter), the collector-to-emitter impedance will be high, and the transistor may be thought of as representing an open set of contact points.

The response of the inverter to a square-pulse input is illustrated in Fig. 4 · 4b. The circuit has a rise (T_r) and fall (T_f) time, just as does the common-base circuit, and also a storage delay (T_s) if the transistor is operated in the saturated condition.

Because of its input-output characteristics, the inverter is the most commonly used transistor configuration in digital systems.

4 · 6   The emitter follower

There are three transistor configurations which produce a power gain from input to output. The common-base and common-emitter configurations have been discussed; the third configuration is the common collector, which is often called an *emitter follower*. This basic circuit is illustrated in Fig. 4 · 5. The emitter follower is so named because its operation resembles that of the electronic tube *cathode-follower* circuit. An emitter follower, like a cathode follower, is very

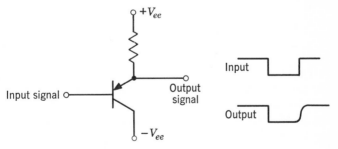

Fig. 4 · 5   Emitter follower or common-collector circuit.

useful for impedance matching, driving coaxial lines and other circuits, and for providing isolation between input and output. Unlike the cathode follower, which has a marked difference in potential between the input d-c level at the grid and the d-c level at the cathode, the transistor emitter follower has only a small difference in potential between the base and emitter connection. As a result of this small shift in d-c level (generally about 0.5 volts d-c), the emitter follower makes an excellent d-c current amplifier which may be used without shifting the signal level from input to output. The emitter follower is generally operated in the active region.

The following are some of the pertinent characteristics of the emitter follower:

1   The voltage gain of the circuit is approximately unity. A change of 3 volts in the input voltage will cause a change of approximately 3 volts at the output.

2   The d-c output level from the emitter follower is approximately equal to the d-c input level. If the input to the base of an emitter follower is at a d-c level of -3 volts and the transistor is operating in the active region, the output level at the emitter will also be at approximately -3 volts dc. For the circuit in Fig. 4·5, the output level at the emitter will be slightly positive with respect to the base, and the output d-c level will effectively "follow" the input level.

3   The current gain of the emitter follower is greater than unity. For most transistors, the current gain through the emitter follower will be greater than 25. Since the voltage gain of the circuit is approximately unity and the current gain is greater than unity, the emitter follower has power gain.

4   The output of the emitter follower is *in phase* or follows the input. This applies to both input and output currents and input and output voltages.

5   The emitter follower has a high input resistance and a low output resistance. The input resistance is approximately $R_L/(1 - \alpha)$ and is usually at least of an order of magnitude greater than the load resistance at the emitter R_L.

4·7   The AND gate

There are two basic functions which are performed by logical circuits. The first is storing signals (information), and the second is performing logical operations on the signals (information) in the system. The AND gate belongs in the latter category, performing a basic logical operation on a set of inputs and yielding an output which is a function of the inputs at any given time.

Since the information processed by a digital computer is represented by sets of electric signals which may be considered to represent binary values, a given signal may be thought of as representing either a 0 or a 1. Assume that a positive d-c voltage represents a 1, and a negative voltage a 0. In this case, the function of an AND gate with two inputs is to produce a positive output signal (a 1) only when both of the inputs are positive (1's). If the AND gate has three inputs, the output will be positive only when all three of the inputs are positive (in all other cases the output level will be negative, representing a 0).

In some systems, 0's and 1's are represented by the absence (representing a 0) or presence of pulses (representing a 1). The function of the AND-gate circuit is then to produce a pulse at its output only when a pulse is applied to all the inputs to the circuit simultaneously. If the inputs to the circuit are labeled x, y, and z, the circuit will produce an output pulse only when a pulse is simultaneously applied to x AND y AND z. When 0's and 1's are represented by both pulses and d-c levels, an AND gate produces an output only when all input signals represent a 1. For instance, there may be three inputs to an AND gate, two of which are d-c levels and the third of which is a pulse. In this case, the circuit will produce a pulse at its output only when both d-c levels are positive and a pulse is applied. It is important to note that if any one of the three inputs signals is a 0—if either of the d-c levels is negative or if the pulse is not applied—the circuit will have no output pulse.

4 · 8   The diode AND circuit

Figure 4 · 6 illustrates a two-input diode AND gate. In the circuit illustrated, a -5 volt d-c level represents a 0 and a $+5$ volt signal a 1. If both inputs are at -5 volts, both of the diodes will be forward biased and the output will be held at -5 volts by the diodes. The total voltage drop across the resistor will be 35 volts.

If the x input line goes to $+5$ volts and the y input remains at -5 volts, the diode connected to the y input will still be forward biased, and the output will remain at -5 volts d-c. (Notice that in this case the x-input diode will be reverse biased and 10 volts will be dropped across the diode.) If the input at y goes to $+5$ volts and x remains at -5 volts, the output will be at -5 volts d-c.

When the inputs at x and y both go to the $+5$ volt level, the output level will then rise to $+5$ volts and the output will represent a 1.

The responses of the diode AND gate to several types of inputs are illustrated in Fig. 4 · 6. The output response to d-c level inputs was just described and is illustrated in the figure. Figure 4 · 6 also

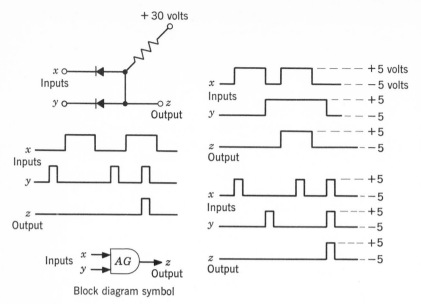

Fig. 4 · 6   Diode AND gate.

illustrates the response when a d-c level and a pulse are used as inputs. The pulse will appear at the output only when the d-c voltage is at the +5 volt (representing a 1) level.

The diode AND gate will also perform the AND function for pulse inputs. If a positive pulse represents a 1 and the absence of a pulse a 0, the circuit in Fig. 4 · 6 will have a pulse at the output only when pulses are applied to both the x and y input lines simultaneously. If one of the pulses is of shorter duration (width) than the other, the output of the circuit will have the pulse width of the smaller pulse. If the input pulses are of different amplitudes, the output will be of the amplitude of the smaller pulse.

The circuit in Fig. 4 · 6 could have more than two inputs. In this case, a diode would be required for each input, and each additional diode would be connected just as the two diodes are connected in the figure. If four diodes are connected in this manner, the output will rise to the +5 volt signal level only when the input signals to all four diodes are positive. There is a practical limit to the number of diodes which can be connected in this manner, however, due to the fact that the diodes do not actually have an infinite back resistance or zero forward resistance. With a large number of inputs, the finite forward and back resistances of the diodes will cause varying output levels, depending on the state of the inputs.

Figure 4·6 also shows the block diagram symbol for the AND gate. This symbol will be used to represent the AND gate in the logical diagrams which follow. The *AG* stands for "AND gate."

··9 Diode-and-transistor AND gate

The circuit illustrated in Fig. 4 · 7 has four inputs, labeled w through z, each of which is at a d-c level of either $+3$ or -1.4 volts. The 3-volt input represents a 1 and the -1.4 volt level a 0. The output level is at $+3$ volts only when all four of the inputs are at $+3$ volts; if any one of the inputs is at -1.4 volts, the output will be at -1.4 volts. The circuit is therefore a multiple-input AND gate.

If all the four inputs to the circuit in Fig. 4 · 7 are at the -1.4 volt d-c level, all the diodes will be forward biased by the $+6$ volts d-c power supply voltage connected through the 18-kilohm resistor. The diodes will conduct, holding the base of the *npn* transistor at approximately -1.4 volts (there will be some voltage drop across the diodes so the potential will actually be somewhat more positive than this). This will effectively "hold" the emitter of the emitter follower at -1.4 volts d-c. If any one of the inputs goes to the $+3$ volt level, the other diodes will still be forward biased and the base and emitter of the transistor will remain at approximately -1.4 volts.

If all the inputs go to the $+3$ volt d-c level at the same time, the potential at the base of the transistor will rise to the $+3$ volt level. (Again, the actual potential at the base will be slightly above $+3$ volts because of the drop in voltage across the diodes.) In this case, the emitter will "follow" the base to the 3-volt level.

In order to maintain the signal levels through this circuit, the cir-

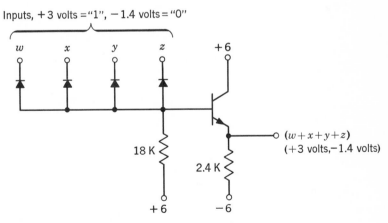

Fig. 4 · 7   Diode-and-transistor AND gate.

cuit has been designed so that the drop across the base-emitter junction of the transistor compensates for the drop across the input diodes.[3] The drop across the diodes will be such that the potential at the base of the transistor will be more positive than the input level. For instance, if the w input is at -1.4 volts, the drop across the respective diode will be on the order of 0.5 to 0.7 volts, and the potential at the base of the transistor will be -0.9 to -0.7 volts d-c. The emitter of the transistor is biased negative with respect to the base; therefore, the voltage drop across the base-to-emitter junction will be in the negative direction and will counteract the drop across the diodes. If the base-to-emitter voltage drop is on the order of 0.5 to 0.7 volts, the output level will be at approximately the input level.

The principal advantage of the circuit is the current gain provided by the emitter follower. The current gain through the circuit will be greater than 30 for most transistors. This will enable the circuit to "drive" more circuits connected to the output than would be otherwise possible.

Since speed is an important factor in many computers, it is of interest to note that with the parameters illustrated and with silicon transistors, the state of the output can be changed at a repetition rate of up to 120 megacycles per sec. The circuit has rise and fall times of less than 0.01 μsec (microsecond) with a 0.005 μsec rise and fall time input pulse, since the transistor is always in the active region, eliminating the storage delay.

4 · 10 Transistor AND gate

An AND gate using a transistor at each input is illustrated in Fig. 4 · 8. Each of these transistors is connected as an emitter follower in the circuit; however, the transistors share a common load resistor. The inputs to the AND gate consist of $+5$ volts, representing a 1, and -5 volts, representing a 0. If any one of the inputs is at the -5 volt level, the base of the transistor in that leg of the circuit will be at -5 volts; and since the emitter is biased positive with respect to the base by the $+30$ volt supply, the emitter will be positive with respect to the base, causing the transistor to conduct heavily and clamping the output of the circuit at the -5 volt level.

If any of the other transistors has its input at the $+5$ volt level, the base-to-emitter junction will be reverse biased since the output line is clamped at -5 volts, and the transistor will be in the cutoff

---

[3]The circuit in the drawing was designed at Lincoln Laboratory for use in an airborne computer, and uses silicon transistors and diodes which have excellent temperature characteristics. The configuration is basic, however, and other types of diodes and transistors may be used.

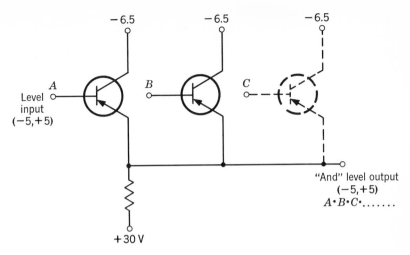

Fig. 4 · 8   Transistor AND gate.

condition. Any one of the transistors will be capable of supplying enough current to maintain the output at the −5 volt level. If, however, all of the inputs are at the +5 volt level, the output will also be held at +5 volts. The circuit therefore performs as an AND gate.

The transistor AND gate has a high input impedance, since all inputs are to a transistor base, and low output impedance. Since the basic transistor configuration is that of the emitter follower, there will be a substantial current gain through the circuit, dependent on the value of β for the transistor. The output level will be shifted slightly from the input level, however, because of the base-to-emitter voltage drop. For the circuit in Fig. 4 · 8, the output level will be slightly higher than the input level.

11   The OR gate

The OR gate has the property that a signal representing a 1 will appear at the output if any one of the inputs represents a 1. That is, if the input signals are pulses, and if a pulse represents a 1, there will be an output pulse representing a 1 from the OR circuit when any one of the inputs lines contains a pulse. If the inputs are d-c levels representing 0's and 1's, the output will be at the 1 level if any input represents a 1. From a circuit viewpoint, the main function of the OR gate is to prevent interaction between inputs.

Figure 4 · 9 illustrates a diode OR-gate circuit. There are two inputs to the circuit (x and y) and one output. The input signals to the circuit consist of −5 volt signals representing 0's, and +5 volt signals

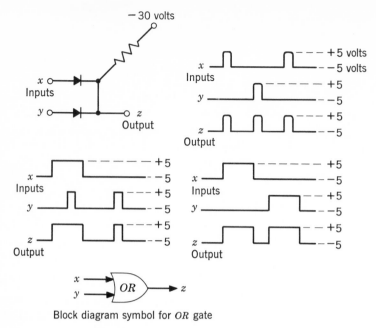

Block diagram symbol for OR gate

Fig. 4·9   Diode OR gate.

representing 1's. If both of the inputs to the circuit are at -5 volts d-c, both diodes will be forward biased and the output of the circuit will be at -5 volts d-c, representing a 0. If either of the inputs to the circuit rises to $+5$ volts d-c, the diode at this input will be forward biased and the output will rise to $+5$ volts representing a 1. The diode at the input remaining at -5 volts will then be reverse biased by the $+5$ volt signal at the output. This circuit has the property that the output level will be at the level of the most positive input.

If both of the inputs to the circuit rise to $+5$ volts, the output will again be at $+5$ volts. This circuit is sometimes referred to as an inclusive OR circuit, because the output is a 1 when both inputs are 1's.

More inputs may be added to the circuit illustrated in Fig. 4·9. A diode is then required for each input. If any one or any combination of the inputs rises to the $+5$ volt level, then the output will be at $+5$ volts.

As in the case of the diode AND gate, it is not practical to have too many inputs to the circuit because the forward and back resistances of the diodes are finite, and different combinations of input signals will then cause different signal levels at the outputs. The diode OR gate will also function with either pulse inputs or mixed-pulse and d-c level inputs.

The logical block diagram symbol which will be used for the OR gate is illustrated in Fig. 4 · 9.

If the convention that a positive signal represents a 1 and a negative signal a 0 is reversed, the circuit in Fig. 4 · 9 will then perform the AND function. Also notice that if the AND gate which is illustrated in Fig. 4 · 6 has negative inputs representing 1's and positive input signals representing 0's, the circuit will then perform the OR function. In order to avoid confusion, the circuit in Fig. 4 · 9 is sometimes referred to as a *positive* OR gate or as a *negative* AND gate. The circuit in Fig. 4 · 6 would then be referred to as a *positive* AND gate or a *negative* OR gate. Unless otherwise noted, we will consider relatively positive signals to represent 1's and relatively negative signals to represent 0's. The term AND gate will then refer to a positive AND gate, such as the one in Fig. 4 · 6, and an OR gate will mean a positive OR gate, such as that in Fig. 4 · 9.

4 · 12   A diode-and-transistor OR gate

Figure 4 · 10 illustrates the use of both diodes and a transistor to construct an OR gate. There are four inputs to the circuit (labeled *w* through *z*), and one output. Each input to the circuit can be either at +3 volts d-c, representing a 1, or at −1.4 volts d-c, representing a 0. The output from the circuit is either at +3 volts or at −1.4 volts d-c, but will be at +3 volts if any of the inputs are at +3 volts.

If all of the inputs are at −1.4 volts d-c, the diodes will all be forward biased and the voltage level at the base of the transistor will be at −1.4 volts, less the voltage drop across the diodes. This will be on

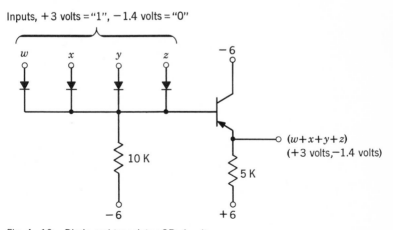

Inputs, +3 volts = "1", −1.4 volts = "0"

Fig. 4 · 10   Diode-and-transistor OR circuit.

the order of 0.7 volt, so the input to the transistor base will be at approximately −2.1 volts.[4] The transistor is connected as an emitter follower. Since the potential at the emitter will essentially "follow" the base potential, the emitter will be at essentially −2.1 volts; however, there will be a voltage drop from base to emitter which will cancel the drop across the diodes, and the output level will be at approximately −1.4 volts, the desired signal level.

If any one of the inputs to the circuit rises to the +3 volt level, the diode at the input will be forward biased, bringing the potential at the transistor base to the +3 volt level. The voltage drop across the diode or diodes which are forward biased will cause the actual signal level at the transistor base to be somewhat less than this, at perhaps +2.3 volts. When the input to the transistor base is at the +2.3 volt level, the emitter "follows" the base to this level; however, there will be a voltage drop from emitter to base. Since this drop is in the direction of the +6 voltage, the voltage will add to the +2.3 voltage at the base, bringing the output signal level to the +3 volt d-c level.

Besides performing the OR function on the input signals, this circuit provides power gain because of the emitter follower. With the transistors (silicon) used in the circuit illustrated, the output signal level may be changed at a repetition rate of 20 megacycles per sec. If the signal input levels have a 0.01 μsec rise and fall time, this OR circuit will have rise and fall times of less than 0.015 μsec.

4 · 13   Transistor OR gates

An all-transistor OR gate is illustrated in Fig. 4 · 11. It consists of several *npn* emitter followers connected in parallel, and the inputs to this OR gate are either +5 or −5 volt d-c levels. Notice that these levels are the same as the levels from the AND circuit in Fig. 4 · 8. These circuits were designed for the same machine, and they are therefore compatible. The output from the OR circuit in Fig. 4 · 11 is −5 volts d-c only when all three of the inputs are at −5 volts d-c. If any one or any combination of the three inputs is at the +5 volt d-c level, the output will be at the +5 volt level.

The three transistors in Fig. 4 · 11 are all connected as emitter followers in parallel, sharing a common emitter resistance. Any one of the transistors is capable of supplying enough current to bring the output to the +5 volt level. If only one of the inputs is at +5 volts, the

[4]The voltage drops across various types of diodes and transistors will vary. The voltage-drop values presented are intended to be illustrative and are characteristic of silicon diodes and transistors. Germanium diodes and transistors will generally have smaller drops when forward biased.

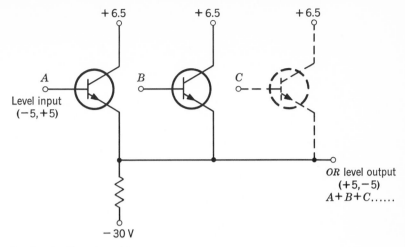

+6.5   +6.5   +6.5

A
Level input
(−5,+5)

B

C

OR level output
(+5,−5)
$A+B+C\ldots\ldots$

−30 V

Fig. 4 · 11   Transistor OR gate.

other transistors will be reverse biased from base to emitter by the +5 volt level on the output line. This will effectively isolate the inputs from each other.

4 · 14   Inverter circuit

The circuit illustrated in Fig. 4 · 12 has a common-emitter configuration and is commonly referred to as an *inverter*. The input signal to the inverter is applied to the base, and the output is taken at the collector. The particular circuit in Fig. 4 · 12 is from the TX-2 computer, which represents 1's and 0's with 0 and −3 volt d-c levels. With a 0-volt input, the 5- and 180-kilohm resistors will act as a voltage divider connected between 0 and +10 volts, and the voltage at the base of the transistor will be slightly positive. The transistor will therefore be cut off, with little current flowing in the emitter and collector circuits. Since the collector-to-emitter impedance will be high, the collector will tend toward the −10 volt supply level. It will, however, be clamped by the diode to the −3 volt level, and diode *CR*1 (which will be forward biased) will supply the additional current through the resistor to maintain the output at −3 volts.

If the input at x is at the −3 volt level, the transistor base will be held negative with respect to the emitter and the transistor will conduct heavily. The emitter-to-collector impedance will then be low, and the output will be effectively shorted to ground through the transistor.

The output of the transistor is therefore the *inverse* or *complement* of the input. If the inputs are 0 volts and −3 volts as in Fig. 4 · 12, with 0 volts representing a 1 and −3 volts a 0, the output will be the 1's complement of the input.

The block diagram symbol for the inverter is a hollow block with an I inside it, as shown in Fig. 4·12. Beneath the block diagram symbol is a table of input-to-output values. If the input to the circuit is designated as X, the output will be X', the inverse or complement of the input. The term "complement" will be further explained in Chap. 5.

The capacitor in Fig. 4·12, which is connected in parallel with the 5-kilohm input resistor, is used to overdrive the base when the negative-going edge of a pulse appears. If the transistor is cut off and the leading edge of a negative pulse appears, a surge of current will be applied directly to the transistor base, speeding up the rise time. The capacitor serves an even more important function in turning the transistor off. When the transistor is on and conducting heavily, minority carriers are accumulated in the transistor; when the input signal is returned to the 0-volt level, the capacitor serves to "sweep out" the minority carriers, reducing the storage time and decreasing the total fall time of the output.

The transistor-inverter configuration is very useful, not only for

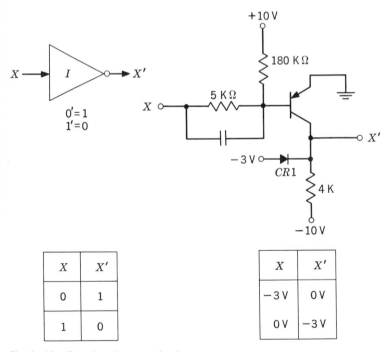

Fig. 4·12   Transistor-inverter circuit.

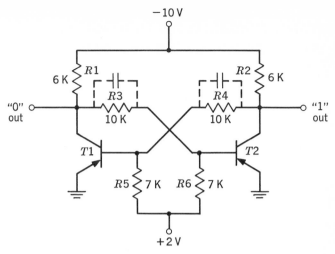

Fig. 4 · 13   Two-transistor flip-flop.

the logical function it performs, but also because of the power amplification it provides. The input resistance is high and the output resistance relatively low. Also, the voltage gain through the circuit makes it useful as a level restorer. If the signal levels through the circuitry connected to the input of the inverter have caused the basic logic d-c levels of the computer to shift, or if the amplitude of the pulses through the system has degenerated, the inverter circuit will amplify the signals and restore them to the proper values, although output polarities will be reversed. Sometimes "level restorer" or "buffer" circuits are used which consist of two inverters connected in series, that is, with the collector of the first connected to the base of the second.

4 · 15   The transistor flip-flop

The fundamental characteristic of the flip-flop circuit[5] is that at any given time it can be in only one of two possible states. For this reason the flip-flop circuit is called "bistable."

A basic two-transistor flip-flop circuit is shown in Fig. 4 · 13. The two states the circuit may be in are as follows: (1) transistor $T1$ is conducting and transistor $T2$ is cut off; and (2) transistor $T2$ is conducting and transistor $T1$ is cut off.

[5]The circuit is also referred to as a "bistable multivibrator," "Eccles-Jordan circuit" (after the inventors), and a "trigger" or "toggle." The designation "flip-flop" appears to be the most common in computer literature and will be used here.

If we assume positive logic, where ground or 0 volts represents a 1 and a negative potential represents a 0, the output labeled "1" will represent a 1 when $T2$ is conducting or *on* (and $T1$ is off) and will represent a 0 when $T2$ is *off* (and $T1$ is on).

The transistor flip-flop illustrated in Fig. 4·13 consists of two inverters coupled together. The circuit has two outputs, one at the collector of each of the transistors. For the parameters shown, the output voltage levels are approximately 0 and -7 volts. Since the circuit is bistable, one of the outputs will always be at -7 volts when the other output is at 0 volts. The transistor whose collector is at -7 volts will be cut off.

The circuit can be best explained if it is assumed to be in one of the two possible states and if the switching action is then described. Assume that transistor $T2$ is saturated and transistor $T1$ is cut off. Transistor $T2$ will then present a low resistance from collector to emitter and the collector potential will be at essentially 0 volts. If the collector of $T2$ is at ground potential, resistors $R4$ and $R5$ will act as voltage dividers from the $+2$ volt supply to ground and will bias the base of transistor $T1$ positive with respect to the emitter, which is grounded. This will cause transistor $T1$ to be cut off, and $T1$ will present a high emitter-to-collector impedance. Resistors $R1$, $R3$, and $R6$ are in series between the -10 and $+2$ volt supplies, and the collector of $T1$ will be held at approximately -7 volts. The current flowing through $R1$, $R3$, and $R6$ will also bias the base of $T2$ negative with respect to the grounded emitter, maintaining the transistor in saturation. The circuit will be stable in this condition.

If a negative pulse of sufficient amplitude is applied at the base of transistor $T1$, the base will be biased negative with respect to the emitter and the transistor will begin to conduct. As the transistor begins to conduct, the current through resistor $R1$ will increase and the potential at the 0 output will start positive. As the voltage at the junction of $R3$ and $R6$ becomes more positive, transistor $T2$ will start toward cutoff and current through $T2$ will decrease, causing the 1 output to become more negative. When the collector of $T1$ approaches 0 volts, $R3$ and $R6$ will hold the base of transistor $T2$ positive with respect to the emitter and the transistor will be held in the cutoff condition. The flip-flop will then be in the other of its two stable states with transistor $T2$ cut off and $T1$ conducting heavily. In this state, the voltage level at the 0 output will be relatively positive (0 volts) with respect to the voltage at the 1 output (-7 volts).

The switching action of the circuit can be speeded up by adding capacitors (indicated by dotted lines) in parallel with resistors $R3$ and $R4$. These commutator capacitors will then bypass the coupling resistors during switching, increasing the gain during the switching action. However, the frequency at which different flip-flops must operate and the loads which the flip-flops must drive generally vary within a given machine. For this reason, several flip-flops compatible with the other logical circuits are generally made available to the logical designer. This is not to say that a different flip-flop is designed for each application; instead, several general types of flip-flops are usually designed. The characteristics which determine the use of a particular flip-flop in a specific application are generally dependent upon the loads that the flip-flop must drive and the highest frequency at which the flip-flop must operate.

4 · 16   A SET - CLEAR flip-flop

The flip-flop circuit's basic characteristic is that it can be in only one of two possible states at a given time and that it will remain in that state until commanded to change states. In order to introduce information into the flip-flops of a machine, we must be able to read a 0 or a 1 into a flip-flop. A simple method for doing this is shown in Fig. 4 · 14. This flip-flop is the same in basic configuration as the flip-flop shown in Fig. 4 · 13, except that it has SET and CLEAR lines each connected to the bases of the transistors through a diode. The transistors in this circuit are *pnp* transistors, and we will assume positive logic so a negative signal will represent a 0 and a 0-volt signal a 1.

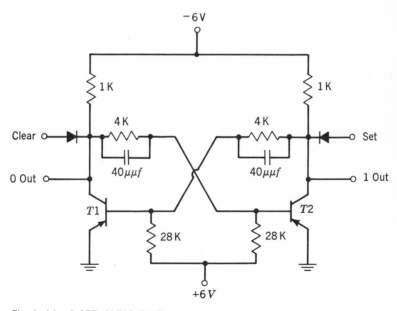

Fig. 4 · 14   A SET - CLEAR flip-flop.

Assume the flip-flop is in the 1 state with the transistor $T1$ off and transistor $T2$ on. If we apply a 0-volt signal at the CLEAR input, the base of $T2$ will be carried positive by current flowing through the diode at the CLEAR input and through the 4-kilohm resistor to the base of $T2$. This will cause $T2$ to be cut off, and when the collector of $T2$ goes negative, current flowing through the 4-kilohm resistor connected to the base of $T1$ will cause $T1$ to be turned on. The flip-flop will now be in the 0 state with $T1$ on and $T2$ off.

If the flip-flop is in the 0 state and we apply a 0-volt signal to the SET input, $T1$ will be turned off and this will turn on $T2$, thus setting a 1 into the flip-flop.

The purpose of the diodes at the SET and CLEAR inputs is to prevent negative signals from affecting the flip-flop. If, for instance, the flip-flop is in the 1 state, the only signal which will affect the state of the flip-flop will be a 0-volt signal at the CLEAR input. A negative signal at the SET input will backbias the diode at that input, and no current will flow into the circuit, thus leaving it unaffected. Similarly, a 0-volt signal at the SET input will have no effect, since the collector of $T2$ is already at 0 volts.

4 · 17   A clocked SET - CLEAR flip-flop

Quite often, computer circuits are operated in a clocked mode. From the viewpoint of the flip-flop circuit, this means that a given flip-flop will be allowed to change values only when a clock pulse occurs in the system. This greatly alleviates timing problems and simplifies both design and maintenance of a machine. As a result, almost all commercial computers have their timing derived from a master clock.

Let us assume we have a system where the clock consists of a 0.1 μsec duration positive pulse occurring at a rate of 1 megacycle (one million pulses per second). The information in the system is to be represented by the d-c levels from flip-flops and gates in the system. We therefore will use d-c levels to determine whether a 0 or 1 is to be read into a given flip-flop and will introduce new information only when a clock pulse occurs.

The flip-flop in Fig. 4 · 15 is a clocked SET - CLEAR flip-flop which will go to the 1 state if the SET input lead is at 0 volts (representing a 1) and an input clock signal occurs, and will go to the 0 state if the CLEAR input is at 0 volts (representing a 1) and an input clock pulse occurs. If both the SET and CLEAR inputs are at 0 volts and an input clock pulse occurs, the flip-flop will be unaffected. The designer must see that both the SET and CLEAR inputs are not positive when an input clock signal occurs, for the state of the flip-flop after this occurrence is indeterminate.

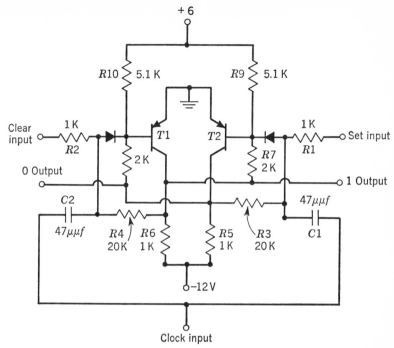

Fig. 4 · 15   Clocked SET · CLEAR flip-flop.

The two transistors with their associated resistors form a standard two-transistor flip-flop with the same basic operation as the flip-flop in Fig. 4 · 14. The capacitors, $C2$ and $C1$, the diodes $CR1$ and $CR2$, and the resistors $R1$ and $R2$ form a SET and a CLEAR input network. Assume that the SET input is at 0 volts and that the positive-going edge of the clock pulse appears; the intersection of $C1$ and $CR5$ will go positive by the amplitude of the leading edge of the positive clock pulse. This positive-going signal will pass through diode $CR1$ turning $T2$ off and setting the flip-flop to the 1 state, if it was not already in the 1 state. Similar reasoning will show that when the CLEAR input is at the 0-volt level and the clock pulse appears, the flip-flop will be reset to the 0 state.

If both the SET and CLEAR inputs are negative voltages less than the amplitude of the clock pulse, the clock pulses will not affect the flip-flops because the intersection of $CR1$ and $C1$, for instance, will never go positive. And, since each transistor base will be at either 0 volts or slightly positive, neither diode will ever conduct and the state of the flip-flop will not be changed. Figure 4 · 16 shows a typical sequence of input waveforms and their corresponding effects on the flip-flop.

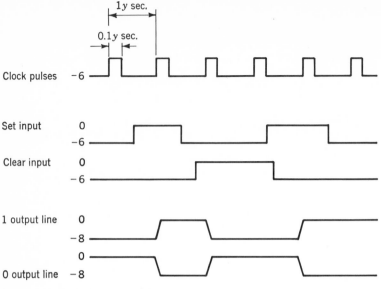

Fig. 4 · 16   Typical waveforms for the flip-flop in Fig. 4 · 15.

4 · 18   The complementing or triggering flip-flop

One other type of flip-flop input circuit is sometimes used, and this is an input circuit which routes an input pulse in a manner such that the state of the flip-flop is always changed.

If the CLEAR input of Fig. 4 · 15 is connected to the 1 OUTPUT line of the flip-flop and the SET input to the 0 OUTPUT line, we will have such a circuit. In this case there will be a single input line marked the clock input. When a positive-going signal of sufficient amplitude is applied at this input, the flip-flop will always change states.

Figure 4 · 17 shows such a flip-flop, which uses different resistors from those shown in Fig. 4 · 15 but has the same basic configuration.

The reasoning behind the operation of this flip-flop can be seen if we consider that when the flip-flop is in the 0 state, the 0 OUTPUT line will represent a 1 and tell the SET input to read a 1 into the flip-flop; while if the flip-flop is in the 1 state, the 1 OUTPUT line will be a 1 and cause a positive pulse to read a 0 into the flip-flop. Therefore, whenever a positive pulse appears at the clock input, the flip-flop will change states.[6]

The clock input would then be called a *complement* or *trigger* input,

[6]Actually, a positive-going signal of sufficient amplitude is what is needed to cause the flip-flop to change states. A negative-going portion of a signal at the input will not affect the flip-flop, provided it does not follow a positive edge too closely.

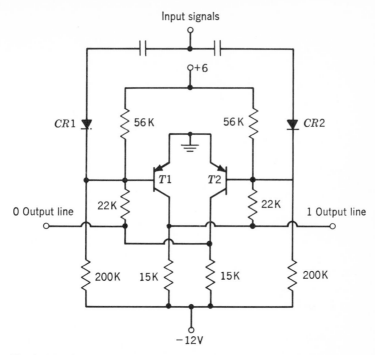

Input signals

+6

CR1   56 K   56 K   CR2

T1   T2

0 Output line   22 K   22 K   1 Output line

200K   15K   15K   200K

−12V

Fig. 4·17   A triggering or complementing flip-flop.

and we say that whenever the flip-flop changes states, it is *complemented* or *triggered.*

4·19   Symbolic representation of flip-flop

The symbols used to represent the flip-flop are illustrated in Fig. 4·18. Figure 4·18a illustrates a flip-flop with two inputs, CLEAR and SET, and with a 0 and 1 output.[7] Sometimes the SET and CLEAR and the 0 and 1 are omitted from drawings. In this case, it is generally understood that the CLEAR input is drawn to the left of the SET input and the 0 output to the left of the 1 output. Figure 4·18b illustrates a flip-flop with only one input. This is the trigger or complementing flip-flop. Any input pulse to this flip-flop results in a change in the state of the flip-flop. Notice that the conventions of using an arrow to represent a pulse (at the inputs) and a hollow diamond to represent a d-c level (at the outputs) are also used. When a flip-flop has TRIGGER, SET, and CLEAR inputs, the block diagram symbol is a combination of the two symbols illustrated.

[7]Sometimes the CLEAR input is called the RESET input.

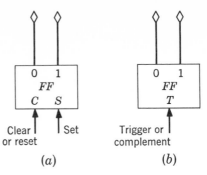

Fig. 4 · 18   Block diagram symbols for flip-flops.

4 · 20   The binary counter

A basic function which digital circuits must perform is that of counting. A counter, by definition, is a device which records the number of events which have occurred. The input to an electronic counter commonly consists of a series of pulses, and the counter records the number of pulses which have occurred during a given time. Memory is involved in this process, as the counter must record in some way the total number of pulses. In the two examples which follow, flip-flops are used as the basic memory devices, and the state of the flip-flops will indicate the number of pulses which have been transmitted.

Figure 4 · 19 illustrates a 4-bit binary counter. There are two input lines to the counter: an input line which is used to clear each flip-flop in the counter, setting it to the 0 state, and an input line for the pulses to be counted.

Since the counter illustrated has only four storage devices, it can represent only 16 different numbers (from 0000 to 1111 binary, or from 0 to 15 decimal). The total number of states which a given counter may have is equal to 2^n, where n is the number of binary storage elements in the counter. A 6-bit counter could therefore represent 2^6 or 64 numbers. The counter illustrated starts at 0000 when the flip-flops are cleared, and counts to 1111 by increments of 1, that is, 0000, 0001, 0010, 0011, . . . , 1111.

The flip-flops used in the counter can only be complemented by *positive* pulses; that is, a *negative-going* signal will *not* change the state of a flip-flop. (The flip-flop in Fig. 4 · 17 could be used.) The rightmost flip-flop, $FF4$, represents the least significant bit of the number represented by the counter; the next flip-flop, $FF3$, the second least significant bit; and $FF1$, the most significant.

After the flip-flops have been cleared, all the 0 output lines will be high. The first positive pulse will then complement $FF4$. The 0 output of $FF4$ will go negative and the 1 output line positive. The input to

*FF*3 is from the 0 line of *FF*4, so the input pulse to *FF*3 will be negative and the flip-flop will remain in the 0 state. The counter will then contain 0001.

When the second pulse arrives, *FF*4 will again be complemented; however, this time the 0 output line will go positive, and a positive pulse will appear at the complement input of *FF*3, changing the state of the flip-flop. A negative pulse will appear at the input to *FF*2, so flip-flop *FF*2 will not change states. The counter will then contain 0010. The waveform at the 1 output of each flip-flop is shown in Fig. 4 · 19.

When the counter is in the 1111 state, the input pulse will first complement *FF*4, causing *FF*3, *FF*2, and finally *FF*1 to be complemented in turn. The counter will then contain 0000. The counter is cyclic, returning to its original state after every sequence of 16 pulses.

The counter also performs another important function, that of frequency division. If the pulse repetition rate of the input pulses is

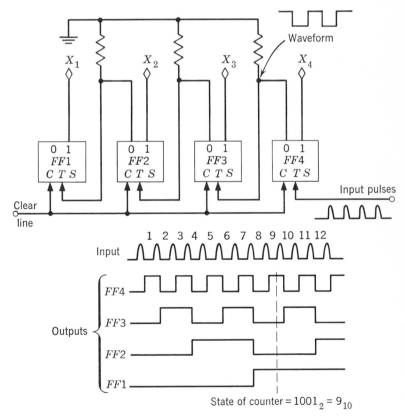

Fig. 4 · 19   Four-stage binary counter.

1 megacycle, the frequency at which $FF3$ changes states will be 500 kc (kilocycles); $FF2$ will change states at a rate of 250 kc, and $FF1$ at a rate of 125 kc.

4 · 21   A more flexible counter

A higher-speed and more flexible counter is illustrated in Fig. 4 · 20. This counter uses AND gates to sense the states of the flip-flops and decide whether to complement the next flip-flop in the chain. Assume the counter contains 0111: the AND gates connected to $FF2$, $FF3$, and $FF4$ will then be enabled, and an input pulse will cause all four of the flip-flops to be complemented, changing the state of the counter to 1000.

For instance, if the counter contains 0101, an input pulse will complement $FF4$ and will also pass through the rightmost AND gate and complement $FF3$. The pulse will not pass through the second AND gate, however, as the input to the gate from $FF3$ will represent a 0 and the pulse will be inhibited. After the pulse, the counter will contain 0110.

The counter in Fig. 4 · 20 is more flexible than the counter in Fig. 4 · 19 because the states of the flip-flops may be changed without interaction between flip-flops. Suppose that the counter in Fig. 4 · 19 contains 0111, where $FF1$ contains 0, $FF2$ contains 1, $FF3$ contains 1, and $FF4$ contains 1. If we attempt to "put" a 0 into $FF2$, a positive-going signal will appear at the 0 output of $FF2$ as it changes states, and this will cause $FF1$ to change states. If the counter contains 0111 and we try to change the state of $FF4$ from 1 to 0, the counter will change to the 1000 state. The counter in Fig. 4 · 20 will not behave in this manner. The state of any flip-flop may be changed by applying

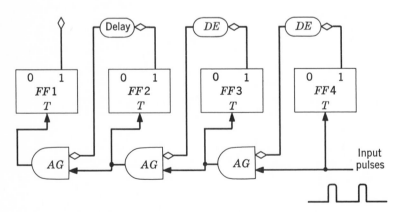

Fig. 4 · 20   Parallel binary counter.

a pulse to the SET or RESET line of the flip-flop and, unless an input pulse to the counter circuitry line is applied at the same time, the other flip-flops will not be affected.

4 · 22 The race problem

There is one problem connected with the counter in Fig. 4 · 20. Suppose that a flip-flop changes state during an input pulse. If the flip-flop originally held a 0 and changes to a 1 during a pulse, the associated AND gate will be enabled and will pass the latter part of the input pulse, perhaps complementing an incorrect flip-flop. This basic problem, that of storage devices changing states during a pulse, is called the *race problem*.

A possible solution, shown in Fig. 4 · 20, is the addition of delay lines between the outputs of the storage devices and the inputs to the gates. If the storage device changes states during a pulse, the change will be delayed until after the fall of the pulse and the race problem will thus be eliminated.

Another technique involves having an inherent delay in the action of the storage devices; several types of storage devices have been designed which will change their states only when a certain period has passed after an input to the circuit. This is also a form of delay; in this case, the response of the storage devices is delayed.

Still another technique involves storage devices which change states only on the trailing edge of a pulse. Flip-flops are often used which are triggered only by positive pulses, but which will change states only at the trailing or negative-going portion of a positive input pulse. This offers another solution, as the flip-flops will not change states during a pulse, but only at the trailing edge.

4 · 23 Delay lines

The *bit-time* interval is the basic time interval for a serial-type machine. The duration of a bit time is equal to the inverse of the pulse-repetition rate for the machine. For instance, if a basic clock pulse rate of the machine is 250 kc, a bit time will be 4 μsec. Delays in a serial machine will often be expressed as multiples of the basic bit-time period; for instance, in the case mentioned, 1 bit time would be 4 μsec; 2 bit times, 8 μsec; etc.

The total time period which elapses from the beginning of the signal representing the first bit of a serial computer word until the signal representing the first bit of the next word is defined as a *word time*. For instance, if the pulse-repetition rate for the machine is 250 kc, a bit time will be 4 μsec; that is, the time allocated to each signal representing a bit of the number. If the basic computer word contains 30 bits, the word time for the machine will be 120 μsec.

Storage or memory can be made using electrical or electro-mechanical devices called *delay lines*. A signal connected at the input to a delay line appears at the output after some finite fixed-time interval. The time which elapses between the input and output is called the *delay time*.

If a delay line is made long enough, it will be able to delay a whole sequence of signals. Suppose that a serial machine has a 15-bit number to be stored in pulse form (a positive pulse represents a 1 and the absence of a pulse a 0) and that a bit-time period for the machine is 2 μsec. If the delay time for the line is 30 μsec, the entire sequence of pulses which represents a number may be inserted at the input to the line, and it will appear at the output after a delay of 30 μsec. If the output of the line is connected back to the input, then the line will be in the shape of a loop, and the entire sequence of pulses representing a number will continue to circulate around this loop.

Figure 4·21 illustrates a length of delay line connected in this way, except that a retiming and reshaping amplifier has been inserted between the output from the line and the input to it. The basic clock pulses of the machine are used to reestablish the timing of the pulses so that they remain in synchronization with the rest of the machine. Storage of this type is called *dynamic storage* because the information stored is continually changing position.

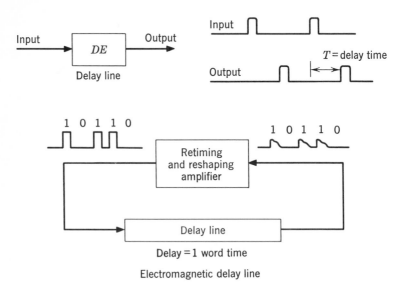

Fig. 4·21   Delay lines.

The delay time required to store a number of words is liable to be from several hundred microseconds to several milliseconds. In order to construct lines with delay times in this region, *sonic delay lines* are generally used. A sonic delay line consists of a sonic conductor and two transducers, i.e., a *transmitter* which transforms an incoming electrical pulse into a sonic pulse and a *receiver* which detects the sonic pulse and transforms it back into electrical form.

The delay time of a sonic delay line is dependent on the velocity of acoustic wave propagation in the medium used. Mercury and quartz delay lines were used in several of the earlier computers, but magnetostrictive and glass delay lines are now in use almost exclusively. Magnetostriction is a property of materials which change their length under the influence of a magnetic field. Magnetostrictive delay lines consist of a length of magnetostrictive material (which is generally a special type of metal wire) with a transmitter at one end and a receiver at the other. The transmitter consists of a coil wound around the magnetostrictive material at one end of the delay line. Current through this coil causes a stress in the magnetostrictive material, launching an acoustic wave. This wave is propagated along the line and is then detected at the other end, where it induces a voltage in a receiving coil. The line is terminated at each end so that reflections do not occur.

Glass delay lines are now quite popular. While glass delay lines do not in general provide the amount of delay which can be obtained in magnetostrictive delay lines, they may be operated at a much higher frequency. For instance, bits may be stored in magnetostrictive delay lines at a rate of perhaps 2 megacycles, but glass delay lines may be operated at rates of 20 megacycles. As a result, a 0.1-msec delay line of magnetostrictive material would hold 200 bits, but a glass delay line with the same delay would hold 2,000 bits. The situation is not quite that simple, however, as cost per unit of delay and a number of other considerations enter the picture, so that the two types of lines have been very competitive for different types of machines.

Glass delay lines have a delay of approximately 1 μsec for each 0.1 in. That is, the velocity of sound in glass is approximately 0.1 in. per μsec. Sometimes glass delay lines are made in the shape of rods; the length of the rod determines the delay of the line. Glass delay lines are also made in flat plates which are shaped so that the beam of sound launched by the transmitter is bounced back and forth off several walls before it reaches the receiver. In this case, the delay is equal to the total path length of the beam from transmitter to receiver.

4 · 24   Shift registers

A *register* is defined as a device which is capable of storing information. In digital computers, registers generally consist of a set of storage devices. For instance, in a binary machine, a register composed of 15 flip-flops would be capable of storing 15 bits of information. The register illustrated in Fig. 4 · 22 contains n storage devices, each a flip-flop. In this register, the binary bit stored in each flip-flop will be shifted one place to the right each time a clock pulse is applied. A register that is constructed in this manner is called a *shift register.*

The sequence of signals representing the number to be read in is connected to the input lines at the left in Fig. 4 · 22. Each time a bit is to be read into the register, a clock pulse is applied. This causes all the bits in the register to be shifted right, and the new bit to be stored in the leftmost storage device. If the series of signals representing the number to be read in are contained on a single line, an inverter may be used to form the necessary waveshape for the other input line since there are two input lines to the register.

If a steady train of clock pulses is applied to the shift input line, the input waveform will be reproduced at the outputs from the register after a number of clock pulses equal to the number of storage devices (bits) in the register have been applied. If the clock pulses are spaced 2 μsec apart, and the length of the register is 12 bits, the input waveform will appear at the output from the shift register after a delay of 24 μsec. The outputs from the flip-flops will be in essentially d-c form; however, the d-c signals may be converted to pulses with the width and amplitude of the clock pulses by connecting an AND gate to the 1 output of the last flip-flop and pulsing it with the clock pulses (refer to Fig. 4 · 22).

The block diagram symbol for the shift register is illustrated at the bottom of Fig. 4 · 22. Two input lines and two output lines are shown, but only one input and one output line will often be drawn.

Other types of storage devices are also used to construct shift registers. Shift registers using ring-shaped pieces of ferromagnetic material (called cores) for storage devices are often used. The direction of magnetization of the material used in these cores indicates whether a 0 or a 1 is stored. The properties of these storage devices will be discussed in Chap. 7. Shift registers may also be constructed using other configurations than that shown in Fig. 4 · 22. Regardless of the construction, the characteristics of the shift register are the same. Each bit of the information stored is shifted each time a SHIFT pulse is applied.

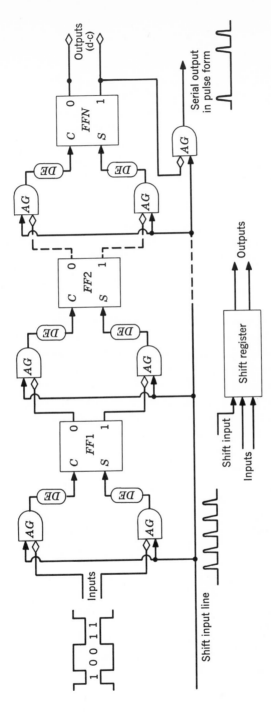

Fig. 4 · 22 Shift register.

4 · 25 Circulating registers

A register using a delay line and a retiming and reshaping amplifier (the dynamic storage technique described in Sec. 4 · 23) will have characteristics very similar to those of the shift register. Both are capable of storing a number of bits; both have serial inputs and outputs. If the output of a shift register is connected back to its input, it will resemble the circulating storage of the delay line. Figure 4 · 23 shows a circulating register in which either a dynamic storage loop or a shift register may be used.

A series of pulses representing a number in serial form may be read into the register and then circulated, and information stored in the register may also be "cleared." The "control flip-flop" is used to control the operation of the register illustrated in Fig. 4 · 23. SHIFT pulses are assumed to be applied continuously. If the control flip-flop is set to the 1 state by a pulse on the READ IN NEW DATA line, a binary number transmitted in serial form may be read into the register through the INPUT line connected to the AND gate. After the last bit of the number is in the register, the number may be caused to circulate around the register by pulsing the CIRCULATE input, setting the control flip-flop to the 0 state.

If the control flip-flop is set to the 1 state for a length of time equal to the time required for a signal to traverse the length of the register (the total delay time of the delay line for dynamic storage) and no pulses are applied at the input during this period, the register will be cleared. It is not necessary to clear this register before reading in new information, however, as the AND gate in the feedback loop will

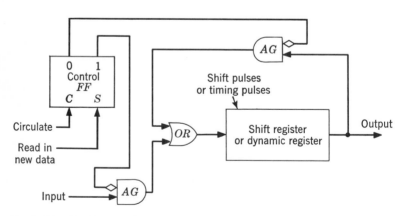

Fig. 4 · 23   Circulating register.

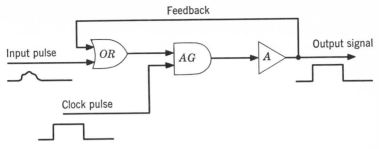

Fig. 4 · 24   Retiming and reshaping amplifier.

block the circulation of old data when the control flip-flop is in the 1 state.

4 · 26   Retiming and reshaping amplifier

The retiming and reshaping of pulses is an important function in synchronous serial computers. When dynamic registers such as those just described are used, the pulses circulating through the delay line will be attenuated and the delay time of the delay line will not exactly correspond to the timing of the computer. If, for example, a number of dynamic registers are used, the pulses circulating through the various registers will drift slowly out of synchronization. In order to prevent this, each register utilizes a retiming and reshaping amplifier which regenerates the pulses and maintains them in synchronization with the central timing. Retiming and reshaping amplifiers are also used to restore pulses after they have passed through logical circuitry.

The block diagram of the amplifier in Fig. 4 · 24 shows one possible configuration. The leading edge of each input pulse representing the information stored is arranged to arrive slightly in advance of the clock pulse. Coincidence between the input pulse and the clock pulse causes the AND gate to conduct. The output of the AND gate is amplified by the amplifier (noninverting), and the amplified signal is fed back to the OR gate. The increased signal to the OR gate will regenerate the input signal. If the input pulse falls before the trailing edge of the clock pulse occurs, the feedback path will cause the OR gate to continue to conduct and the output pulse will stay "up." When the clock pulse falls, however, the lower input to the AND gate will be discontinued and the output pulse will fall. Thus the feedback loop causes the output to be sustained until the clock pulse is terminated.

If no input pulse arrives, the process will not be initiated and no pulse will appear at the output.

4 · 27   Integrated circuits

The circuitry presently used in digital machines can be roughly broken into two categories: discrete component circuitry and integrated circuitry. Historically, the discrete component circuitry came first; discrete component transistors, resistors, diodes, etc., are each packaged separately, and a circuit is made by interconnecting a number of individual components on a printed circuit board. In this case, one or more gates or flip-flops are usually mounted on a given printed circuit board, and then the boards are interconnected to make a machine. Generally, each board holds several circuits of the same type, such as flip-flop and AND-gate circuits.

With integrated circuitry, entire flip-flop circuits or several gate circuits or perhaps several inverters are all placed in the same small container. Two of the most popular means for packaging integrated circuits are the small top hat or TO-5 can, and the flat pack shown in Fig. 4 · 25. The TO-5 can was for a long time a container for a single transistor; so the difference in size between ordinary and integrated circuitry can be readily observed. The increased packing density is also of considerable advantage from a speed viewpoint, since interconnecting leads between circuits can be made quite short, reducing capacity and propagation time for signals. Also, the circuits themselves can be made quite fast.

From a circuit theory viewpoint, the principles of integrated circuits are much the same as the principles of discrete component circuits. The schematic diagrams for integrated circuits almost duplicate the schematics for discrete component circuits. For reasons of manufacture, integrated circuits tend to have the following characteristics, however.

1 Integrated circuits use very few capacitors and almost no inductances.
2 The power supply voltages and the signal voltages are smaller for integrated circuits than for discrete component circuits.
3 The values of the components in integrated circuits tend to be smaller than for discrete components. The resistances in integrated circuits tend to be in hundreds of ohms, while the resistances for discrete components circuits tend to be in thousands of ohms.

As an example, a diode AND gate for discrete components would likely use a 15-kilohm resistor similar to that in Fig. 4 · 6 and would use a power supply voltage from $+10$ to $+30$ volts d-c, while an integrated circuit would probably have a power supply voltage of $+2$ to $+6$ volts. The resistor to the positive voltage might be one or two hundred ohms for integrated circuits, and will likely be from 5 to

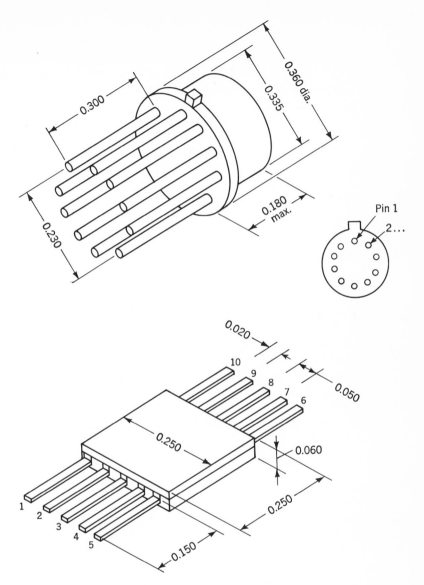

Fig. 4 · 25   Integrated and discrete component circuits.

15 kilohms for discrete circuits. Similarly, the signals for integrated circuits would be on the order of 0 volts for a binary 0 and perhaps +1 to +3 volts for a 1, while discrete component circuits with a 0-volt signal for a 0 would have signals of from +3 to + 10 volts for binary 1. Nevertheless, the principle of operation is the same; for instance, the operation of the diodes would be the same.

There is a natural tendency to classify digital circuits according to the types of components they consist of. Whole systems of circuits are then categorized as, for instance, "diode-transistor logic" or "resistor-transistor logic," etc. These classifications are somewhat artifical, but are helpful nonetheless. The major classifications are:

1 DTL—diode-transistor logic
2 RTL and TRL—resistor-transistor logic
3 DCTL—direct-coupled transistor logic
4 TTL—transistor-transistor logic

There are a few other types of circuits, such as current-steering circuits and current-switching circuits, but the above four are the major categories. We shall examine these types, bearing in mind that each of the circuits already shown falls into one of the four classes.

4·28 Diode-transistor logic

As may be deduced from the title, diode-transistor logic circuits use combinations of diodes and transistors to perform the desired logical functions. Almost all the circuits which have been shown in previous sections are diode-transistor logic circuits (or, when capacitors are used, diode capacitor or DCTL circuits). A typical diode-transistor logic circuit, and one which is particularly emphasized in integrated circuitry, is shown in Fig. 4·26. Just as diode-transistor logic is among the most popular logical systems in use today, the diode-transistor NAND circuit shown in Fig. 4·26 is one of the most popular logical gates now manufactured in computer circuitry. The particular resistor values shown in the figure are those which are used in the IBM 360 series. However, almost any manufacturer of inte-

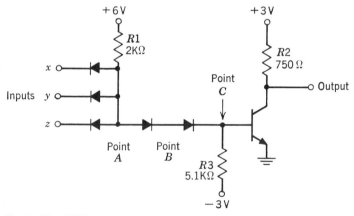

Fig. 4·26   NAND gate.

grated circuitry produces a gate with this basic configuration; the primary difference between the circuits manufactured by different companies lies in the values of the resistances and the speeds obtainable in the diode and transistor circuits.

The NAND circuit in Fig. 4 · 26 has three inputs which are labeled x, y, and z, and a single output. The term "NAND gate" is a contraction of the term "NOT AND gate," and sometimes this circuit is called a NOT AND gate. The reason is that the circuit is actually a composite of two circuits, an AND gate, and an inverter. Since an inverter is sometimes called a "NOT gate," we have the contraction NAND gate for NOT AND gate.

The AND gate in Fig. 4 · 26 consists of the three diodes connected to the x, y, and z inputs and resistor $R1$ connected to $+6$ volts, which corresponds exactly to the AND gate shown in Fig. 4 · 6. The remaining two diodes, two resistors, and transistor then comprise an inverter circuit. The difference between this circuit and the inverters shown earlier consists of the two diodes connected in series to the base of the transistor. Both the transistor and these two diodes are silicon semiconductors. When a diode is forward biased, it will have a relatively constant voltage drop across it, for reasonable variations in current through the diode. The diodes connected to the base of the transistor in Fig. 4 · 26 will be kept permanently forward biased by current flowing from $+6$ volts to -3 volts through resistors $R1$ and $R3$. Since the two diodes are silicon diodes, they will each drop about 0.7 volt.

We can check the operation of the circuit as follows: Suppose the three inputs, x, y, and z, are all at 0 volts d-c. The silicon diodes connected to these inputs will also drop about 0.7 volt, since each diode will be forward biased by current flowing through $R1$ from $+6$ volts. The potential at point A will then be at about $+0.7$ volt d-c. Since current is flowing through the diode connected between point A and point B, this diode will drop this potential 0.7 volt negative making point B approximately 0 volts d-c. Another 0.7 volt will then be dropped across the second diode which is connected to the base of the transistor, and point C will therefore be at approximately -0.7 volt d-c, biasing the transistor off. This being the case, the output of the transistor will tend toward $+3$ volts, and if there is no load on the output, it will indeed be at $+3$ volts d-c. (Sometimes the second diode, which is connected directly to the base of the transistor, is made so that it will drop somewhat greater than 0.7 volt, thus biasing the transistor more negatively when the input levels are at 0.)

Now let us assume that all three inputs are at $+3$ volts. The transistor will be on in this case, owing to the current through $R1$, and the drop across the base-to-emitter junction of the transistor will also

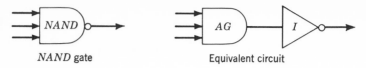

NAND gate   Equivalent circuit

Fig. 4·27   NAND gate symbol.

be at about 0.7 volt d-c. Therefore, point C will be at 0.7 volt d-c, point B will be at 1.4 volts d-c, point A will be at 2.1 volts d-c, and the three diodes connected to the x, y, and z inputs will be reversed biased by this potential. At this time, since the transistor will be on, the output potential will be clamped to approximately 0 volts d-c although there may be some voltage drop from emitter to collector when the transistor is in saturation. This will seldom exceed some fractions of a volt (on the order of less than 0.5 volt).

If we let $+3$ volt signal levels represent 1's and 0-volt signal levels represent 0's, the output from this NAND-gate structure will be a 1 at all times except when all three of the inputs, x, y, and z, are at $+3$ volts or 1 input signals. If, however, all three of the inputs are $+3$ volts d-c representing 1's, the output of the circuit will be at 0 volts d-c representing a logical 0. This is precisely the action produced by the NAND-gate circuit. If any one of the inputs represents a 0, the NAND gate will have a 1 output. If, however, all of the inputs represent 1's, the NAND gate will have a 0 output. Whether the NAND gate has two inputs, three inputs, four inputs, or more, the principle is still the same. All of the inputs must be at the 1 level in order for the output to be a 0. For all other input combinations the output of the NAND gate will be a logical 1.

The block diagram symbol for the NAND gate is shown in Fig. 4·27, as is the combination of the AND gate and inverter which is logically equivalent to the NAND-gate circuit.

4·29   Resistor-transistor logic

Figure 4·28 shows a typical gate in a resistor-transistor logic system. Instead of using diodes at the inputs-to-gates as in diode-transistor logic systems, the gating structures are forms of resistors and transistors only.

We can diagnose the operation of the circuit in Fig. 4·28 as follows: Consider that a 0-volt logic signal represents a 0 and a $+3$ volt logic signal represents a 1. If all three of the inputs to x, y, and z are at 0 volts d-c, then point A will be negative with respect to ground because of the current flowing through the 10-kilohm resistor to -3 volts. This will turn the *npn* transistor in the circuit off and the

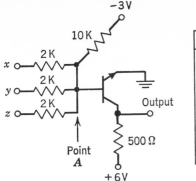

Signals				Logical valves			
x	y	z	Out	x	y	z	Out
0V	0V	0V	+6	0	0	0	1
0	0	+3	0	0	0	1	0
0	+3	0	0	0	1	0	0
0	+3	+3	0	0	1	1	0
+3	0	0	0	1	0	0	0
+3	0	+3	0	1	0	1	0
+3	+3	0	0	1	1	0	0
+3	+3	+3	0	1	1	1	0

Fig. 4 · 28   RTL NOR gate.

output will tend to go toward +6 volts. It will in fact be at +6 volts if there is no output load on the circuit. If, however, one of the inputs, x, y, or z, is carried to +3 volts, representing a 1, the voltage divider consisting of the other two resistors which will be at 0 volts and of the 10-kilohm resistor at −3 volts will not carry the junction of the three resistors negative. Instead, the base of the transistor will be positive, turning the transistor on and bringing the output of the transistor to approximately 0 volts, representing a logical 0. The same situation will occur if any two inputs or if all three inputs are at +3 volts d-c. In each of these cases, the transistor will be turned on and the output from the gate will be a logical 0. A table of combinations showing the input-output relations for the RTL NOR-gate circuit is also shown in Fig. 4 · 28.

A block diagram symbol for the NOR gate is shown in Fig. 4 · 29, as is an equivalent circuit which illustrates that the NOR gate performs the same logical function as an OR gate followed by an inverter. As may be deduced, the term "NOR" is a contraction of "NOT OR," signifying that the logical function performed is that of the OR gate followed by an inverter or NOT circuit. While resistor-transistor logic has been fairly popular in discrete component circuitry, it is not used much in integrated circuitry because of the difficulty in manufacturing circuits with precise resistor values and because of the greater speeds attainable with diode-transistor logic, direct-coupled transistor logic, and transistor-transistor logic.

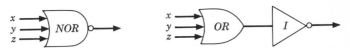

Fig. 4 · 29   NOR-gate block diagram symbol.

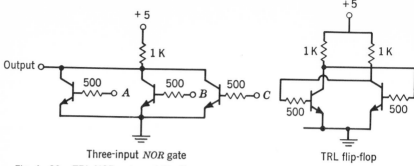

Three-input *NOR* gate   TRL flip-flop

Fig. 4 · 30   TRL NOR gate and flip-flop.

The circuit in Fig. 4 · 30 is called a TRL NOR gate, a contraction of transistor-resistor-logic. The circuit has three inputs, *A*, *B*, and *C*, and the output will be a 1 only when all inputs are 0's. The logic levels for the circuit shown are 0 volts for a binary and +1⅔ volts for a 1, and the output will be at 0 volts only when all three inputs to *A*, *B*, and *C* are positive levels.

This type of circuit is very popular in microcircuit or integrated circuit systems. The resistors are small and they need not be precise in value. Also, there is gain through every stage. The circuits are simple and with good transistors can be very fast. Notice that only transistors and resistors are used, this being the reason for the name TRL. Flip-flops are made of two NOR gates connected together as shown in Fig. 4 · 30, and also consist only of resistors and transistors.

Entire machines have been made of just the NOR-gate type of circuit by making flip-flops consisting of cross-coupled NOR gates of the type shown. NOR gates can be used to make both AND gates and OR gates as will be shown in the next chapter.

4 · 30   Direct-coupled transistor logic

Quite small voltage swings are found in a class of circuitry known as *direct-coupled transistor logic* (DCTL). The circuits in DCTL systems are characterized by their simplicity. Figure 4 · 31 illustrates two inverters, a flip-flop, a NAND gate, and a NOR gate.

The basic DCTL circuits use only transistors and resistors. Coupling between circuits is by direct connection and coupling capacitors or resistor nets are not used; instead, the output of each gate is directly coupled to the input of the next. While the voltages associated with 1's and with 0's are measurably different in this system, the difference in levels is quite small, perhaps 0.3 volts. The difference in the currents associated with the 0 and 1 states is quite distinct, however. For this reason, it is profitable to examine the logic levels from both a voltage and current viewpoint.

If the input to the base of the first inverter in Fig. 4·31a is at 0 volts, the transistor will be effectively cut off, and the collector-to-emitter resistance will be high. The base of the second transistor will therefore "see" only the 1-kilohm resistor connected to the −2 volt supply. This will bias the base of transistor $T2$ negative with respect to the emitter and the transistor will conduct current heavily, effectively shorting the collector of $T2$ to ground. The base current of $T2$ will prevent the base from going very negative; the voltage at the base of $T2$ in this state will be about −0.3 volts.

If the input to $T1$ is lowered to the −0.3 to −0.5 volt region, $T1$ will begin to conduct heavily and the collector of the transistor will approach the 0-volt level, finally stopping at perhaps −30 to −60 mv. This will cause transistor $T2$ to be effectively cut off, and the output of $T2$ will swing toward the −2 volt level. In actual practice, the output of $T2$ would be connected to the input of another logical circuit and be held at the −0.3 to −0.5 volt level.

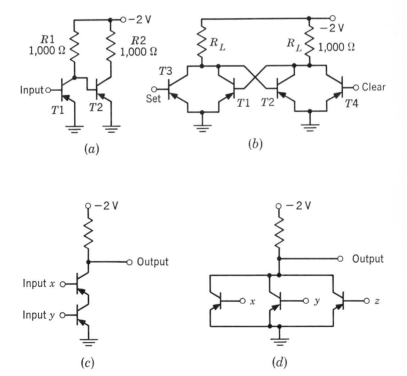

Fig. 4·31 DCTL circuits.

It may be seen that for the circuit to operate efficiently, the transistor characteristics must be such that the voltage drop across the emitter-to-collector junction must be very low when the transistor is conducting heavily. The drop in potential from emitter to collector must, in fact, be sufficiently low to cut off the next stage effectively. Surface-barrier and alloy-junction transistors have the necessary characteristics to do this, and are generally used.

Notice that the current through $R1$ will remain almost constant regardless of the state of the input. If transistor $T1$ is cut off, the base of transistor $T2$ will supply about 1.7 ma, holding $T2$'s base at about -0.3 volts. This magnitude of current will cause the voltage drop across $T2$ to be quite small. If the base of $T1$ is then driven negative, the collector of $T1$ will rise to about -30 mv, and the current through $R1$ will be approximately 2 ma, a change of 0.3 ma. This circuit effectively performs "current switching" as a current on the order of 2 ma is switched in and out of the base of $T2$, while the current through the resistors, and by consequence the output voltage levels, remains almost constant.

4 · 31 DCTL flip-flop, NAND gate, and NOR gate

The DCTL flip-flop in Fig. 4 · 31b consists of four inverters connected together. The two inner transistors comprise the basic flip-flop, while the two outer transistors are used to set and clear the flip-flop circuit. The difference between this and the flip-flops described previously lies in the omission of the resistor and capacitor cross-coupling network generally used. Instead, the collector of each transistor is directly connected to the base of the other.

Assume that $T1$ is conducting heavily; the base of $T2$ will then be at about -30 mv and $T2$ will be cut off. As a result, about 1.7 ma of current will flow in the base circuit of $T1$, and the collector of the transistor will be near ground, holding $T2$ cut off. If a negative pulse of current is applied to the CLEAR input, $T4$ will begin to conduct heavily, bringing the collector of $T4$ and at the same time the base of $T1$ to about -30 mv, and cutting $T1$ off. This will cause the collector of $T1$ and the base of $T2$ to become more negative, and transistor $T2$ will begin to conduct, placing the flip-flop in the 0 state.

We will assume the DCTL circuits shown to use a negative logic, that is, the -0.3 volt level represents a 1 and the -30 mv level a 0.

The NAND gate shown in Fig. 4 · 31c contains two transistor inverters stacked together. The output from this circuit will be a 1 whenever the inputs x AND y are NOT 1's. That is, if either x or y represents a 0, the output will be a 1, but if both x and y represent 1's, the output will be a 0. If both inputs to the NAND gate are at the

−0.3 volt level, the base of each transistor will be negative with respect to the emitter and both transistors will be saturated, causing the output voltage (minus the sum of the emitter-to-collector voltage drops) to be clamped to ground. If either of the inputs to a base goes to the 0-volt level, however, the transistor base will be biased sufficiently near 0 to effectively cut the transistor off, and the output voltage will tend toward the −2 volt supply level. Since in actual practice the output will be connected to another transistor input, the output level will be clamped at the −0.3 level by the next stage.

The drops from emitter-to-collector tend to build up when a number of transistors are connected in this manner, although as many as five transistors stacked in this configuration have been used in machines. If there are five inputs, the output will be a 1 unless all five of the inputs represent a 0.

A NOR gate is shown in Fig. 4·31d. This circuit resembles the AND gates and OR gates shown in Figs. 4·8 and 4·12, except that the transistors are connected in an inverter configuration. In the circuit in Fig. 4·31d, if any of the three inputs is at the 1 level, the output will be a 0, but if three inputs are at the 0 level, the output will be a 1. Negative logic is again used: a −0.3 volt signal represents a 1 and a 0-volt signal a 0.

Notice that if the relatively positive d-c level is used to represent a 1 and the relatively negative d-c level a 0, the NAND and NOR gates perform different functions. The gate in Fig. 4·31c will then perform as a NOR gate and will have a relatively positive (or 1) output only when all inputs are at the lower potential. The gate in Fig. 4·31d will perform as a NAND gate in this case, and will have a relatively positive (or 1) output wherever any of the inputs is at the lower potential representing a 0.

The DCTL type of circuitry has as its basic advantages simplicity and low power consumption. However, there are also disadvantages: the transistor parameters must be held within relatively close tolerances, more transistors are required than with diode logic, and, since the transistors are operated saturated, the speed of circuitry is somewhat limited.

32 Transistor-transistor logic systems

The circuit shown in Fig. 4·32 is called a "transistor-transistor NAND gate" and is a circuit which is indigenous to integrated circuitry systems. The reason for this is that it is particularly easy to fabricate a single transistor with a single base and collector but with several emitters when certain types of integrated circuits are made. A class of transistor circuits called *transistor-transistor logic* (TTL)

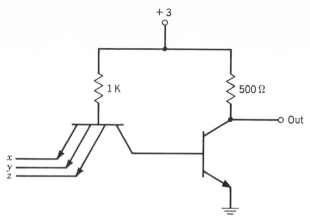

Fig. 4 · 32   Transistor-transistor NAND gate.

utilizes this type of transistor, and the TTL circuit as shown in Fig. 4 · 32 is typical of these circuits.

The operation of the circuit in Fig. 4 · 32 can be described as follows: The multiple-emitter transistor, with its emitters connected to the inputs x, y, and z, operates in the same manner as if three diodes were connected together in a conventional AND-gate circuit as was shown in Fig. 4 · 6, except that the plates of the three diodes are effectively made in one piece. If any one of the three inputs, x, y, or z, is at 0 volts d-c, the collector of the transistor will be effectively at 0 volts d-c holding the output transistor in the circuit off, as no current will flow into the base of this transistor. The output transistor will then be off and the output will rise to a positive voltage, representing a 1. If, however, all three of the inputs, x, y, and z, are at +3 volts d-c, the collector of the circuit will be carried positive, turning the output transistor on, and at this time the output of the circuit will be effectively at 0 volts d-c or logical 0. It may be seen that this particular circuit operates in a manner which is logically equivalent to that of the other NAND gates which have been shown. That is, the output of the circuit will be a 1 if any one of the inputs is a logical 0. If, however, all of the inputs are logical 1's, the output of the circuit will be a logical 0.

QUESTIONS

1   If the base of a *pnp* transistor is positive with respect to the emitter and if the collector is negative with regard to the base, in which region is the transistor?

a. active   *b.* cutoff   *c.* saturated

2   If the input x in Fig. 4·6 is at -5 volts d-c and the input y is at $+5$ volts d-c, what will be the current through the diodes if the diodes have infinite resistance when back biased, passing 0 current in this case, and 0 resistance when forward biased?

3   If the base of a *pnp* transistor is negative with respect to the emitter and the collector is negative with respect to the base, in which region is the transistor?
    a. active   *b.* cutoff   *c.* saturated

4   If we connect 10 diodes in parallel in the circuit of Fig. 4·6 so that there are 10 inputs to the AND gate, and if diodes have a 200-ohm resistance when forward biased and a 145,000-ohm resistance when back biased, what will be the output potential if 1 input is at -5 volts d-c and the other 9 are at $+5$ volts d-c?

5   In which region are the transistors in class A amplifiers generally operated?

6   Assume the circuit is as in Question 4. If all inputs are at $+5$ volts d-c, what will be the output voltage be? Suppose all inputs are at -5 volts d-c; then what will be the output voltage?

7   Does the circuit in Fig. 4·4a have a storage delay time when the input level falls? Does the circuit in Fig. 4·5? Why or why not?

8   Assume that the diodes and the transistors base-to-emitter junction drop the same voltage when they are forward biased in Fig. 4·7. What will the output level be if all inputs are at $+3$ volts d-c?

9   Two positive pulses, one having a duration of 1 μsec and the other a duration of 2 μsec, are connected to inputs x and y in Fig. 4·6. What is the duration of the output pulse?

10 *a.* If the load on the output of the circuit in Fig. 4·7 is 2,400 ohms to $+6$ volts and all inputs are at -1.4 volts, what will be the voltage at the output?
    b. If we again have a 2,400-ohm load on the output of circuit 4·7, what will be the output level be if all inputs are at $+3$ volts d-c? What do you deduce from this?

11 If the voltage drop across the emitter-to-base junction of the transistor in Fig. 4·7 is larger than the voltage drop across a diode which is forward biased, will the output levels be slightly (*a*) negative? (*b*) positive with respect to the input levels?

12 If we have a three-input AND gate as in Fig. 4·8 with inputs A, B, and C as shown, suppose that the transistor at the B input opens from collector to emitter (the transistor fails) so that it always presents an infinite resistance from collector to emitter. There are eight different voltage combinations of $+5$ and -5 volts which the inputs can take. What will be the output voltage from the circuit for each input state? Table 4·1 has two of the output voltages filled in. We assume a transistor drops 0.5 volt from base to emitter when on and presents an infinite impedance to the circuit when off.

TABLE 4 · 1

a	b	c	OUTPUT
−5	−5	−5	−4.5
−5	−5	−5	
−5	+5	−5	
−5	+5	+5	
+5	−5	−5	
+5	−5	+5	
+5	+5	−5	
+5	+5	+5	+5.5

13 If one of the inputs to the circuit in Fig. 4 · 7 is (erroneously) at a −2 volt d-c level, what will be the approximate output level?

14 In Question 12, several of the output levels were wrong and several were right for the input voltages in the table. Which were wrong and which were right?

15 In Fig. 4 · 9, if the d-c input level at x is at +5 volts and the d-c level at y is at −5 volts, will the diode connected to the y input be
   a. forward biased?   b. reverse biased?

16 If the diodes in Fig. 4 · 9 have a 0.5-volt drop when forward biased and an infinite resistance when reverse biased, fill in the output levels in Table 4 · 2.

17 If silicon transistors and germanium diodes are used in the circuit in Fig. 4 · 10, will the output levels be higher or lower in potential than the input levels?

18 Suppose we eliminate the z input from Fig. 4 · 10 leaving only the inputs w, x, and y. Further, let the diode at input x be broken in half so that the diode always presents an infinite resistance in the circuit. What will the output level be for each input combination in Table 4 · 3, assuming the diode drops cancel the transistor drop?

19 When the flip-flop in Fig. 4 · 15 is in the 1 state, what will be the potentials at the 0 and 1 output terminals?

TABLE 4 · 2

INPUTS		OUTPUT
x	y	z
+5 V	+5 V	
+5 V	−5 V	
−5 V	+5 V	
−5 V	−5 V	

TABLE 4 · 3

INPUTS			OUTPUT
w	x	y	z
−1.4	−1.4	−1.4	−1.4
−1.4	−1.4	+3	+3
−1.4	+3	−1.4	
−1.4	+3	+3	
+3	−1.4	−1.4	
+3	−1.4	+3	
+3	+3	−1.4	
+3	+3	+3	+3

20 For the circuit with the bad diode analyzed in Question 8, some of the output voltages were correct and some were in error. Which were in error?

21 If the flip-flop in Fig. 4 · 17 is in the 1 state and a +6 volt pulse is applied at the COMPLEMENT input, will diode $CR1$ or diode $CR2$ be forward biased by the input pulse?

22 Make a table of voltage input combinations as in Question 12. Then assume that we are analyzing the circuit in Fig. 4 · 11 and the transistors at the A and B inputs are OK, but the transistor at input C has failed and is permanently open from emitter to collector. Fill in the output section of the table assuming this situation exists. Which outputs are in error?

23 If the SET and CLEAR inputs to the flip-flop in Fig. 4 · 15 are at −5 volts and a positive pulse is applied at the clock input, will the flip-flop change states?

24 If the flip-flop in Fig. 4 · 13 is erroneously constructed with a 100,000-ohm resistor for $R1$ instead of a 10-kilohm resistor, the circuit will always be in the same state. In this case what will the output d-c levels be at the 0 and 1 outputs?

25 Draw a block diagram for a 4-bit binary counter which counts downward (1111, 1110, 1101, . . . , 0000).

26 What will be the output level from Fig. 4 · 32 if x and y are at +2 volt levels and z is at a +2.5 volt level?

27 If the basic pulse rate of a computer is 200 kc and the word length is 20 binary bits, what will be the delay time required of a delay line which is used in a one-word circulating register?

28 What will be the output level for Fig. 4 · 32 if x and y are at +2 volts d-c and z is at 0 volts d-c?

29 When the input level to a cascaded set of DCTL inverters (Fig. 4 · 31a) is changed, not only does the current through the re-

sistors connected to the transistor collectors remain relatively constant, but the current flowing from emitter to collector for each transistor remains relatively constant as well. Is this statement true or false? Explain why.

30 If we connect the NOR gate output of Fig. 4 · 30 to the A input of another NOR gate the same as in Fig. 4 · 30, leaving the B and C inputs of this circuit disconnected, what will be the d-c level of the output of the first NOR gate if the three inputs A, B, and C are at 0 volts d-c? Assume an off transistor presents an infinite resistance from emitter to collector and an on transistor drops 0.7 volt from base-to-emitter when saturated.

31 With the circuit as in Question 30, what will be the output level from the first NOR gate be if the inputs were all there at $+3$ volts d-c? What will be the output level from the second NOR gate?

32 If the resistor at the z input of Fig. 4 · 28 is erroneously a 20-kilohm resistor instead of 2-kilohm resistor, analyze the circuit's operation by filling in Table 4 · 4. We assume that an on transistor has a $+0.3$ volt drop from emitter to collector and an off transistor presents an infinite resistance in the circuit.

33 Suppose we connect the output of the circuit in Fig. 4 · 28 to the x input of another circuit which is also the same as that in Fig. 4 · 27, leaving the other two inputs free. What will the output level be from the first circuit if we have the inputs shown in Table 4 · 5?

34 Suppose we connected the output of the NOR gate in Fig. 4 · 28 as an input to eight other identical NOR gates. Would the circuit work satisfactorily? If not, why not?

35 Using the voltage drops across diodes and transistor as given in the text, what will be the voltage at point B of Fig. 4 · 26 if the z input is at $+0.5$ volts and the x and y inputs are at $+3$ volts?

TABLE 4 · 4

INPUTS			OUTPUT
x	y	z	
0	0	0	$+3$
0	0	$+2$	
0	$+2$	0	
0	$+2$	$+2$	
$+2$	0	0	
$+2$	0	$+2$	
$+2$	$+2$	0	
$+2$	$+2$	$+2$	$+0.3$

TABLE 4 · 5

INPUTS			OUTPUT OF SECOND NOR GATE
x	y	z	
0	0	0	0.3
0	0	−2	
0	−2	0	
0	−2	−2	
−2	0	0	
−2	0	−2	
−2	−2	0	
−2	−2	−2	−3

36   If we connect the output of a NAND gate to the input of an inverter, the output from the circuit will have the same input-output binary relations as if we had simply used an AND gate. True or false?

37   If we connect the 1 output line in Fig. 4 · 18 to a 1,000-ohm resistor which is then connected to ground, the circuit will always be in which state? What will be the output levels at the 0 and 1 output lines?

38   If we connect the 1 output of the flip-flop in Fig. 4 · 15 to the CLEAR input leaving the SET input disconnected, in which state will the flip-flop always be after two clock pulses? Explain.

39   Describe the difference between positive and negative logic and examine the AND gate in Fig. 4 · 6 and the OR gate in Fig. 4 · 9. Make tables of input-output voltages assuming the logic levels in the system are 0 and −5 volts and letting 0 volts represent first a 0 and then a 1.

5

Logical

design

In 1854, George Boole, an English mathematician, published his classic book "An Investigation of the Laws of Thought, on Which Are Founded the Mathematical Theories of Logic and Probabilities." Boole's stated intention was to perform a mathematical analysis of logic. The work of Boole is perhaps best introduced by the following quotation from the first chapter:

> The design of the following treatise is to investigate the fundamental laws of those operations of the mind by which reasoning is performed; to give expression to them in the symbolical language of a Calculus, and upon this foundation to establish the science of Logic and construct its method; to make that method itself the basis of a general method for the application of the mathematical doctrine of Probabilities; and, finally, to collect from the various elements of truth brought to view in the course of these inquiries some probable intimations concerning the nature and constitution of the human mind.

Starting with his investigation of the laws of thought, Boole constructed a "logical algebra." This investigation into the nature of logic and ultimately of mathematics led subsequent mathematicians and logicians into several new fields of mathematics. Two of these, known as "the calculus of propositions" and "the algebra of classes," were based principally on Boole's work. This book will designate the algebra now used in the design of logical circuitry as "Boolean algebra."

Boolean algebra was first brought to bear on problems which had arisen in the design of relay switching circuits in 1938 by Claude E. Shannon, a research assistant in the department of electrical engineering at the Massachusetts Institute of Technology. An abstract of Shannon's thesis, written at MIT for the degree of Master of

Science, was published under the title "A Symbolic Analysis of Relay and Switching Circuits." This paper presented a method for representing any circuit consisting of combinations of switches and relays by a set of mathematical expressions, and a calculus was developed for manipulating these expressions. The calculus used was shown to be exactly analogous to the calculus of propositions used in the field of symbolic logic. The basic techniques described by Shannon were adopted almost universally for the design and analysis of switching circuits. Because of the analogous relationship between the actions of relays and of transistor circuits, the same techniques which were developed for the design of relay circuits are still being used in the design of modern high-speed computers.

There are several advantages in having a mathematical technique for the description of switching circuits. For one thing, it is far more convenient to calculate with expressions used to represent switching circuits than it is to use schematic or even logical diagrams. Just as an ordinary algebraic expression may be simplified by means of the basic theorems, the expression describing a given switching-circuit network may also be reduced or simplified. This enables the logical designer to simplify the circuitry used, achieving economy of construction and reliability of operation. Boolean algebra also provides an economical and straightforward way of describing the circuitry used in computers. In all, a knowledge of Boolean algebra is indispensable in the computing field.

5 · 1   Fundamental concepts of Boolean algebra

When a variable is used in a normal algebraic formula, it is assumed that the variable may take any numerical value. For instance, in the formula $2x + 5y = z$, we assume that x, y, and z may range through the entire field of real numbers.

The variables used in Boolean equations have a unique characteristic, however; they may assume only one of two possible values. These two values may be represented by the symbols 0 and 1. As we have seen, if the letter x is used to designate an input signal to a circuit, it is understood that there are only two values which x may assume. As previously stated, a 0 may represent a negative voltage and the 1 a positive voltage, or the 0 might represent the absence of a pulse and the 1 the presence of a pulse. In any case, the input signal may be thought of as representing either a 0 or a 1. If an equation describing logical circuitry has several variables, it is still understood that each of the variables can only assume the values 0 or 1. For instance, in the equation $x + y = z$, z may have only the value 0 or 1, regardless of the values of x and y.

This concept will become clearer if another symbol is defined, the + or logical addition symbol. Several circuits which yield this function were introduced in the previous chapter where they were described as OR gates. Each of these had the same characteristic: If every input to an OR-gate circuit represents a 0, the output will represent a 0. If any single input or any combination of inputs to the circuit represent 1's, the output will represent a 1.

For the OR-gate circuit with two inputs, there are four possible combinations of values which the inputs may take (Fig. 5·1). For each set of inputs, there is a resulting output. For instance, if the input designated as x is a 0 and the input designated y is 1, the output of the circuit will be a 1.

The possible input and output combinations may be arranged as follows:

$$0 + 0 = 0$$
$$0 + 1 = 1$$
$$1 + 0 = 1$$
$$1 + 1 = 1$$

This is a "logical addition" table and could represent a standard binary addition table except for the last entry. When both x and y

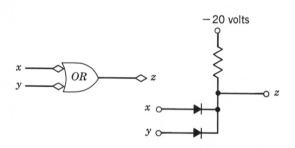

| Input | | Output | | Input | | Output |
x	y	z		x	y	z
0	0	0		0	0	0
0	1	1		0	+10	+10
1	0	1		+10	0	+10
1	1	1		+10	+10	+10

Fig. 5·1   The OR circuit.

represent 1's, the output from the circuit still represents a 1. The $+$ symbol therefore does not have the "normal" meaning but is a logical addition symbol.[1] The equation $x + y = z$ can be read x or y equals z or "x plus y equals z." This concept may be extended to any number of variables; for instance, in the equation $a + b + c + d = e$, even if a, b, c, and d all had the value of 1, the sum of the values, or e, would only represent a 1.

In order to avoid any ambiguity, a number of other symbols have been recommended as replacements for the $+$ sign. Some of these are: $\cup$,[2] v, and $\vee$. The majority of logical designers still use the $+$ sign, however, which was the symbol originally proposed by Boole.

5 · 2   Logical multiplication

Circuits which physically realize the logical multiplication operation were described in the last chapter where they were titled AND gates. The important characteristics of each of these circuits, from a logical algebra viewpoint, is that the output represents a 1 only when *all* inputs to the circuit have the value of 1. The AND-gate circuit in Fig. 5 · 2 has two inputs which are designated x and y. This circuit performs logical multiplication and the symbol which will be used to designate this operation is the dot product sign ($\cdot$).[3] The usual contraction of $x \cdot y$ to xy will also be used.

Parentheses are used to group related terms. For instance, the expression $x(y + z)$ means multiply x by the value of y plus z. Sums or products enclosed within the parentheses are to be taken collectively.

A table of inputs to the AND circuit and each resulting output is illustrated in Fig. 5 · 2. There are four possible combinations of inputs to the circuit and only one of these, when both x and y represent 1's, yields a 1 at the output. At the right of the table is a list of values for x and y and the resulting values for z written in equation form. The four relations shown are the four postulates which define logical multiplication.

Several of the AND-gate circuits in Chap. 4 had more than two inputs. The expression representing the multiple-input AND circuit is simply an extension of the two-input expression. If there are three

---

[1]In order to avoid misunderstanding, E. V. Huntington recommended that the symbol $\oplus$ be used to signify that the operation performed was logical addition as opposed to normal addition. This symbol is now more commonly used to represent the exclusive OR operation and has a different meaning from that which was originally proposed. The plus sign $+$ will therefore be used to represent the inclusive OR relationship.

[2]The preceding equation might then be written $a \cup b \cup c \cup d = e$.

[3]Other symbols have been used to designate logical multiplication such as $\cap$, $\wedge$, $\odot$.

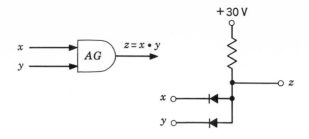

+30 V

$$z = x \cdot y$$

x ──▶ AG ──▶

y ──▶

x ○

y ○

○ z

x	y	z	
0	0	0	0 · 0 = 0
0	1	0	0 · 1 = 0
1	0	0	1 · 0 = 0
1	1	1	1 · 1 = 1

Inputs x	y	Outputs z
0	0	0
0	+10	0
+10	0	0
+10	+10	+10

Fig. 5 · 2   Diode AND circuit.

inputs to the circuit, labeled x, y, and z, and the output is labeled a, the logical equation will be written $xyz = a$. The value of a will be equal to 1 only when all inputs to the circuit, and hence all the variables x, y, and z, have the value 1.

5 · 3   Two-level AND - OR circuit

Figure 5 · 3 presents a schematic diagram for a two-level AND - OR circuit which combines the logical addition and multiplication operations. There are six inputs to this circuit, designated a, b, c, d, e, and f. The a, b, c and d, e, f inputs are divided into two separate branches with the a, b, and c inputs to a diode AND-gate circuit and the d, e and f inputs to another AND-gate circuit. The resistors from both sets of three AND diodes are connected to $+30$ volts. If the inputs to the AND-gate circuits are $+5$ and -5 volt d-c levels, with a $+5$ volt level representing a 1, the output level at the lower end of the resistor for each AND circuit will be at -5 volts d-c unless all three of the inputs to that branch are at $+5$ volts d-c. That is, unless a AND b AND c are at $+5$ volts d-c, the output at that branch of the circuit will be at -5 volts d-c. The same applies to the d, e, and f branches of the circuit.

The outputs of the two AND-gate circuits are connected to an OR circuit consisting of two diodes and a resistor. If either of the AND gates has a $+5$ volt level output, the entire network will have a $+5$

volt output. Notice that the inputs are isolated from each other by the diodes. If *a*, *b*, and *c* are positive and *d*, *e*, and *f* are negative, the lower OR diode will be reverse biased, isolating the lower branch of the circuit.

The symbolic block diagram for this two-level circuit is illustrated at the right of Fig. 5·3. The output is defined by the expression *abc* + *def*, and it will therefore be 0 unless *a* AND *b* AND *c* or *d* AND *e* AND *f* are equal to 1. The two-level diode circuit illustrated in Fig. 5·3 is a very prevalent configuration in digital computer circuitry and is referred to as a two-level circuit because there are two stages of logic, arranged in an AND-to-OR or multiplication-to-addition relationship.

5·4 Complementation

The logical operation of complementation is performed by the inverter, which was explained in Sec. 4·16. Characteristically, the output is not equal to the input of an inverter circuit. There are only two possible values a variable may take, 0 and 1. Therefore, if the input is 1, the output must be 0; and if the input is 0, the output must be 1. This operation is sometimes referred to as "negation" or "inversion" as well as complementation. The symbol used to represent the complement of a variable is the prime sign (′). This symbol may be read

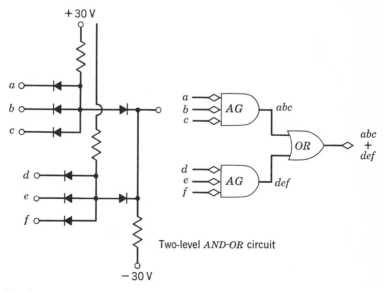

Fig. 5·3 Two-level AND · OR circuit.

as either "not" or "the complement of," so that x' might be read as "not x" or "the complement of x." Since the variables used can take only one of two possible values, there are only two postulates for inversion. These are $0' = 1$ and $1' = 0$. The block diagram symbol for the inverter is a hollow square with an I inside.

Three basic logical operations have now been introduced: addition, multiplication, and complementation. A logical equation containing all of these operations is: $xy + z' = m$. This equation may be read as either: m equals the product of x and y, plus the complement of z; or, m equals x and y or "not z."

5 · 5 Evaluation of logical expressions

The tables of values for the three operations which have been explained are sometimes called *truth tables* or *tables of combinations*. In order to study a logical expression it is very convenient to construct a table of values for the variables and then to evaluate the expression for each of the possible combinations of variables in turn. Consider the expression $x + yz'$. There are three variables in this expression: x, y, and z, each of which can assume the values 0 or 1. The possible combinations of values may be arranged in ascending order,[4] as shown in Table 5 · 1.

One of the variables, z, is complemented in the expression $x + yz'$, so a column is now added to the table listing values of z' (see Table 5 · 2).

TABLE 5 · 1

x	y	z
0	0	0
0	0	1
0	1	0
0	1	1
1	0	0
1	0	1
1	1	0
1	1	1

TABLE 5 · 2

x	y	z	z'
0	0	0	1
0	0	1	0
0	1	0	1
0	1	1	0
1	0	0	1
1	0	1	0
1	1	0	1
1	1	1	0

[4]Notice that the variables in each row of this table may be combined into a binary number. The binary numbers will then count from 000 to 111 in binary, or from 0 to 7 decimal. Sometimes each row is numbered in decimal according to the number represented. Reference may then be made to the row by using the decimal number. For instance, row 0 has values of 0, 0, 0 for x, y, and z, row 6 has values of 1, 1, 0, and row 7 has values of 1, 1, 1.

TABLE 5 · 3

x	y	z	z'	yz'
0	0	0	1	0
0	0	1	0	0
0	1	0	1	1
0	1	1	0	0
1	0	0	1	0
1	0	1	0	0
1	1	0	1	1
1	1	1	0	0

A column is now added listing the values yz' assumes for each y and z'. This column will contain the value 1 only when both y and z' are equal to 1 (see Table 5 · 3).

Now the logical addition of the values of x to the values which have been calculated for yz' is performed in a final column (see Table 5 · 4).

The final column contains the value of $x + yz'$ for each set of input values which $x, y,$ and z may take. For instance, when $x = 1, y = 0,$ and $z = 1$, the expression has the value of 1.

5 · 6   Evaluation of an expression containing parentheses

The following example illustrates the procedure for constructing a truth table for the expression $x + y(x' + y')$. There are only two variables in the expression: x and y. First a table of the values which x and y may assume is constructed (Table 5 · 5).

Now, since the expression contains both x' and y', two columns are added listing complements of the original values of the variables (Table 5 · 6).

TABLE 5 · 4

x	y	z	z'	yz'	$x + yz'$
0	0	0	1	0	0
0	0	1	0	0	0
0	1	0	1	1	1
0	1	1	0	0	0
1	0	0	1	0	1
1	0	1	0	0	1
1	1	0	1	1	1
1	1	1	0	0	1

TABLE 5 · 5   TABLE 5 · 6

x	y
0	0
0	1
1	0
1	1

x	y	x'	y'
0	0	1	1
0	1	1	0
1	0	0	1
1	1	0	0

TABLE 5 · 7

x	y	x'	y'	$(x' + y')$
0	0	1	1	1
0	1	1	0	1
1	0	0	1	1
1	1	0	0	0

The various values which the term inside parentheses $(x' + y')$ assumes are now calculated (Table 5 · 7).

The values for $x' + y'$ are now multiplied by the values of y in the table, forming another column representing $y(x' + y')$ (Table 5 · 8).

Finally, the values for $y(x' + y')$ are added to the values for x which are listed, forming the final column and completing the table (see Table 5 · 9).

An inspection of the final column of the table indicates that the values taken by the function $x + y(x' + y')$ are identical to the values found in the logical addition table. This indicates that the function $x + y(x' + y')$ is equivalent to the function $x + y$. This equivalence has been established by the "proof by perfect induction." If a logical circuit were constructed for each of the two expressions, one circuit would require two inverters, two OR circuits, and an AND circuit, while the other circuit would require only an OR circuit. Both circuits would perform the same function, yielding identical outputs for each combination of inputs.

TABLE 5 · 8

x	y	x'	y'	$x' + y'$	$y(x' + y')$
0	0	1	1	1	0
0	1	1	0	1	1
1	0	0	1	1	0
1	1	0	0	0	0

TABLE 5 · 9

x	y	x'	y'	$x' + y'$	$y(x' + y')$	$x + y(x' + y')$
0	0	1	1	1	0	0
0	1	1	0	1	1	1
1	0	0	1	1	0	1
1	1	0	0	0	0	0

5 · 7 Basic relations of Boolean algebra

The fundamental relations of Boolean algebra have been presented, with logic gates used to illustrate the three operations defined. A complete set of the basic operations is listed below.[5] Although simple in appearance, these rules may be used to construct a Boolean algebra, determining all of the relations which follow:

$$\text{If } x \neq 0, \text{ then } x = 1 \quad \text{and}$$
$$\text{if } x \neq 1, \text{ then } x = 0$$

LOGICAL ADDITION	LOGICAL MULTIPLICATION	COMPLEMENT RULES
$0 + 0 = 0$	$0 \cdot 0 = 0$	$0' = 1$
$0 + 1 = 1$	$0 \cdot 1 = 0$	$1' = 0$
$1 + 0 = 1$	$1 \cdot 0 = 0$	
$1 + 1 = 1$	$1 \cdot 1 = 1$	

A list of useful theorems is presented in Table 5 · 10. Most of the basic rules by which Boolean algebraic expressions may be simplified are contained in this table. Each of these theorems may be proved using the ten basic postulates which have been presented by means of the "proof by perfect induction." An example of this proof for theorem 3 in Table 5 · 1 is as follows: the variable x can have only the values 0 or 1; if x has the value 0, then $0 + 0 = 0$; if x has the value 1, then $1 + 1 = 1$. Therefore $x + x = x$.

The same basic technique may be used to prove the remainder of the theorems. Theorem 9 states that double complementation of a variable results in the original variable. If x equals 0, then the first complement is 1 and the second will be 0, the original value. If the

---

[5]There are actually a number of possible sets of postulates which may be used to define the algebra. The particular treatment of Boolean algebra given here is derived from that of E. V. Huntington and M. H. Stone. The author would also like to acknowledge the influence of I. S. Reed and S. H. Caldwell on this development of the concepts of the algebra.

TABLE 5·10   BOOLEAN ALGEBRA THEOREMS

1. $0 + x = x$
2. $1 + x = 1$
3. $x + x = x$
4. $x + x' = 1$
5. $0 \cdot x = 0$
6. $1 \cdot x = x$
7. $x \cdot x = x$
8. $x \cdot x' = 0$
9. $(x')' = x$
10. $x + y = y + x$
11. $x \cdot y = y \cdot x$
12. $x + (y + z) = (x + y) + z$
13. $x(yz) = (xy)z$
14. $x(y + z) = xy + xz$
15. $x + xz = x$
16. $x(x + y) = x$
17. $(x + y)(x + z) = x + yz$
18. $x + x'y = x + y$

original value for x is 1, then the first complement will be 0 and the second 1, the original value. Therefore $(x')' = x$.

Theorems 10 and 11, which are known as the *commutative* laws, express the fact that the order in which a combination of terms is performed does not affect the result of the combination. Theorem 10 is the commutative law of addition which states that the order of addition does not affect the sum $(x + y = y + x)$. Theorem 11 is the commutative law of multiplication $(xy = yx)$ which states that the order of multiplication does not affect the product.

Theorems 12 and 13 are the *associative* laws. Theorem 12 states that in the addition of several terms, the sum which will be obtained if the first term is added to the second and then the third term is added will be the same as the sum obtained if the second term is added to the third and then the first term is added $[x + (y + z) = (x + y) + z]$. Theorem 13 is the associative law of multiplication, stating that in a product with three factors, *any* two may be multiplied together, followed by the third, $x(yz) = (xy)z$.

Theorem 14, the *distributive law*, states that the product of a monomial (x) multiplied by a polynomial $(y + z)$ is equal to the sum of the products of the monomial multiplied by each term of the polynomial, $x(y + z) = xy + xz$.

The three laws, commutative, associative, and distributive, may be extended to include any number of terms. For instance, the commutative law for addition states that $x + y = y + x$. This may be extended to

$$x + y + z + a = a + y + z + x$$

The commutative law for multiplication may also be extended: $xyz = yzx$. These two laws are useful in rearranging the terms of an equation.

The associative laws may also be extended:

$$(x + y) + (z + a) = (a + y) + (x + z)$$

and $(xy)(za) = (xa)(zy)$. These two laws are useful in regrouping the terms of an equation.

The distributive law may be extended in several ways:

$$x(y + z + a) = xy + xz + xa$$

If two polynomials, such as $(w + x)$ and $(y + z)$ are to be multiplied together, one of the polynomials is first treated as a monomial and multiplied by the individual terms of the other polynomial. The results are then multiplied out according to the distributive law. For instance,

$$(w + x)(y + z) = w(y + z) + x(y + z) = wy + wz + xy + xz$$

5 · 8   Proof by perfect induction

Notice that, among others, theorem 17 does not apply to "normal" algebra. The theorem may be obtained from the preceding theorems as follows:

$$(x + y)(x + z) = x(x + z) + y(x + z) = x + xz + xy + yz$$
$$\text{(by theorem 14)}$$

and by theorem 15, $x + xz + xy = x$

Therefore, $(x + y)(x + z) = x + yz$

Since theorem 17 does not apply to normal algebra, it is interesting to test the theorem, using the "proof by perfect induction." It will therefore be necessary to construct truth tables for the right-hand $(x + yz)$ and left-hand $(x + y)(x + z)$ members of the equation and compare the results (see Tables 5 · 11 and 5 · 12).

TABLE 5·11

x	y	z	zy	$x + yz$
0	0	0	0	0
0	0	1	0	0
0	1	0	0	0
0	1	1	1	1
1	0	0	0	1
1	0	1	0	1
1	1	0	0	1
1	1	1	1	1

The last column of the table for the function $x + yz$ is identical to the last column of the table for $(x + y)(x + z)$. This proves (by means of the "proof by perfect induction") that the expressions are equivalent.

5·9 Simplification of equations

Theorems may be used to simplify Boolean expressions just as the theorems of normal algebra may be used to simplify expressions. Consider the expression

$$(x + y)(x + y')(x' + z)$$

The first two terms consists of $(x + y)(x + y')$; these terms may be multiplied together and, since $x + xy' + xy = x$ and $yy' = 0$, reduced to x.

The function has now been reduced to $x(x' + z)$ which may be expressed as $xx' + xz$ (theorem 14), and since xx' is equal to 0, the entire expression $(x + y)(x + y')(x' + z)$ may be reduced to xz.

TABLE 5·12

x	y	z	$x + y$	$x + z$	$(x + y)(x + z)$
0	0	0	0	0	0
0	0	1	0	1	0
0	1	0	1	0	0
0	1	1	1	1	1
1	0	0	1	1	1
1	0	1	1	1	1
1	1	0	1	1	1
1	1	1	1	1	1

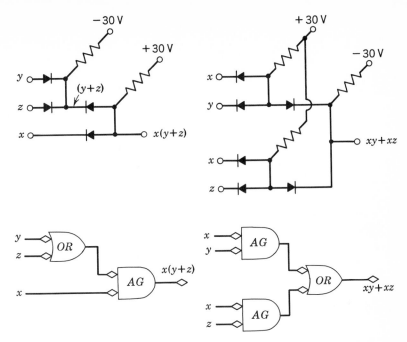

Fig. 5 · 4   Equivalent diode networks.

Another function which may be simplified is $xyz + xy'z + xyz' + y'z'$. First the three terms $xyz + xy'z + xyz'$ may be expressed as $x(yz + y'z + yz')$, using theorem 14. Then using theorem 14 again: $x[y(z + z') + y'z]$, and since $z + z'$ equals 1, we have $x(y + y'z)$.

The function $x(y + y'z)$ may be further reduced to $x(y + z)$ by using theorem 18. The final expression can be written in two ways: $x(y + z)$ or $xy + xz$. The first expression is generally preferable if the equation is to be constructed as an electronic circuit, as it requires only one AND circuit and one OR circuit requiring only four diodes (Fig. 5 · 4), whereas $xy + xz$ requires six diodes. Both circuits are two-level, one however, $x(y + z)$, is an OR-to-AND configuration while the other, $xy + xz$, is an AND-to-OR configuration.

5 · 10   De Morgan's theorems

The following two theorems are known as De Morgan's theorems.

$$(x + y + z)' = x'y'z'$$
$$(xyz)' = x' + y' + z'$$

The complement of any Boolean expression, or a part of any expression, may be found by means of these theorems. In general, two steps are used to form a complement:

1 Addition symbols are replaced with multiplication symbols or multiplication symbols with addition symbols, and
2 Each of the variables (terms) in the expression is complemented.

The use of De Morgan's theorem may be demonstrated by finding the complement of the expression $(x + yz)$. First it is important to notice that a multiplication sign has been omitted and the expression could be written $x + (y \cdot z)$. In order to complement this, the addition symbol is replaced with a multiplication symbol and the two terms are complemented $x' \cdot (y \cdot z)'$ then the remaining term is complemented $x'(y' + z')$. The following equivalence has been found, $(x + yz)' = x'(y' + z')$.

The complement of $(w'x + yz')$ may be formed with the following two steps:

1 First the addition symbol is changed: $(w'x + yz')'$ is changed to $(w'x)' \cdot (yz')'$.
2 The complement of each term is formed

$$(w' \cdot x)'(y \cdot z')'$$

become $(w + x')(y' + z)$. Notice that since w and z were already complemented, they become uncomplemented by the theorem $(x')' = x$.

It is sometimes necessary to complement both sides of an equation. This may be done in the same way as before:

$$wx + yz = 0$$

complementing both sides, $\qquad (wx + yz)' = 0'$

$$(w' + x')(y' + z') = 1$$

5 · 11 Basic duality of Boolean algebra

De Morgan's theorem expresses a basic duality which underlies all of Boolean algebra. The postulates and theorems which have been presented can all be divided into pairs. For example, $(x + y) + z = x + (y + z)$ is the "dual" of $(xy)z = x(yz)$, and $x + 0 = x$ is the dual of $x \cdot 1 = x$.

Often the postulates and theorems are listed in an order which illustrates the duality of the algebra. In proving the theorems of the

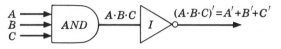

Fig. 5·5   The NAND gate.

algebra, it is then necessary only to prove one theorem and the "dual" of the theorem follows necessarily. For instance, if you prove that $x + xy = x$, you can immediately add the theorem $x(x + y) = x$ to the list of theorems as the "dual" of the first expression.[6] In effect, all of Boolean algebra is predicated on this "two-for-one" basis.

5·12   NAND gates and NOR gates

Since NAND gates and NOR gates are quite often used in digital machines, it is fortunate that the Boolean algebra which has been described can be easily made to analyze the operation of these gates.

Consider the NAND gate in Fig. 5·5. The inputs are A, B, and C and the output from the gate is written as $A' + B' + C'$. The output will therefore be a 1 if A is a 0 or B is a 0 or C is a 0, and the output will be a 0 only if A AND B AND C are all 1's.

The NAND gate can be analyzed using the equivalent block diagram circuit shown in Fig. 5·5 which has an AND gate followed by an inverter. If the inputs are A, B, and C, the output of the AND gate will be $A \cdot B \cdot C$ and the complement of this is $(A \cdot B \cdot C)' = A' + B' + C'$ as shown in the figure.

The NOR gate can be analyzed in a similar manner. Figure 5·6 shows the NOR-gate block diagram symbol with inputs A, B, and C and output $A'B'C'$. This says the NOR gate's output will be a 1 only when all three inputs are 0's. If any input represents a 1, the output of a NOR gate will therefore be a 0.

Below the NOR-gate block diagram symbol in Fig. 5·6 is an equivalent circuit showing an OR gate and an inverter. The inputs A, B, and C are ORed by the OR gate giving $A + B + C$, which is complemented by the inverter giving $(A + B + C)' = A'B'C'$.

---

[6]When the first expression, $x + xy = x$, has been complemented, $x'(x' + y') = x'$ is obtained. Uncomplemented variables may then be substituted on both sides of the equation without changing the basic equivalence of the expression.

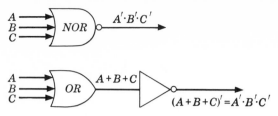

Fig. 5 · 6   The NOR gate.

Multiple-input NAND gates may be analyzed similarly. A four-input NAND gate with inputs A, B, C, and D has an output $A' + B' + C' + D'$ which says that the output will be a 1 if any one of the inputs is a 0 and will be a 0 only when all four inputs are 1's.

Similar reasoning will show that the output of a four-input NOR gate with inputs A, B, C, and D can be represented by the Boolean algebra expression $A'B'C'D'$, which will be equal to 1 only when A, B, C, and D are all 0's.

If one of the two input lines to a two-input NAND gate contained the inputs $A + B$ and the other contained $C + D$ as shown in Fig. 5 · 7a, the output from the NAND gate would be

$$[(A + B)(C + D)]' = A'B' + C'D'$$

We can show this by noting that the NAND gate first ANDs the inputs (in this case $A + B$ and $C + D$) and then complements this.

If one of the input lines to a two-input NOR gate contained the

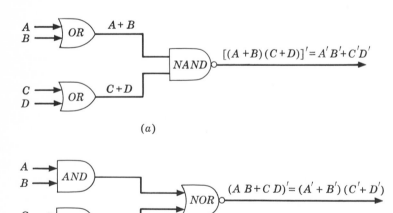

(a)

(b)

Fig. 5 · 7   OR-to-AND and AND-to-NOR networks.

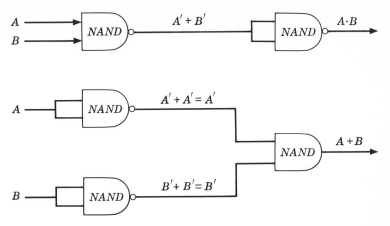

Fig. 5·8   Making AND and OR gates from NAND gates.

signal $A \cdot B$ and the other input line contained the signal $C \cdot D$, the output from the NOR gate would be $(A \cdot B + C \cdot D)' = (A' + B')(C' + D')$, as shown in Fig. 5·7b.

Notice that we can make an AND gate from two NAND gates using the trick shown in Fig. 5·8 and a two-input OR gate from three NAND gates as is also shown in the figure. A set of NAND gates can therefore be used to make any combinational network, by substituting the block diagrams shown in Fig. 5·8 for the AND and OR blocks. (Complementation of a variable, when needed, can be obtained from a single NAND gate by connecting the variable to all inputs.)

The NOR gate can also be used to form any Boolean function which is desired and the fundamental tricks are shown in Fig. 5·9.

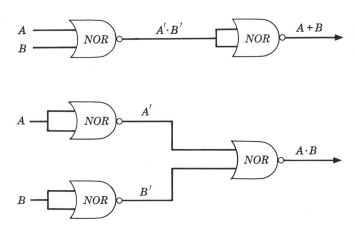

Fig. 5·9   Making AND and OR gates from NOR gates.

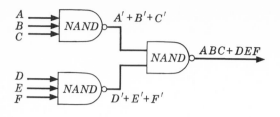

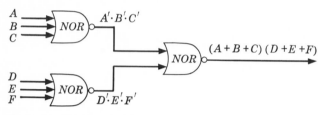

Fig. 5 · 10   NAND and NOR gates in two-level networks.

Actually it is not necessary to use the boxes shown in Figs. 5 · 8 and 5 · 9 to replace AND and OR gates singly, for a two-level NAND-gate network yields the same function as a two-level AND-to-OR–gate network, and a two-level NOR-gate network yields the same function as a two-level OR-to-AND–gate network. This is shown in Fig. 5 · 10. Compare the output of the NAND-gate network with that in Fig. 5 · 3, for example.

5 · 13   Derivation of a Boolean expression

When designing a logical circuit, the logical designer works from two sets of known values: (1) the various states which the inputs to the logical network can take and (2) the desired outputs for each input condition. The logical expression is derived from these sets of values.

Consider a specific problem. A logical network has two inputs, x and y, and an output z. The relationship between inputs and outputs is to be as follows:

1 When both x and y are 0's, the output (z) is to be 1.
2 When x is 0 and y is 1, the output (z) is to be 0.
3 When x is 1 and y is 0, the output (z) is to be 1.
4 When x is 1 and y is 1, the output (z) is to be 1.

These relations may be expressed in tabular form as shown in Table 5 · 13.

It is now necessary to add another column to the table. This column will consist of a list of "product terms" obtained from the values of the input variables. The new column will contain each of the input variables listed in each row of the table, with the letter representing the respective input complemented when the input value for this variable is 0, and not complemented when the input value is 1. The terms obtained in this manner are designated as "product terms." With two input variables x and y, each row of the table will contain a product term consisting of x and y, with x or y complemented or not depending on the input values for that row (see Table 5 · 14).

Whenever z is equal to 1, the x and y product term from the same row is removed and formed into a "sum-of-products." Therefore the product terms from the first, third, and fourth rows are written as follows: $x'y' + xy' + xy$.

There are now three sets of terms, each the product of two variables. The sum of these products is equal to the expression desired. This type of expression is often referred to as a *canonical expansion* for the transmission function. The complete expression in normal form is:

$$x'y' + xy' + xy = z$$

The left-hand side of this expression may be simplified as follows:

$$x'y' + xy' + xy = z$$
$$x'y' + x(y' + y) = z$$
$$x'y' + x = z$$

therefore
$$x + y' = z$$

The truth table may then be constructed to check the function which has been derived (see Table 5 · 15).

The last row of this column agrees with the last row of the truth table of the desired function, showing that the expressions are equivalent.

TABLE 5 · 13

INPUTS		OUTPUT
x	y	z
0	0	1
0	1	0
1	0	1
1	1	1

TABLE 5 · 14

INPUTS		OUTPUT	PRODUCT TERMS
x	y	z	
0	0	1	$x'y'$
0	1	0	$x'y$
1	0	1	xy'
1	1	1	xy

TABLE 5 · 15

x	y	y'	$x + y'$
0	0	1	1
0	1	0	0
1	0	1	1
1	1	0	1

The expression $x + y'$ may be constructed in one of two ways. If only the inputs x and y are available, as might be the case if the inputs to the circuit were from another logical network or from certain types of storage devices, an inverter would be required to form y'. The circuit would then require an inverter plus a two-diode OR gate. If the inputs were from flip-flops, however, the complement of the y input would be available, since the 0 output of the flip-flop could be used instead of the 1 output (refer to Chap. 4).

Another expression, with three inputs (designated as x, y, and z) to the logical net, will be derived. Assume that the desired relationships between the inputs and the output have been determined, as shown in Table 5 · 16.

1 First, a truth table is formed (Table 5 · 17).
2 A column is added listing the inputs x, y, and z according to their value in the input columns (Table 5 · 18).
3 The product terms from each row in which the output is a 1 are collected ($x'y'z'$, $x'yz'$, $xy'z'$, and xyz'), and the desired expression is the sum of these products ($x'y'z' + x'yz' + xy'z' + xyz'$). Therefore, the complete expression in standard form for the desired network is

$$x'y'z' + x'yz' + xy'z' + xyz' = a$$

TABLE 5 · 17

INPUTS			OUTPUT
x	y	z	a
0	0	0	1
0	0	1	0
0	1	0	1
0	1	1	0
1	0	0	1
1	0	1	0
1	1	0	1
1	1	1	0

TABLE 5 · 16

INPUTS			OUTPUT
When: $x = 0, y = 0, z = 0$			1
$x = 0, y = 0, z = 1$			0
$x = 0, y = 1, z = 0$			1
0	1	1	0
1	0	0	1
1	0	1	0
1	1	0	1
1	1	1	0

TABLE 5·18

INPUTS			OUTPUT	PRODUCT TERMS
x	y	z	a	
0	0	0	1	$x'y'z'$
0	0	1	0	$x'y'z$
0	1	0	1	$x'yz'$
0	1	1	0	$x'yz$
1	0	0	1	$xy'z'$
1	0	1	0	$xy'z$
1	1	0	1	xyz'
1	1	1	0	xyz

This expression may be simplified as shown below:

$$x'y'z' + x'yz' + xy'z' + xyz' = a$$
$$x'(y'z' + yz') + x(y'z' + yz') = a$$
$$x'[z'(y' + y)] + x[z'(y' + y)] = a$$
$$x'z' + xz' = a$$
$$z' = a$$

The function can therefore be performed by a single inverter connected to the z input. Inspection of the truth table will indicate that the output a is always equal to the complement of the input variable z.

5·14 Sum-of-products and product-of-sums

The sequence of steps just explained derived a *sum-of-products* expression for a given circuit. Another technique, really a dual of the first, forms the required expression as a *product-of-sums*. The expression derived in this manner is made up, before simplification, of terms each consisting of sums of variables $(x + y + z)$ .... The final expression is the product of these sum terms and has the form $(x + y + z)(x + y + z') ... (x' + y' + z')$.

The method for arriving at the desired expression is as follows:

1 Construct a table of the input and output values.
2 Construct an additional column containing complemented and uncomplemented variables (depending on the values in the input columns) for each row of the table. In each of these rows, a sum term is formed; however, in this case if the input value for a given variable is 1, the variable will be complemented, and if 0, not complemented.

INPUTS		OUTPUT
x	y	z
0	0	1
0	1	0
1	0	0
1	1	1

INPUTS		OUTPUT	SUM TERMS
x	y	z	
0	0	1	$(x + y)$
0	1	0	$(x + y')$
1	0	0	$(x' + y)$
1	1	1	$(x' + y')$

3   The desired expression is the product of the sum terms from the rows in which the output is 0.

5·15   Derivation of Boolean expression using product-of-sums

Table 5·19 contains the input and output values which describe a function to be realized by a logical network.

A column containing the input variables in sum-term form is now added in each row. A given variable is complemented if the input value for that variable is 1 in the same row, and not complemented if the value is 0 (Table 5·20).

A product-of-sums expression is now formed by selecting those sum terms for which the output is 0 and multiplying them together. In this case 0's appear in the second and third rows, showing that the desired expression is $(x + y')(x' + y)$. A sum-of-products expression may be found by multiplying the two terms of this expression together, yielding $xy + x'y'$. In this case, the same number of diodes would be required to construct circuits corresponding to both the sum-of-products and the product-of-sums expressions.

TABLE 5·21

INPUTS			OUTPUT
x	y	z	a
0	0	0	0
0	0	1	0
0	1	0	1
0	1	1	1
1	0	0	0
1	0	1	0
1	1	0	1
1	1	1	0

TABLE 5 · 22

INPUTS			OUTPUT	PRODUCT TERMS	SUM TERMS
x	y	z	a		
0	0	0	0	$x'y'z'$	$x + y + z$
0	0	1	0	$x'y'z$	$x + y + z'$
0	1	0	1	$x'yz'$	$x + y' + z$
0	1	1	1	$x'yz$	$x + y' + z'$
1	0	0	0	$xy'z'$	$x' + y + z$
1	0	1	0	$xy'z$	$x' + y + z'$
1	1	0	1	xyz'	$x' + y' + z$
1	1	1	0	xyz	$x' + y' + z'$

· 16 Derivation of a three-input-variable expression

Consider Table 5 · 21 expressing an input-to-output relationship for which an expression is to be derived.

Two columns will be added this time, one containing the sum-of-products terms and the other the product-of-sums terms (Table 5 · 22).

The two expressions may now be written in the following way:

Sum-of-products: $(x'yz') + (x'yz) + (xyz') = a$

Product-of-sums: $(x + y + z)(x + y + z')(x' + y + z)$
$$(x' + y + z')(x' + y' + z') = a$$

The two expressions may be simplified as shown below:

SUM - OF - PRODUCTS

$$(x'yz') + (x'yz) + (xyz') = a$$
$$x'(yz' + yz) + (xyz') = a$$
$$x'y + xyz' = a$$
$$y(x' + xz') = a$$
$$x'y + yz' = a$$
$$y(x' + z') = a$$

or

PRODUCT - OF - SUMS

$$(x + y + z)(x + y + z')(x' + y + z)(x' + y + z')(x' + y' + z') = a$$
$$(x + y)(x' + y)(x' + z') = a$$
$$y(x' + z') = a$$

The two final product-of-sums expressions obtained are identical. Notice, however, that the shortest sum-of-products expression, which is $x'y + yz'$, requires two AND gates and an OR gate, and would require six diodes if constructed using diode logic. The shortest product-of-sums expression $y(x' + z')$ requires only a single AND gate and a single OR gate, and will require only four diodes if constructed. In some cases, the minimal sum-of-products expression will require fewer logical elements to construct, and in other instances the construction of the minimal product-of-sums expression will require fewer elements. If the sole criterion is the number of logical elements, it is necessary to obtain both a minimal sum-of-products expression and also a minimal product-of-sums expression in order to compare the two. It is possible to derive the canonical expansion expression for the network to be designed in one of the forms—for instance, product-of-sums—to simplify the expression, and then to convert the simplified expression to the other form using the distributive laws. Any additional simplification which is required can then be performed. In this way, minimal expressions in each form may be obtained without deriving both canonical expansions.

The simplification techniques which have been described are algebraic and depend on judicious use of the theorems which have been presented. The problem of simplifying Boolean expressions so that the shortest expression is always found is quite complex; however, it is possible, by means of the repeated use of certain algorithms, to derive minimal sum-of-products and product-of-sums expressions. These techniques will not be described in this book; several of the references, including those of the author, deal with this subject in some detail.

5 · 17 Sequential circuits

So far, the logical equations and the logical diagrams have been analyzed as networks in which the output was completely determined by the inputs at any given time. That is, the inputs to the circuits were assumed to have certain values, and the output was completely determined by the input values.[7] There is another broad class of circuits, however, known as "sequential switching circuits." These circuits contain memory elements such as flip-flops or delay lines. As the circuits operate, the storage elements change their state so that the various outputs of the logical networks are time-dependent. It should be noted, however, that although the states of the memory elements vary with time, the functions performed by the logical circuits such as the AND and OR circuits remain the same. The changes which occur are sequential; the memory elements proceed from one state

[7]A logical network for which the input states at any given time completely determine the outputs is called a "combinational" network.

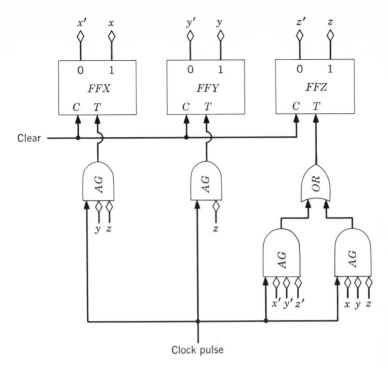

Fig. 5 · 11   Operation counter.

to another. The operation of the circuits may therefore be considered from a static standpoint; first the memory elements assume one state, and later they assume another state. The particular outputs of the circuits are therefore dependent, not only on the inputs at a given time, but on the states of the memory elements prior to the inputs.

Figure 5 · 11 illustrates the logical diagram for an *operation counter*, which is a simple type of sequential circuit. This counter is stepped from state to state by a clock pulse. The counter contains three flip-flops; however, it does not count 000, 001, 010, . . . , etc., as does the counter described in the previous chapter, but instead it counts 000, 001, 011, 101, 111, 000 (in binary) or 0, 1, 3, 5, 7, 0, 1, 3, . . . (decimal). Counters may be designed to step through any desired sequence, and logical circuits of this sort are very useful. In general, an operation counter is a sequential switching circuit in which the memory elements change from one to the next of a predetermined sequence of states each time an input signal is applied.

In Fig. 5 · 11, the three flip-flops are labeled *FFX*, *FFY*, and *FFZ*. The 0 output line of *FFX* is labeled x' and the 1 output as x. The outputs of *FFY* and *FFZ* are labeled in the same manner. The d-c out-

TABLE 5 · 23

x	y	z	
0	0	0	
0	0	1	
0	1	1	cycle length
1	0	1	
1	1	1	
0	0	0	
.	.	.	
.	.	.	

puts from these flip-flops are then connected to the AND gates and OR gates which determine when each flip-flop is to be complemented. *Notice that the connections from the flip-flop outputs to the inputs of the AND gates and OR gates are not shown, but instead the inputs are labeled as are the flip-flop outputs.* The inputs to the rightmost AND gate in the figure are from the 1 outputs of *FFX*, *FFY*, and *FFZ*. This AND gate will therefore conduct a pulse only when all three flip-flops are in the 1 states.

A table of the successive states which the flip-flops assume may be constructed as in Table 5 · 23.

The counter is first cleared to the all-zero state by applying a pulse on the CLEAR line. Successive pulses then step the counter through each state. The flip-flops are assumed to have an inherent delay so that the race problem does not occur.[8] The counter has a cycle length of five, since the counter memory devices assume their original state after five changes.

When each of the flip-flops is in the 0 state, the AND gates to the $x'y'z'$ input will conduct the clock pulse. This will cause *FFZ* to be complemented, and after the first pulse, *FFZ* will contain a 1 and *FFX* and *FFY* will remain in the 0 state. Since *FFZ* now contains a 1. the AND gate connected to *FFY* will conduct the second pulse, complementing *FFY* and changing the state of the counter to 011. Successive states of the counter may be checked by noting the input levels from the flip-flops to the AND gates before and after each clock pulse.

As may be seen, the four AND gates and the OR gates comprise a combinational circuit, the inputs to which are determined by the

---

[8]The race problem arises when a flip-flop changes its state during a clock pulse. This may cause the input levels to the AND gates to change and interfere with the correct operation of the counter. The race problem was described in more detail in Sec. 4 · 22.

TABLE 5 · 24

x	y	F_1	F_2	F_3	F_4	F_5	F_6	F_7	F_8	F_9	F_{10}	F_{11}	F_{12}	F_{13}	F_{14}	F_{15}	F_{16}
0	0	0	1	0	1	0	1	0	1	0	1	0	1	0	1	0	1
0	1	0	0	1	1	0	0	1	1	0	0	1	1	0	0	1	1
1	0	0	0	0	0	1	1	1	1	0	0	0	0	1	1	1	1
1	1	0	0	0	0	0	0	0	0	1	1	1	1	1	1	1	1

states of the memory devices. The functioning of this section of the counter may be analyzed just as the previous logical nets were analyzed.

· 18 Table of functions

So far, we have dealt with three operations on binary variables. Other operations have been defined, named, and are often used in the literature on computers and Boolean algebra. The three operations which have been explained and used are: (1) complementation, (2) logical addition (the OR operation), and (3) logical multiplication (the AND operation). For each of these a truth table was constructed which defined each operation. There are 16 possible functions of two variables. Table 5 · 24 is a list of the values for the 16 functions.

Several of the possible functions are very simple. For example, F_1 is equal to 0 and F_{16} is equal to 1. All of the functions may, of course, be expressed by means of the three operations so far defined, and the minimum forms for all of the functions in the list above in terms of logical multiplication, addition, and the complementation operations, are shown in Table 5 · 25.

Functions 4 and 6 are complements of one of the variables, function 15 is the addition function, and function 9 is the multiplication function. Two of the functions, F_2 and F_8, are used considerably in mathematical papers. F_2, $x'y'$, is commonly referred to as the Peirce function and F_8, $x' + y'$, is designated as the Sheffer stroke function. Special symbols are sometimes used to designate these functions; the symbol for the Peirce function is a vertical arrow $\downarrow$ so that F_2 may

TABLE 5 · 25

$F_1 = 0$	$F_5 = xy'$	$F_9 = xy$	$F_{13} = x$
$F_2 = x'y'$	$F_6 = y'$	$F_{10} = x'y' + xy$	$F_{14} = x + y'$
$F_3 = x'y$	$F_7 = xy' + x'y$	$F_{11} = y$	$F_{15} = x + y$
$F_4 = x'$	$F_8 = x' + y'$	$F_{12} = x' + y$	$F_{16} = 1$

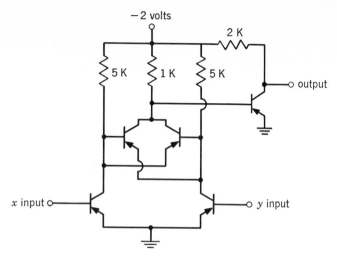

−2 volts

2 K

5 K   1 K   5 K

o output

x input o

o y input

Fig. 5 · 12   DCTL exclusive OR circuit.

be written $x \downarrow y$, and the Sheffer stroke function with a $/$, so that F_8 may be written x/y. Since these operations correspond to those of two input NOR and NAND gates, either of these two functions may be used to generate all possible Boolean functions and, as a result, they are sometimes referred to as "universal connective elements."

Function F_7 ($xy' + x'y$) is the exclusive-OR function. (The most common symbol for this function is $\oplus$.) This function is often used in computer design; however, the circuitry is generally composed of several AND gates, OR gates, and complement circuits. Figure 5 · 12 illustrates a DCTL exclusive-OR circuit.

The OR or logical-addition function for which the symbol $+$ has been used is more properly called the inclusive-OR operation. The everyday usage of OR is ambiguous for it can mean "one or the other or both" or "one or the other and not both." Both usages are perfectly proper, so the problem is only one of definition. The inclusive-OR operation has therefore arbitrarily been designated by the $+$ symbol, and is the "one or the other or both" case, while the symbol $\oplus$ is used for the exclusive-OR operation.

QUESTIONS

1   The circuit in Fig. 5 · 3 has six inputs labeled a through f. If $a = 1$, $b = 1$, $c = 0$, $d = 1$, $e = 0$, and $f = 1$, will the signal at the output represent a 0 or a 1? What if the variables have the previous values except that $c = 1$?

2 Prepare a truth table for the following Boolean expressions:
   a. $xyz + xy'z'$ b. $abc + ab'c' + a'b'c'$
   c. $a(bc' + b'c)$ d. $(a + b)(a + c)(a' + b')$
3 Prepare a truth table for the following Boolean expressions:
   a. $ab' + a'b$ b. $ab' + bc'$
   c. $ac' + ac$ d. $ab'c + abc' + a'bc$
   e. $ab(ab'c + ab'c' + abc')$
4 Simplify the following expressions and draw a block diagram of the
   circuit for each simplified expression using AND and OR gates.
   Assume the inputs are from flip-flops.
   a. $ab'c' + a'b'c' + a'bc' + a'b'c$
   b. $abc + a'bc + ab'c + abc' + ab'c' + a'bc' + a'bc'$
   c. $a(a + b + c)(a' + b + c)(a + b' + c)(a + b + c')$
   d. $(a + b + c)(a + b' + c')(a + b + c')(a + b' + c)$
5 Simplify the following expressions:
   a. $abc(abc' + ab'c + a'bc)$ b. $ab + ab' + a'c + a'c'$
   c. $xy + xyz + xyz' + x'yz$ d. $xy(x'yz + xy'z' + x'y'z')$
6 Form the complements of the following expressions. For instance,
   the complement of $(xy + yz)$ is equal to

$$(xy + xz)' = (x' + y')(x' + z') = x' + y'z'.$$

   a. $(a + bc + ab)$ b. $(a + b)(b + c)(a + c)$
   c. $ab + b'c + cd'$ d. $ab(c'd + b'c)$
   e. $a(b + c)(c' + d')$
7 Prove the two basic De Morgan theorems in Sec. 5 · 10 using the
   "proof by perfect induction."
8 Convert the following expressions to sum-of-products form:
   a. $(a + b)(b' + c)(a' + c)$
   b. $(a + c)(a' + b' + c')(a + b)$
   c. $(a + c)(ab + ac)(a'c' + b)$
9 Which theorem is the dual of theorem 12 in Table 5 · 1?
10 Multiply the following sum terms together forming a sum-of-
   products expression in each case. Simplify while multiplying when
   possible.
   a. $(a + c)(b + d)$
   b. $(a + c + d)(b + d + c)$
   c. $(ab + c + dc)(ac + bc + d)$
   d. $(ab' + a'b + ac)(a'b' + ab + ac')$
11 Write the Boolean expression (in sum-of-products form) for a logical
   circuit which will have a 1 output when $x = 0$, $y = 0$, $z = 1$, and
   $x = 1, y = 1, z = 0$; and a 0 output for all other input states. Draw
   the block diagram for this circuit assuming the inputs are from
   flip-flops.

TABLE 5 · 26

INPUTS			OUTPUT
x	y	z	a
0	0	0	0
0	0	1	1
0	1	0	1
0	1	1	0
1	0	0	0
1	0	1	1
1	1	0	1
1	1	1	0

12 Prove theorem 17 in Sec. 5 · 7 by multiplying out the left side and using theorem 15 to simplify.

13 Write the Boolean expression (in sum-of-products form) for a logical network which will have a 1 output when $x = 0, y = 1, z = 1; x = 1,$ $y = 0, z = 0;$ $x = 1, y = 1, z = 0;$ and $x = 1, y = 1, z = 1$. The circuit will have a 0 output for all other sets of input values. Simplify the expression derived and draw a block diagram for the simplified expression.

14 Prove theorem 18 in Sec. 5 · 7 using the proof by perfect induction.

15 Develop both the sum-of-products and product-of-sums expressions which describe Table 5 · 16 showing combinations, and then simplify both expressions. Draw a block diagram for logical circuitry which corresponds to the simplified expressions using only NAND gates for sum-of-products and NOR gates for product-of-sums.

TABLE 5 · 27

INPUTS			OUTPUT
a	b	c	z
0	0	0	0
0	0	1	1
0	1	0	1
0	1	1	0
1	0	0	1
1	0	1	1
1	1	0	0
1	1	1	0

TABLE 5 · 28

INPUTS			OUTPUT
a	b	c	z
0	0	0	1
0	0	1	0
0	1	0	0
0	1	1	1
1	0	0	1
1	0	1	0
1	1	0	0
1	1	1	1

TABLE 5 · 29

INPUTS			OUTPUT
x	y	z	p
0	0	0	1
0	0	1	1
0	1	0	1
0	1	1	1
1	0	0	1
1	0	1	0
1	1	0	0
1	1	1	0

16   What are the values of the following expressions of $A = 1$, $B = 0$, and $C = 1$:
   a. $A(B' + C')$ b. $B'A + AC'$
   c. $A(B'C' + B'C + C')$ d. $AB'C' + AB'C + A'BC$

17   Write the Boolean algebra expressions for Tables $5 \cdot 27$, $5 \cdot 28$, and $5 \cdot 29$ showing combinations in sum-of-products form; then simplify the expressions and draw a block diagram of the circuit corresponding to each expression.

6

The arithmetic

element

The most obvious definition of the arithmetic element is that it is the part of a computer which performs arithmetic operations. Although this definition would have been reasonably satisfactory for earlier machines, the continually expanding list of instructions performed by present-day machines includes many functions not normally included in the category of arithmetic operations. Certainly many logical operations must be included in the list of functions performed by this section of the computer. It has been suggested that the characteristic of arithmetic operations lies in the fact that numerical quantities form the elements of the calculation. Even this is a somewhat restrictive definition, since much of the operating time of many machines is used for the performance of logical operations, especially those operations dealing with alphanumeric characters.

Regardless of the many functions now being performed by the arithmetic elements of present-day machines, the basic arithmetic operations—addition, subtraction, multiplication, and division—continue to be the "bread-and-butter" operations which the computer performs. Even the literature gives evidence of the fundamental nature of these operations, for when a new machine is described, the times required for addition and multiplication are always included as significant features. Accordingly, a large part of this chapter describes the means by which a computer adds, subtracts, multiplies, and divides. Other basic operations, such as shifting, logical multiplication, and logical adding, will also be described.

It should be remembered that the control element directs the operation of the arithmetic unit. What the arithmetic element does is to add, subtract, multiply, etc., when it is provided with the correct sequence of pulses or levels. It is up to the control element to provide these signals, as it is the function of the storage units to provide the arithmetic element with the information which is to be used. It will therefore be assumed that the control and storage sections of the machine are capable of delivering the correct pulse sequences and d-c levels, and that the numerical quantities on which the operations are to be performed are available. The function of the arithmetic element is therefore to add, subtract, or perform whatever operation the control element directs. Again, the control element is likely to be designed after the arithmetic element, as the questions confronting the designer of the control element are likely to be those concerned with delivering the correct sequence of signals to the arithmetic element.

6 · 1 Construction of the arithmetic element

It was explained in Chaps. 2 and 3 that the information handled in a machine is divided into "words" consisting of a number of bits. For instance, the words handled by a given binary machine may be 40 bits in length. In this case, the arithmetic unit would have to be capable of adding, multiplying, etc., words of 40 bits in length. The words used in the calculations are supplied from computer storage, and the control element directs the operations which are performed. If addition is to be performed, the addend and augend will be supplied to the arithmetic element which must add the numbers and then at least temporarily store the result (sum).

In order to introduce several concepts, let us consider the construction of a typical computer arithmetic element. The storage devices in an arithmetic element consist of a set of registers, each of which is capable of storing a certain amount of information. The length of a register is defined as the maximum amount of information the register can store. In a binary register, the register length is equal to the maximum number of binary digits which can be stored; and in a binary-coded-decimal register, the register length will be the number of decimal digits the register can store.

For convenience, the various registers of the arithmetic element are generally given designations such as x register, b register, mq register, accumulator, etc. The basic register of the arithmetic element of a single-address machine is generally designated as the *accumulator*, which is the register in which the result of each arithmetic operation is stored. In general, an accumulator register is a storage device consisting of flip-flops or a dynamic register which can store a given number, and which is capable of adding a second number to the first number and then storing the sum. An accumulator register, plus its associated circuitry, is generally also capable of performing other operations, such as shifting the number stored in it to the right or left and complementing the number stored.

The accumulator is therefore the basic storage register of the arithmetic element. If the machine is instructed to clear and add, the control element will first clear the accumulator of whatever number may have been stored in it and then put the number selected in storage into the accumulator register. If the computer is instructed to add, the number stored in the accumulator will represent the augend. The addend will then be located in memory and the computer's circuitry will add this number (the addend) to the number previously stored in the accumulator (the augend) and store the sum in the accumulator. Notice that the original augend will no longer be stored in the arithmetic element after the addition. Furthermore, the sum may then either remain in the accumulator or be transferred to memory, depending on the type of computer. This chapter will deal only with the processes of adding, subtracting, etc., and not the process of locating the number to be added in memory, or the transferring of numbers to memory.

These operations will be covered in following chapters.

6 · 2   Basic register operations

There are several operations which are basic to the registers of digital machines. These operations will be described in terms of flip-flop registers, although the operations can be performed on other types of storage devices which may be used for the registers of the arithmetic element. The first of these is the CLEAR-REGISTER operation. Figure 6 · 1 illustrates a 3-digit or 3-bit parallel storage register composed of three flip-flops. A pulse at the CLEAR-PULSE input will remove any information which is in the flip-flops, returning them all to the 0 state. If information is to be read into a register, it is necessary in some machines to clear the register first.

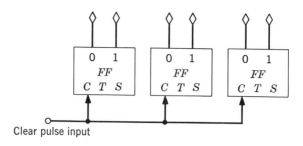

Fig. 6 · 1   CLEAR-REGISTER operation.

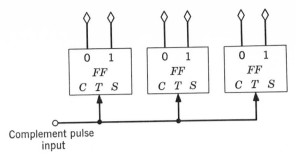

Fig. 6 · 2   COMPLEMENT-REGISTER operation.

The COMPLEMENT operation is illustrated in Fig. 6 · 2. The 3-bit register is assumed to contain a binary number from 000 to 111. When the COMPLEMENT pulse is connected, the 1's complement of the number previously held is formed. For instance, if the flip-flops initially represent 101, after the COMPLEMENT pulse is applied they will represent 010. If the flip-flops initially represent 000, the complement pulse will change them to 111.

Figure 6 · 3 illustrates a TRANSFER-AFTER-CLEAR operation. A number contained in the lower flip-flops is to be transferred into the upper set of flip-flops. First, the upper set of flip-flops are cleared by means of a CLEAR pulse, which resets the three upper flip-flops to the 0 state. A pulse then is applied to the transfer line AND gates.

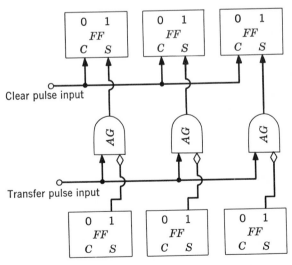

Fig. 6 · 3   TRANSFER-AFTER-CLEAR operation.

If any of the lower three flip-flops are in the 1 state, the output d-c level from these flip-flops, in coincidence with the TRANSFER pulse, will write 1's into the corresponding flip-flops of the upper register. If a lower flip-flop contains a 0, the corresponding AND gate will not conduct a pulse, and the upper flip-flop will continue to contain a 0.

Figure 6 · 4 illustrates a double-line TRANSFER circuit. This circuit will transfer a number from the lower three flip-flops into the upper flip-flops, regardless of the previous state of the upper flip-flops and upon receipt of only one pulse. When the TRANSFER pulse is applied, either the AND gate connected to the 0 output or the AND gate connected to the 1 output of each flip-flop will conduct a pulse to the corresponding flip-flop in the upper register. Notice that each flip-flop in the upper register will receive a pulse from one of the two AND gates connected to it. If one of the upper flip-flops contains a 0 and receives a pulse on its RESET input, it will remain in the 0 condition. If, however, the flip-flop contains a 0 and a pulse is received at the SET input, the flip-flop will be set to the 1 state. If an upper flip-flop originally contains a 1, the converse is true. This will cause each flip-flop in the upper register to contain the same value as the corresponding flip-flop in the lower register after the TRANSFER pulse is applied.

The upper and lower sets of flip-flops each contain a letter designation beside the FF symbol. These designations range from X_1 to X_3 for the upper register and from Y_1 to Y_3 for the lower register. It is convenient to refer to a given flip-flop or set of flip-flops by means

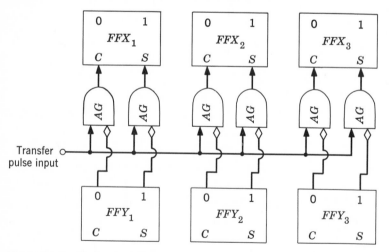

Fig. 6 · 4   Double-line transfer.

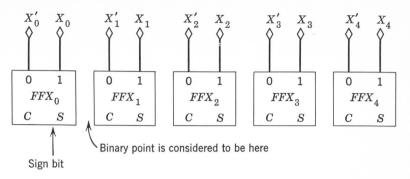

Fig. 6·5 Register designations.

of letter designations, so all of the flip-flops in the same register are generally assigned the same basic letter, plus a numerical subscript which corresponds to the position of the flip-flop within the register. In Fig. 6·4 we may therefore write that the information in FFY_1 is transferred into FFX_1, FFY_2 into FFX_2, and FFY_3 into FFX_3 when the TRANSFER pulse is applied. The three X flip-flops are then referred to as register X, and the three Y flip-flops as register Y, and we may write that the contents of register Y are transferred into register X.

Figure 6·5 contains more information on the representation system that is generally used. The leftmost flip-flop is here designated as X_0 and the remaining flip-flops are designated as X_1 through X_4. These flip-flops therefore constitute a register 5 bits in length, which is designated as register X. The two outputs from flip-flop X_0 are designated x_0' and x_0. If a positive d-c level represents a 1 and a negative d-c level a 0, the x_0' output will be positive when the flip-flop contains a 0, and at the same time the x_0 output will be negative. When the flip-flop contains a 1, the x_0' output will be negative and the x_0 output positive.

The leftmost bit of a register used to store numerical values is generally a sign bit, which indicates whether the number represented by the register is positive or negative. If the sign-bit flip-flop is in the 0 state, the number in the remaining flip-flops is assumed to be positive, and if the sign-bit flip-flop is in the 1 state, the number represented by the remaining flip-flops is assumed to be negative. Further, the flip-flop immediately to the right of the sign-bit flip-flop contains the most significant digit of the number represented. The next flip-flop to the right then stores the next most significant digit and so on to the end of the register. The state of the rightmost flip-flop therefore represents the least significant bit of the output word.

The register illustrated is typical of the sort of register used in the arithmetic element of a fixed-point binary machine. The type of operation is referred to as binary because the storage elements (flip-flops in this case) represent binary values, and the designation "fixed-point" is used because each register is assumed to have a binary point in the same position relative to the sign bit. In Fig. 6 · 5 the binary point is assumed to be between the sign bit and the most significant bit. This is the most common practice in fixed-point binary machines.[1]

If flip-flop x_0 is in the 0 state, FFX_1 is in the 0 state, and FF's X_2 through X_4 are all in the 1 state, the number represented will be $+.0111$. Notice that in this system a register cannot actually store a positive 1, but the largest number which can be represented is $+0.111 \ldots$. If the register (including the sign bit) contains 10 bits, positive values from 0 to 0.111111111 may be represented, and for a 4-bit register positive values from 0.0 to 0.111 may be represented. In general, if the register contains n bits including the sign bit, the register can represent positive binary fractions from 0 to $1 - 2^{1-n}$. For the 10-bit register this is from 0 to $1 - 2^{-9}$ or $1 - (\frac{1}{512})$, and for the 5-bit register in Fig. 6 · 5 from 0 to $1 - 2^{-4}$ or from 0 to $\frac{15}{16}$. Since the sign bit extends the range of the numbers which can be represented, an n-bit binary register can store binary fractions ranging from $+(1 - 2^{1-n})$ to $-(1 - 2^{1-n})$ if the negative binary numbers are represented in true magnitude form.

The same notational system may be used for decimal machines. If a decimal register contains five binary-coded-decimal digits, where each decimal digit is represented by a 4-binary-bit code, the total number of storage elements required will be 20 plus 1 bit to indicate whether the number stored is positive or negative. If the decimal number stored is considered to be a fraction, a register consisting of four decimal digits plus a sign bit can represent from $+(1 - 10^{-4})$ to $-(1 - 10^{-4})$, or from -0.9999 to $+0.9999$.

Notice also that the CLEAR and TRANSFER operations are the same if the number stored is in binary-coded-decimal form. The COMPLEMENT operation, however, requires that the decimal digits be coded in some system where complementing each of the storage elements results in the 9's complement of each binary-coded-decimal digit stored. For instance, in an excess 3 code or 2, 4, 2, 1 code (refer to Chap. 3), the 9's complement of the number stored in a register will be formed if each bit of the binary-coded-decimal code groups is complemented. There are techniques for forming the 9's

---

[1] It is possible to consider the binary point in any one of a number of places, however. For instance, the binary point may be considered to be to the right of the rightmost bit of the register. The description which follows will assume a binary point to the left of the most significant bit of the register.

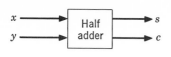

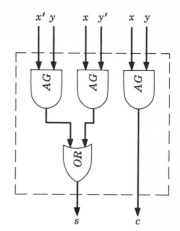

Input		Output	
x	y	s	c
0	0	0	0
0	1	1	0
1	0	1	0
1	1	0	1

$s = x'y + xy'$
$c = xy$

Fig. 6·6 Half adder.

complement of binary-coded-decimal numbers in other systems, such as the 8, 4, 2, 1 code, and these will be described. The CLEAR and TRANSFER operations can also be performed on numbers represented in serial form, and techniques for this have been described in Chap. 4.

6·3 The binary half adder

One of the basic configurations used in the design of binary arithmetic elements is the *half adder* illustrated in Fig. 6·6. There are two inputs to the half adder, designated as x and y in Fig. 6·6, and two outputs, designated as s and c. The half adder performs the binary addition operation for two binary inputs. This is "arithmetic addition," not logical or Boolean algebra addition. Chapter 3 described the principles of binary addition; the basic addition is shown in Table 6·1.

The half adder performs this operation. There are two inputs to the circuit, each representing a binary 0 or 1, and two outputs. If

TABLE 6·1

INPUTS	SUM BIT
$0 + 0$	0
$0 + 1$	1
$1 + 0$	1
$1 + 1$	0 with a carry of 1

either of the inputs is a 1, but not both, the output on the s line will be a 1 (refer to the table above). If both of the inputs are 1's, the output on the c line will be a 1; for all other states there will be a 0 output on the carry line. These relationships may be written in Boolean form as follows:

$$s = xy' + x'y$$

$$c = xy$$

The actual circuitry may be constructed in a number of ways, one of which is illustrated in Fig. $6 \cdot 6$. Notice that the half-adder block diagram in Fig. $6 \cdot 6$ has both x and x' and y and y' inputs. If the inputs are from flip-flops, both of these inputs are available. If complemented inputs are not available, inverters may be used to form them. The inputs to a half or full adder are generally the outputs from some storage device. If each storage device has only one output, there will therefore be only one input line available to the adder. In drawing block diagrams of a half or full adder, the x input line may therefore actually consist of two physical connections; however, only a single input line may be shown in the drawing. The meaning of the x then is that the output(s) from storage device x are connected to the adder circuitry.

A *quarter adder* consists of the two inputs to the half adder and the s output only. The logical expression for this circuit is therefore $s = xy' + x'y$. This is also the "exclusive OR" relationship for Boolean algebra (refer to Chap. 5).

6 · 4   The full adder

While the half adder performs the basic operation of binary addition, additional circuitry is required to perform the addition of two binary registers. This is because there is no input to the half adder for the carries generated by previous bits. Consider the addition of the following two binary numbers:

$$
\begin{array}{r}
1\,0\,1\,1 \\
+\quad 1\,1\,1\,0 \\
\hline
1\,1\,0\,0\,1 = \text{sum}
\end{array}
\qquad\qquad
\begin{array}{r}
1\,0\,1\,1 \\
+\quad 1\,1\,1\,0 \\
\hline
0\,1\,0\,1 = \text{partial sum} \\
1\quad 1\quad\ \ \ = \text{carry bits} \\
\hline
1\,1\,0\,0\,1 = \text{complete sum}
\end{array}
$$

The carries generated in each column must be considered during the addition process; therefore adder circuitry capable of adding the contents of two registers together must include provision for handling

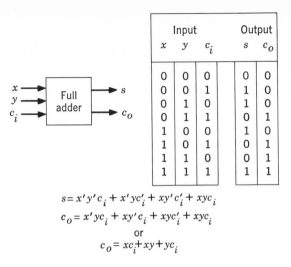

	Input			Output	
x	y	c_i		s	c_o
0	0	0		0	0
0	0	1		1	0
0	1	0		1	0
0	1	1		0	1
1	0	0		1	0
1	0	1		0	1
1	1	0		0	1
1	1	1		1	1

$$s = x'y'c_i + x'yc'_i + xy'c'_i + xyc_i$$
$$c_o = x'yc_i + xy'c_i + xyc'_i + xyc_i$$
$$\text{or}$$
$$c_o = xc_i + xy + yc_i$$

Fig. 6 · 7   The full adder.

carries as well as addend and augend bits. There must therefore be three inputs to each stage of a parallel adder, except the stage for the least significant bits—one for each input from the numbers being added and one for any carry which might have been generated or propagated by the previous stage.

The block diagram symbol for a full binary adder is illustrated in Fig. 6 · 7, as is the complete table of input-output relationships for the full adder. There are three inputs to the full adder: the x and y inputs from the respective digits of the registers to be added, and the c_i input, which is for any carry generated by the previous stage. The two outputs are s, which is the output value for that stage of the addition, and c_o, which produces the carry which is to be added into the next stage. The Boolean expressions for the input-output relationships for each of the two outputs are also presented in Fig. 6 · 7, as is the expression for the c_o output in simplified form.

A full adder may be constructed of two half adders as illustrated in Fig. 6 · 8. Constructing a full adder from two half adders may not necessarily be the most economical technique, however, and generally full adders are designed directly from the input-output relations illustrated in Fig. 6 · 7.

5 · 5   A parallel binary adder

A 4-bit parallel binary adder is illustrated in Fig. 6 · 9. The purpose of this adder is to add together two 4-bit binary numbers. The addend inputs are represented by x_1 through x_4, which are used to designate

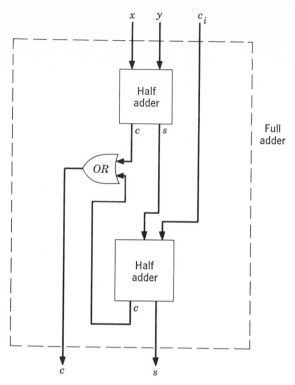

x   y c_i

Half
adder

c   s

Full
adder

OR

Half
adder

c

c   s

Fig. 6·8   Half- and full-adder relationship.

the four storage devices of the addend register; and the augend bits
are represented by y_1 through y_4, designating the inputs from the
register containing the augend. The adder shown does not possess the
ability to handle sign bits for the binary words to be added, but only
adds together the magnitudes of the numbers stored. The additional
circuitry needed to handle the sign bits is dependent on whether
negative numbers are represented in true magnitude or in the 1's or
2's complement systems and this problem will be described later.

Consider the addition of the following two 4-bit binary numbers:

$$0\ 1\ 1\ 1 \text{ where } x_1 = 0, x_2 = 1, x_3 = 1, \text{ and } x_4 = 1$$
$$0\ 0\ 1\ 1 \text{ where } y_1 = 0, y_2 = 0, y_3 = 1, \text{ and } y_4 = 1$$
$$\text{Sum} = \overline{1\ 0\ 1\ 0}$$

The sum should therefore be $s_1 = 1$, $s_2 = 0$, $s_3 = 1$, and $s_4 = 0$.

The operation of the adder may be checked as follows: since x_4 and
y_4 are the least significant digits, they cannot receive a carry from a
previous stage. In the problem above, x_4 and y_4 are both 1's, their

sum is therefore 0 and a carry is generated and added into the full adder for bits x_3 and y_3. Bits x_3 and y_3 are also both 1's, as is the CARRY input to this stage; therefore the SUM output line s_3 carries a 1 and the CARRY line to the next stage also carries a 1. Since x_2 is a 1, y_2 a zero, and the CARRY input is 1, the SUM output line s_2 will carry a 0 and the carry to the next stage will be a 1. Both inputs x_1 and y_1 are equal to 0 and the CARRY input line to this adder stage is equal to 1; therefore the SUM output line s_1 will represent a 1 and the CARRY output line, designated as "overflow" in Fig. 6·9, will have a zero output.

The same basic configuration illustrated in Fig. 6·9 may be extended to any number of bits. A 7-bit adder may be constructed using 7 full adders and a 20-bit adder using 20 full adders.

It should be noted that the OVERFLOW line could be used to enable the 4-bit adder in Fig. 6·9 to have a 5-bit output. This is not generally done, however, because since the addend and augend both come from storage their length is the length of the basic computer word, and a longer word cannot be readily stored by the machine. It was explained earlier that a machine with a word length of n bits [consisting of a sign bit and $(n - 1)$ bits to designate the magnitude] could express positive binary fractions from $-(1 - 2^{1-n})$ to $+(1 - 2^{1-n})$. A number within these limits is called "representable." Since the simple 4-bit adder in Fig. 6·9 has no sign bit, it can only represent binary fractions from 0 to $^{15}/_{16}$. If .1100 and .1100 are added in the adder illustrated in Fig. 6·9, there will be a 1 output on the

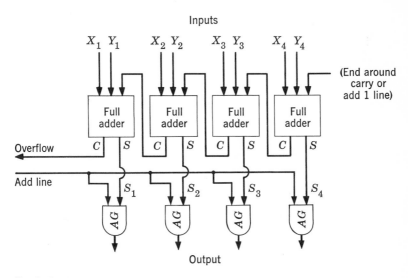

Fig. 6·9   Parallel adder.

OVERFLOW line because the sum of these two numbers is 1.1000. This number is $+1\frac{1}{2}$ decimal and cannot be represented in this system. Such a number is referred to as "nonrepresentable" for this particular very small register. The 1 on the OVERFLOW line therefore indicates an error. The overflow generated in this case is often connected to circuitry which stops the machine, and an alarm is generated which indicates that an illegal addition operation has been performed. It is one of the functions of the machine to detect such errors and to indicate them to the operators of the machine. This is often done by stopping the machine and causing an overflow light to glow.

The AND gates connected to the s output lines from the four adders are used to gate the sum of the two registers into the correct register.

6 · 6 The serial full binary adder

The inputs to the serial adder consist of two numbers, the addend and augend, each represented by a series of signals. Figure 6 · 10 illustrates a block diagram of a serial adder and a set of input and output waveforms. The inputs to the adder are 0110, the addend, and 0011, the augend. Notice that the least significant bits of the numbers to be added are the rightmost parts of the waveforms in Fig. 6 · 10. The most significant bits are the leftmost bits.[2] The signals representing the least significant bits of the two numbers being added arrive at the adder first because the carry bit must be added in with the next least significant pair of augend-addend bits.

There is a DELAY line in the CARRY loop. This delay is equal to one bit time, or the delay which occurs between successive bits to be added. In this manner the carries from the least significant bits are propagated to the more significant bits, just as in the parallel adder. For instance, in Fig. 6 · 10, a carry occurs when both the second and third least significant bits of the augend and addend are added. This carry is delayed and added in with the next pair of addend-augend bits.

Figure 6 · 11 shows how addition may be performed using two circulating registers. The topmost register in the figure is the accumulator register and the lower register is designated the x register. In its normal condition, the control flip-flop (FFA) is in the 0 state and both registers will be circulating the numbers stored. The timing of the machine is arranged so that the signals representing the bits stored

[2]If an oscilloscope is used to examine the input waveforms, the order will be reversed, as the oscilloscope trace will indicate the pulses which occur first in time—i.e., the least significant bits—to the left of the scope face, and the pulses occurring later will be indicated to the right of these.

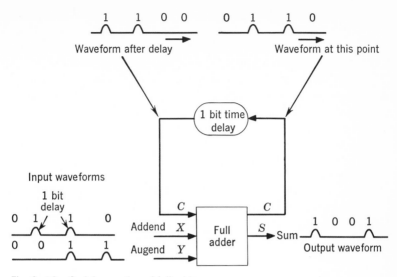

Fig. 6 · 10   Serial operation of full adder.

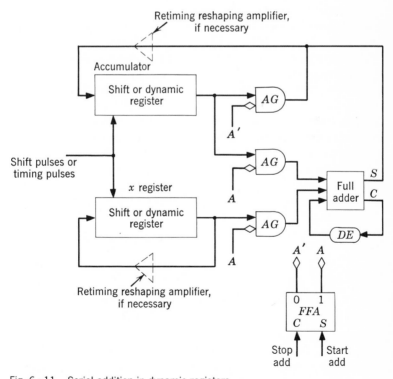

Fig. 6 · 11   Serial addition in dynamic registers.

in the registers are maintained in relative positions; thus the least significant bits in each register leave the registers together and are recirculated; and since the words stored are of the same length, the most significant bits will also be maintained in position.

If the *FFA* is set to the 1 state by a START ADD pulse, the *C* output line will go high (representing a 1) and the two AND gates connected to the full adder will route the signals representing the numbers stored into the full adder. At the same time the *A'* line from the *FFA* will fall, and the loop around which the accumulator contents are normally circulated will be disconnected.

The START ADD pulse arrives at the beginning of a word time, that is, when the signals representing the least significant bits of the numbers stored arrive at the outputs of the registers. At the end of the word time, the STOP ADD line is pulsed and the registers revert to their normal state. After the addition the accumulator register will contain the sum of the numbers previously stored in the accumulator and *x* register.

6 · 7 Positive and negative numbers

When writing numbers in the decimal system, the common practice is to write the number as a magnitude preceded by a plus or minus sign which indicates whether the number is positive or negative. Hence, $+125$ is positive, and -125 is negative 125. The same practice is generally used with binary numbers: $+111$ is positive 7, and -110 is negative 6. In order to handle both positive and negative numbers, the computer must have some means of distinguishing a positive from a negative number. As was previously explained, the computer word usually contains a sign bit, generally adjacent to the most significant bit in the computer word. While notation in such matters is completely arbitrary, in the systems to be described a 1 in the sign bit will indicate a negative number and a 0 in the sign bit a positive number.

The following are several methods for storing negative binary numbers:

1 Negative numbers may be stored in their *true magnitude form*. The binary fraction $-.011$ will therefore be stored as 1.011, where the 1 indicates that the number stored is negative and the .011 indicates the magnitude of the number.

2 The *1's complement* of the magnitude may be used to represent a negative number. The binary fraction $-.0111$ will therefore be represented as 1.1000, where the 1 indicates that the number is negative and the .1000 is the 1's complement of the magnitude. (The 1's complement is formed by simply complementing each bit of the positive magnitude.)

3　The *2's complement* may be used to represent a negative binary number. For instance, $-.0111$ would be stored as 1.1001, where the 1 in the sign bit indicates that the number is negative and the $.1001$ is the 2's complement of the magnitude of the number. (The 2's complement is formed by complementing the actual magnitude $.0111$, giving $.1000$, and then adding 1 to the least significant digit, giving $.1001$.)

6 · 8　Addition in the 1's complement system

The 1's complement system of representing negative numbers is sometimes used in parallel binary machines. The main reason for this is the ease with which the 1's complement of a binary number may be formed. Figure $6 \cdot 2$ illustrated a standard technique for complementing each bit of a binary number stored in a flip-flop register. A second pulse on the COMPLEMENT line will restore the number to its original positive value, making restoration comparatively simple. There are four possible basic situations which may arise in adding combinations of positive and negative numbers in the 1's complement system:

1　When a positive number is added to another positive number, the addition of all bits, including the sign bit, is straightforward. Since both sign bits will be 0's, no sum or carry will be generated in the sign-bit adder and the output will remain 0. Here is an example of the addition of two 4-bit positive numbers. Figure $6 \cdot 9$ illustrates a possible adder configuration if the END-AROUND CARRY line is converted to the OVERFLOW line.

NORMAL NOTATION	COMPUTER WORD
$+ .0011$	0.0011
$+ .0100$	0.0100
$+ .0111$	0.0111

2　When a positive and a negative number are added together, the sum may be either positive or negative. If the positive number has a greater magnitude, the sum will be positive; and if the negative number is greater in magnitude, the sum will be negative. In the 1's complement system, the answer will be correct as is if the sum of the two numbers is negative in value. In this case no carry will be generated when the numbers are added. For instance:

$+ .0011$	0.0011
$- .1100$	1.0011
$- .1001$	1.0110

In this case the output of the adder will be 1.0110, the last 4 bits of which are the 1's complement of .1001, the correct magnitude of the sum. The 1 in the sign bit is also correct, indicating a negative number.

3 If the positive number is larger than the negative number, the sum before the end-around carry is added will be incorrect. The addition of the end-around carry will correct this sum. There will be a 0 in the sign bit indicating that the sum is positive.

$$
\begin{array}{ll}
+.1001 = & 0.1001 \\
-.0100 = & 1.1011 \\
\hline
+.0101 & \overline{0.0100} \\
& \quad\ \ \longrightarrow 1 \\
\hline
& 0.0101
\end{array}
\qquad
\begin{array}{ll}
+.0011 = & 0.0011 \\
-.0010 = & 1.1101 \\
\hline
+.0001 & \overline{0.0000} \\
& \quad\ \ \longrightarrow 1 \\
\hline
& 0.0001
\end{array}
$$

Notice what happens when two numbers of equal magnitude but of opposite sign are added:

$$
\begin{array}{ll}
+.1011 = 0.1011 \\
-.1011 = 1.0100 \\
\hline
\ \ .0000 \quad 1.1111
\end{array}
\qquad
\begin{array}{ll}
+.0000 = 0.0000 \\
-.0000 = 1.1111 \\
\hline
\ \ .0000 \quad 1.1111
\end{array}
$$

The result in these cases will be a negative zero (1.1111), which is correct.

4 When two negative numbers are added together, an end-around carry will always be generated, as will a carry from the adder for the first bits of the magnitudes of the numbers. This will place a 1 in the sign bit.

$$
\begin{array}{ll}
-.0011 = & 1.1100 \\
-.1011 = & 1.0100 \\
\hline
-.1110 & \overline{1.0000} \\
& \quad\ \ \longrightarrow 1 \\
\hline
& 1.0001
\end{array}
\qquad
\begin{array}{ll}
-.0100 = & 1.1011 \\
-.0111 = & 1.1000 \\
\hline
-.1011 & \overline{1.0011} \\
& \quad\ \ \longrightarrow 1 \\
\hline
& 1.0100
\end{array}
$$

The output of the adder will be in 1's complement form in each case, with a 1 in the sign-bit position.

6 · 9 Addition in the 2's complement system

When negative numbers are represented in the 2's complement system, the operation of addition is very similar to that in the 1's complement system. In parallel machines, the 2's complement of a number stored in a register may be formed by first complementing the register and then adding 1 to the least significant bit of the register. This process requires two steps and is therefore more time-consuming than the 1's complement system; however, the 2's complement system has the advantage of not requiring an end-around carry during addition.

It is possible to construct a complementer for serial machines which will form the 2's complement of a serial number as it passes through the complementer; this technique will be shown later. Because it is easy to form 2's complements in serial machines, this system is the most used.

The four situations which may occur in adding two numbers when the 2's complement system is used are as follows:

1   When both numbers are positive, the situation is completely identical to that in case 1 in the 1's complement system which has been discussed.

2   When one number is positive and the other negative, and the larger number is the positive number, a carry will be generated through the sign bit. This carry may be discarded, as the outputs of the adder are correct, as shown below.

$$
\begin{array}{ll}
+.0111 = & 0.0111 \\
-.0011 = & +1.1101 \\
\hline
+.0100 & \llcorner 0.0100 \\
& \rightarrow\text{carry is discarded}
\end{array}
\qquad
\begin{array}{ll}
+.1000 = & 0.1000 \\
-.0111 = & +1.1001 \\
\hline
+.0001 & \llcorner 0.0001 \\
& \rightarrow\text{carry is discarded}
\end{array}
$$

3   When a positive and negative number are added, and the negative number is the larger, no carry will result in the sign bit and the answer will again be correct as it stands.

$$
\begin{array}{ll}
+.0011 = & 0.0011 \\
-.0100 = & 1.1100 \\
\hline
-.0001 & 1.1111
\end{array}
\qquad
\begin{array}{ll}
+.0100 = & 0.0100 \\
-.1000 = & 1.1000 \\
\hline
-.0100 & 1.1100
\end{array}
$$

NOTE: A 1 must be added to the least significant bit of a 2's complement number when converting it to a magnitude. For example:

$$
\begin{array}{l}
1.0011 = -.1100 \\
+.0001 \\
\hline
-.1101
\end{array}
$$

When both numbers are of the same magnitude, or are plus and minus zero, the results are as follows:

$$
\begin{array}{ll}
+.0011 = & 0.0011 \\
-.0011 = & 1.1101 \\
\hline
.0000 & 0.0000
\end{array}
\qquad
\begin{array}{ll}
+.0000 = & 0.0000 \\
-.0000 = & 1.0000 \\
\hline
.0000 & 1.0000
\end{array}
$$

When a positive and negative number of the same magnitude are added, the result will be a positive zero; however, since "negative" zero in this system is 1.0000, the addition of plus and minus zero will be a negative zero.

4 When two negative numbers are added together, an end carry will be generated in the sign bit and also in the bit to the right of the sign bit. This will cause a 1 to be placed in the sign bit, which is correct, and the carry from the sign bit may be discarded.

$$
\begin{array}{ll}
-.0011 = & 1.1101 \\
-.0100 = & 1.1100 \\
\hline
-.0111 & 1.1001 \\
\end{array}
\qquad
\begin{array}{ll}
-.0011 = 1.1101 \\
-.1011 = 1.0101 \\
\hline
-.1110 \quad 1.0010 \\
\end{array}
$$

$\longrightarrow$ carry is discarded

6 · 10 Addition and subtraction in an arithmetic element

If the machine is capable of adding both positive and negative numbers, subtraction may be performed by complementing the subtrahend and then adding. For instance, $8 - 4$ yields the same result as $8 + (-4)$, and $6 - (-2)$ yields the same result as $6 + 2$. Subtraction therefore may be performed by an arithmetic element capable only of adding, by forming the complement of the subtrahend and then adding. For instance, in the 1's complement system, four cases may arise:

TWO POSITIVE NUMBERS

$$
\begin{array}{l}
0.0011 \\
-0.0001 \quad \text{Complementing the subtrahend} \\
\hline
\qquad \text{and adding,}
\end{array}
\qquad
\begin{array}{l}
0.0011 \\
1.1110 \\
\hline
0.0001 \\
\longrightarrow \text{carry } 1 \\
\hline
0.0010
\end{array}
$$

TWO NEGATIVE NUMBERS

$$
\begin{array}{l}
1.1101 \\
-1.1011 \quad \text{complementing,} \\
\hline
\end{array}
\qquad
\begin{array}{l}
1.1101 \\
0.0100 \\
\hline
0.0001 \\
\longrightarrow \text{carry } 1 \\
\hline
0.0010
\end{array}
$$

POSITIVE MINUEND NEGATIVE SUBTRAHEND

$$
\begin{array}{l}
0.0010 \\
-1.1101 \\
\hline
\end{array}
=
\begin{array}{l}
0.0010 \\
0.0010 \\
\hline
0.0100
\end{array}
$$

NEGATIVE MINUEND POSITIVE SUBTRAHEND

$$
\begin{array}{l}
1.0101 \\
-0.0010 \\
\hline
\end{array}
=
\begin{array}{l}
1.0101 \\
1.1101 \\
\hline
1.0010 \\
\longrightarrow \text{carry } 1 \\
\hline
1.0011
\end{array}
$$

The same basic rules apply to subtraction in the 2's complement system except that the carry generated in the sign bits is simply dropped. In this case, the 2's complement of the subtrahend is formed and the complemented number is then added to the minuend with no end-around carry. The complementation of the subtrahend may be performed in several ways. For the 2's complement system, for instance, if the storage register is composed of flip-flops, the number in the register to be subtracted may be complemented by means of a pulse applied at the COMPLEMENT input of all the flip-flops in the register (refer to Fig. 6·2), and then a 1 may be added to the number in the register through the adder circuitry. The 1 may also be added when the two numbers are added, connecting a 1 at the CARRY input (refer to Fig. 6·9) of the adder for the least significant bits. For serial machines, the 2's complement of the subtrahend may be formed by means of the circuit in Fig. 6·12.

The circuit in Fig. 6·12 complements every bit which passes after, but not including, the first 1. For instance, if binary 1010 is the number to be complemented, the complementer will first receive a 0, then a 1, then another 0, and finally a 1. The circuit will not complement the 0, nor will it complement the first 1 it receives, but it will complement every bit thereafter. The final complemented number will be 0110, the 2's complement of 1010. The flip-flop must be reset before the circuit is used to form the 2's complement of another number.

If 1's are represented by pulses and 0's by the absence of pulses, a transistor inverter will not directly form a complement. (The 1's com-

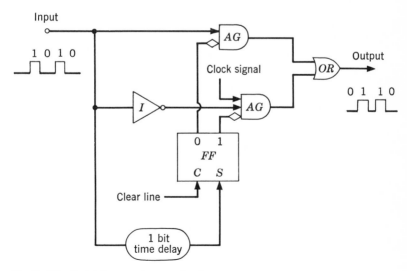

Fig. 6·12   Serial 2's complement circuit.

plement of "no pulse" is a pulse in such a system.) To circumvent this problem, an INHIBIT circuit is used (denoted by a block with an INH inside). In this logical circuit, when a pulse appears on the input line which is circled, no pulse will pass through the circuit. If, however, no pulse appears on the circled input, a pulse on the clock input will pass through the circuit.

6 · 11   A serial-arithmetic element

Figure 6 · 13 shows a two-register serial-arithmetic element which makes possible the following operations:

1   A word can be read from memory into either the accumulator or x register.
2   A word in memory can be added to a word stored in the accumulator and the sum will be stored in the accumulator.
3   A word in memory can be subtracted from a word stored in the accumulator, and the contents stored in the accumulator.

The registers in Fig. 6 · 13 store the signals representing the numbers to be used in serial form. The signals representing the bits of the numbers must be kept in strict synchronization. Several of the earlier computers used sonic delay lines to form both the registers in the arithmetic element and also the registers in the memory element of the machine. All the numbers stored in both the memory element and arithmetic element were then kept strictly synchronized by clock pulses distributed throughout the machine. Several smaller machines utilize magnetic-drum storage to form both the memory-element registers and arithmetic-element registers, and the timing of the signals throughout the machines is kept synchronized by timing signals from the drum. (The magnetic drum will be described in Chap. 7. The registers in a magnetic-drum system are classified as "dynamic registers" and their behavior is similar to that of the registers using delay lines.)

Control of the arithmetic element in Fig. 6 · 13 is via a set of four flip-flops designated FFZ, FFY, FFC, and FFD. The control element of the machine is supplied with timing pulses which indicate the beginning and ending of word times, and these signals are used to operate the flip-flops.

In order to read a word from the memory element into the accumulator, the word must be located in the memory, and then, at the beginning of a word time, FFC is set into the 1 state by a pulse on its SET line. This opens the AND gate connected to the input of the accumulator and closes the AND gate in the circulating loop of the register. During the word time the word located in memory will be

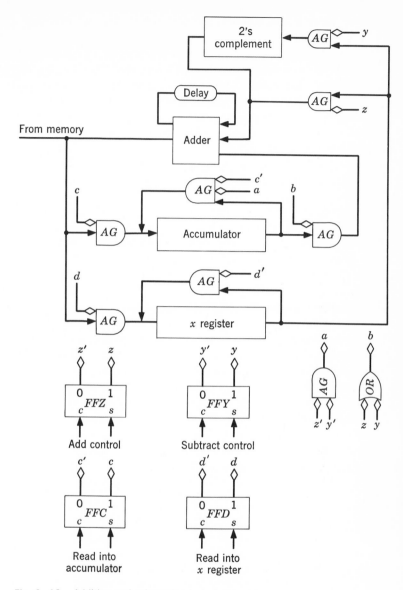

Fig. 6 · 13   Addition and subtraction in serial machine.

read into the accumulator. At the end of the word time, just after the sign bit has been read into the accumulator, a RESET pulse is applied to *FFC*, closing the input path to memory and again causing the word stored in the accumulator to be circulated. The contents of the accumulator will now be the word read from memory.

A word may be read into the x register in the same manner, except that in this case FFD is set to the 1 state at the beginning of a word and reset at the end of the word time.

The ADD control and SUBTRACT control flip-flops are used to control the arithmetic element during addition and subtraction. Notice that the outputs from these flip-flops are also connected to a pair of gates, the outputs of which are designated as a and b. The a and b signals are connected to several AND gates which control the operation of the registers.

When an ADD instruction is given (refer to Chap. 2), the word to be added to the accumulator is first located in memory and then read into the x register. At the beginning of the next word time the ADD control flip-flop (FFZ) is set to the 1 state. The z and b signals become 1's and the a signal becomes 0, routing the outputs from the accumulator circulating loop. The output of the adder represents the sum of the numbers stored in the accumulator and x register, and this sum is read back into the accumulator during the word time. At the end of the word time, FFZ is returned to the 0 state and the sum will be circulated in the accumulator register.

Subtraction is performed in a similar manner except that FFY is set to 1 at the beginning of the word time and reset at the end of the word time. This causes the contents of the x register to be routed into the adder through the 2's complementer, so that the output of the adder will be the difference instead of the sum of the accumulator and x register. After the word time, the difference will be stored in the accumulator register.

6 · 12   The full adder, three examples

The full adder is a basic component of an arithmetic element. Figure 6 · 7 illustrated the block diagram symbol for the full adder, along with a table of combinations for the input-output values and the expressions describing the sum and carry lines. Succeeding figures and text described the operation of the full adder in both parallel and serial systems. Notice that while for serial systems only one full adder is required, a parallel system requires one full adder for each bit in the basic word.

There are of course many configurations for full binary adders. Three examples will be shown: one for parallel registers using storage devices with only one output line, one for parallel registers using flip-flops, and a serial full adder.

1 *Full Binary Adder for IBM* 704-709. Figure 6 · 14 illustrates the full binary adder configuration used in the IBM 704 and 709 general-

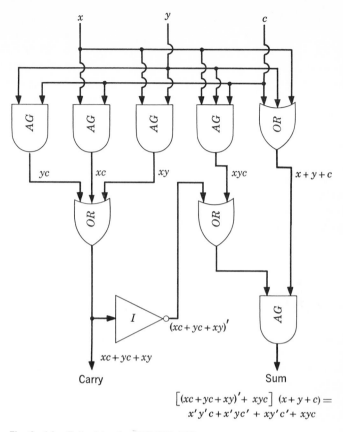

$$\left[(xc+yc+xy)'+xyc\right](x+y+c)=$$
$$x'y'c+x'yc'+xy'c'+xyc$$

Fig. 6 · 14   Full adder for IBM 704–709.

purpose digital computers. There are three inputs to the circuit: the x input is from one of the storage devices in the accumulator, the y input is from the corresponding storage device in the register to be added to the accumulator register, and the third input is the CARRY input from the adder for the next least significant bit. The two outputs are the SUM output and the CARRY output. The SUM output will contain the sum value for this particular digit of the output (if bit x_3 is added to bit y_3, the output on s_3 will be the third most significant bit in the sum). The CARRY output will be connected to the CARRY input of the next most significant bit's adder (refer to Fig. 6 · 9).

The outputs from the three AND gates connected directly to the x, y and c inputs are logically added together by the OR gate circuit directly beneath. If either the x and y, x and c, or y and c input lines contain a 1, there should be a CARRY output. The output of this circuit, written in logical equation form, is shown on the figure. This may be compared with the expression derived in Fig. 6 · 7.

The derivation of the SUM output is not so straightforward. The CARRY output expression $xy + xc + yc$ is first inverted (complemented) yielding $(xy + xc + yc)'$. The logical product of x, y, and c is formed by an AND gate and is logically added to this forming $(xy + xc + yc)' + xyc$. The logical sum of x, y, and c is then multiplied, forming the expression

$$[(xy + xc + yc)' + xyc](x + y + c)$$

When multiplied out and simplified, this expression will be $x'y'c + x'yc' + xy'c' + xyc$, the expression derived in Fig. 6 · 7. Tracing through the logical operation of the circuit for various values will indicate that the SUM output will be 1 when only one of the input values is equal to 1, or when all three input values are equal to 1. For all other combinations of inputs the output value will be a 0.

2 *Full Adders Using Only NOR Gates.* Figure 6 · 15 shows a full-adder circuit using only NOR gates. This circuit was developed for integrated circuits using TRL as described in Chap. 4. The entire circuit can be packaged into one integrated circuit can such as the TO-5 can shown in Fig. 4 · 25. The maximum delay from an input change to an output change for the S output is on the order of 36 nanoseconds (nsec).[3] The maximum delay from input to the C output is about 30 nsec.

The amount of delay associated with each carry is an important figure in evaluating a full adder for a parallel system, because the amount of time required to add two numbers is determined by the maximum time it takes for a carry to propagate through the adders. For instance, if we add 0.1111 to 1.0001 in the 2's complement system, the carry generated by the 1's in the least significant digit of each number must propagate through four carry stages and a sum stage before we can safely gate the sum into the accumulator. A study of the addition of these two numbers using the configuration in Fig. 6 · 9 will make this clear.

This problem is called the *carry-ripple problem.* Let us calculate the maximum time for a carry for the adder in Fig. 6 · 15, assuming that two registers of five flip-flops each (including the flip-flop which stores the sign) are used. We will count the maximum number of NOR gates through which a carry must pass. If there are 1's in the least significant flip-flops, a carry of 1 will be generated in the rightmost adder (refer to Fig. 6 · 9) and the signals must pass through five NOR gates. In the next three stages each carry must pass

---

[3]A nsec is equal to 10^{-9} sec.

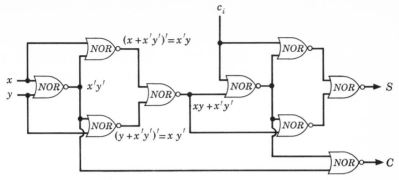

Fig. 6 · 15   NOR-gate full adder.

through three and then two NOR gates per stage, since the x and y inputs will have arrived in advance of the carries-in. For the final leftmost or sign stage a carry signal must pass through 3 NORs so the total number of NORs will be 15. If we assume a delay of 6 nsec maximum per NOR gate, we must then wait $15 \times 6 = 90$ nsec before we may safely gate in a sum.

There are a number of techniques which are used in high-speed machines to alleviate this problem. One of these is a *CARRY bridging circuit* which calculates the carry-out of a number of stages simultaneously and then delivers this carry to the succeeding stages. The references explain several such schemes.

3   *Full Binary Adder for Serial Systems.* The Boolean expression which describes the parallel adder is the same as the expression for the serial adder, as the full adder, whether serial or binary, performs the same function. Figure 6 · 16 is a block diagram of a serial adder. Included in this adder is the 1-bit-time delay line, which causes any carry generated to be propagated and added in with the next most significant pair of bits introduced into the adder.

It should be noted that when pulses are introduced into a serial adder of this sort, the timing of the inputs and the shape of the input pulses are quite critical. If, for instance, one of the x inputs slightly precedes a y input, there are liable to be small spikes throughout the circuit. Since the inputs are not likely to be ideal, the output pulses are also not likely to have an ideal shape. To circumvent this problem, an adder of this sort may be followed by a detecting and reshaping amplifier which samples only a section of the output pulses from the adder, and then amplifies and reshapes the output signal. The reshaping amplifier used will generally discriminate against any low-level signals or spikes which may appear at the output. The output pulse is often sampled when the maximum overlap of the two input pulses is calculated to occur.

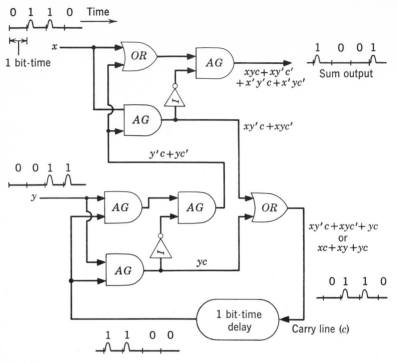

0 1 1 0   Time

1 bit-time

x

OR

AG

$xyc+xy'c'$
$+x'y'c+x'yc'$

Sum output

1 0 0 1

AG

$xy'c+xyc'$

$y'c+yc'$

0 0 1 1

y

AG

AG

OR

$xy'c+xyc'+yc$
or
$xc+xy+yc$

AG

yc

0 1 1 0

1 bit-time
delay

Carry line (c)

1 1 0 0

Fig. 6 · 16   Serial adder.

6 · 13   Half binary subtracter

The use of full adders and numbers represented in either a 1's or 2's complement system have been described, along with the operation of systems which can either add or subtract all combinations of positive and negative numbers. There are systems, however, which express negative numbers in their magnitude forms, so that $+.0110$ is

TABLE 6 · 2

HALF SUBTRACTER			
INPUTS		OUTPUTS	
x	y	d	b
0	0	0	0
0	1	1	1
1	0	1	0
1	1	0	0

expressed in the machine as 0.0110 and −.0110 is expressed as 1.0110. These machines require a subtracter to perform subtraction and also to handle the addition of positive to negative numbers. Also, it is possible to construct a system where the basic operation is subtraction and where addition is performed by complementing the addend and then subtracting the addend. Accordingly, a brief description of circuits which perform subtraction follows.

Chapter 3 described the principles of binary subtraction. The rules for the subtraction of one binary number from another are as follows:

$$0 - 0 = 0$$
$$0 - 1 = 1 \text{ and borrow } 1$$
$$1 - 0 = 1$$
$$1 - 1 = 0$$

A table may be made from these relationships in order to derive the fundamental Boolean relationships for binary subtraction. Just as a half adder performs the basic addition operation for two binary digits, a half subtracter performs the basic subtraction operation. There are therefore two inputs to the half subtracter, the minuend digit and the subtrahend digit; and two outputs, a difference digit and a borrow digit. If x is considered to be the minuend digit and y the subtrahend digit, a table of input-output relationships for a half subtracter may be constructed and the expressions which describe each of the outputs as functions of the inputs may be derived (see Table 6·2).

The difference output line will therefore be 1 only when either x or y is equal to 1, and the borrow will be 1 only when the x input is 0 and the y input 1. The expressions for the difference and borrow outputs are therefore as follows:

$$d = xy' + x'y$$
$$b = x'y$$

The d output line is the same as the sum output line in the half adder. The borrow line, however, is different.

6·14   The full binary subtracter

The problems encountered in subtracting two binary numbers which contain several digits are of the same sort as those in adding. In the case of addition, it is necessary to initiate and propagate carries; and in the case of subtraction, it is necessary to initiate and propagate borrows. In either case, the output of a given subtracter is dependent on the outputs of previous stages.

There are therefore three inputs to a full subtracter (Fig. 6·17) and two outputs. Two of the inputs are from the minuend and subtrahend digits (x and y in Fig. 6·17) and the third input is the *borrow input* (b_i) which is connected to the *borrow output* from the previous stage. The two outputs represent the difference digit and the borrow digit. In case of a borrow, the 1 is borrowed from the full subtracter for the next most significant digits; therefore the borrow output is connected to the borrow input line for the stage which subtracts the next most significant digits.

Table 6·3 shows the input-output relationships for the full subtracter as well as the equations for the difference output line and the borrow line derived from the difference output line. The x in the table represents the minuend digit; y the subtrahend; b_i the

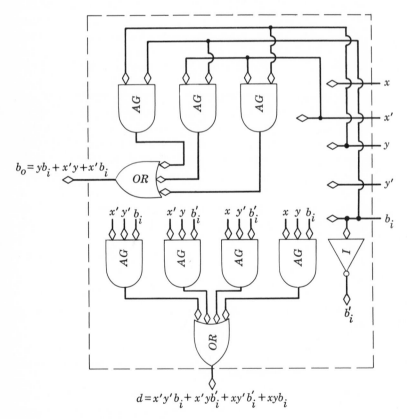

$$d = x'y'b_i + x'yb_i' + xy'b_i' + xyb_i$$

Fig. 6·17   The full binary subtracter.

TABLE 6·3

INPUTS			OUTPUTS		PRODUCT TERMS
x	y	b_i	d	b_o	
0	0	0	0	0	$x'y'b_i'$
0	0	1	1	1	$x'y'b_i$
0	1	0	1	1	$x'yb_i'$
0	1	1	0	1	$x'yb_i$
1	0	0	1	0	$xy'b_i'$
1	0	1	0	0	$xy'b_i$
1	1	0	0	0	xyb_i'
1	1	1	1	1	xyb_i

input borrow from the preceding stage; d the difference output digit; and b_o the output borrow digit.

The logical expression for the difference output d is therefore as follows:

$$d = x'y'b_i + x'yb_i' + xy'b_i' + xyb_i$$

and for the borrow output

$$b_o = x'y'b_i + x'yb_i' + x'yb_i + xyb_i$$

or $$b_o = yb_i + x'y + x'b_i$$

Figure 6·17 illustrates a possible configuration for the full subtracter. The storage devices for both the accumulator and the register to be subtracted are assumed to be flip-flops, so that both complemented and uncomplemented inputs are available. Notice that the expression for the difference output of the full subtracter is the same as the expression for the sum output of the full adder. Only the borrow and carry expressions differ. Combined adder-subtracters have been used in which only a part of the circuit was changed to convert an adder to a subtracter.

6·15 The decimal adder

The circuitry for addition which has been explained has been for machines in which the signals representing numbers were transmitted in either strictly serial or parallel form. Binary-coded-decimal numbers may also be represented in either serial or parallel form, but a third mode of operation called "series parallel" is often used. If a decimal number is written in binary-coded form, the resulting number consists of a set of code groups, each of which represent a single decimal digit. For instance, decimal 463 in a binary-coded-decimal 8, 4, 2, 1 code is 0100 0110 0011. Each group of 4 bits represents one decimal digit. It is convenient to handle each code group which represent a decimal digit as a unit, that is, in parallel. At the same time, the word lengths for decimal computers are apt to be rather long, and therefore, in order to economize in the amount of equipment used, a serial system is desirable.

The series-parallel system provides a compromise in which each code group is handled in parallel, but the decimal digits are handled sequentially. This requires four lines for the 8, 4, 2, 1 binary-coded-decimal character, each input line of which carries a different weight. The block diagram for a full adder operating in this system is shown in Fig. 6 · 18. There are two sets of inputs to the adder; one consists of the four input lines which carry the coded digit for the addend, and the other four input lines carry a coded augend digit. The sets of inputs arrive sequentially, with the least significant addend- and augend-coded-decimal digits arriving first, followed by the more significant decimal digits.

If the 8, 4, 2, 1 code is used, let 24 represent the augend and 38 the addend. The adder will first receive 0100 on the augend lines and at the same time it will receive 1000 on the addend lines. After one bit time, these inputs will be replaced by 0010 on the augend lines and 0011 on the addend lines. During the first bit time, the sum lines should contain 0010, and during the second bit time, 0110. A carry will be generated during the addition of the first two digits; this will be delayed and added in during the second bit time.

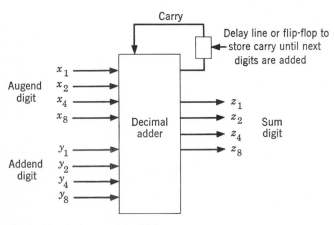

Fig. 6 · 18   Series-parallel addition.

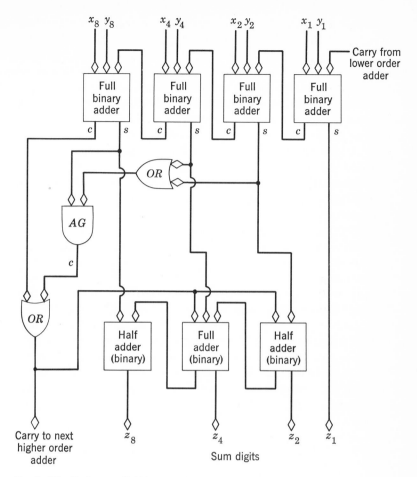

$x_8 \; y_8$ $x_4 \; y_4$ $x_2 \; y_2$ $x_1 \; y_1$

Carry from lower order adder

Full binary adder   Full binary adder   Full binary adder   Full binary adder

c s c s c s c s

OR

AG

c

OR

Half adder (binary)   Full adder (binary)   Half adder (binary)

Carry to next higher order adder z_8 z_4 z_2 z_1

Sum digits

Fig. 6 · 19   Series-parallel binary-coded-decimal adder.

Figure 6 · 19 is a block diagram of an adder configuration for a series-parallel system. There are eight inputs to the adder: four x_i or augend inputs and four y_i or addend digits. Each of these inputs will represent a 0 or a 1 during a given addition. If $3(0011)$ is to be added to $2(0010)$, then $x_8 = 0$, $x_4 = 0$, $x_2 = 1$, and $x_1 = 1$; $y_8 = 0, y_4 = 0$, $y_2 = 1$, and $y_1 = 0$.

The basic adder in Fig. 6 · 19 consists of the four full binary adders at the top of the figure and performs base 16 addition when the intent is to perform base 10 addition. Some provision must therefore be made to, (1) generate carries, and (2) correct sums greater than 9. For instance, if $3_{10}(0011)$ is added to $8_{10}(1000)$, the result should be $1_{10}(0001)$ with a carry generated.

The actual circuitry which determines when a carry is to be transmitted to the next most significant digits to be added consists of the full binary adder to which the sum (s) outputs from the adders for the 8, 4, 2 inputs are connected and of the OR gate to which the carry (c) from the 8-position bits is connected. An examination of the addition process indicates that a carry should be generated when the 8 AND 4, or 8 AND 2, or 8 AND 4 AND 2 sum outputs from the base 16 adder represent 1's, or when the CARRY output from the 8-position adder contains a 1 (this occurs when 8's or 9's are added together).

Whenever the sum of two digits exceeds 9, the CARRY TO NEXT HIGHER ORDER ADDER line contains a 1 for the adder in Fig. 6 · 19.

A further difficulty arises when a carry is generated. If $7_{10}(0111)$ is added to $6_{10}(0110)$, a carry will be generated, but the output from the base 16 adder will be 1101. This (1101) does not represent any decimal digit in the 8, 4, 2, 1 system and must be corrected. The method used to correct this is to add $6_{10}(0110)$ to the sum from the base 16 adders whenever a carry is generated. This addition is performed by adding 1's to the weight 4 and weight 2 position output lines from the base 16 adder when a carry is generated. The two half adders and the full adder at the bottom of the diagram perform this function. Essentially then, the adder performs base 16 addition and corrects the sum, if it is greater than 9, by adding 6. Several examples of this are shown below.

$$8 + 7 = 15$$

$$1000 + 0111 =$$

$$
\begin{array}{cccc}
(8) & (4) & (2) & (1) \\
1 & 1 & 1 & 1 \\
+0 & 1 & 1 & 0 \\
\hline
1 \quad 0 & 1 & 0 & 1 = 5 \\
\end{array}
$$
└—with a carry generated

$$9 + 5 = 14$$

$$
\begin{array}{cccc}
(8) & (4) & (2) & (1) \\
1 & 0 & 0 & 1 \\
0 & 1 & 0 & 1 \\
\hline
1 & 1 & 1 & 0 \\
+0 & 1 & 1 & 0 \\
\hline
1 \quad 0 & 1 & 0 & 0 \text{ or } 4 \\
\end{array}
$$
└—with a carry generated

The choice of the number system to be used will determine the construction of the adder for a given machine. The adder for a machine representing decimal digits in an excess 3 code must, for instance, be different from the adder for a machine using a 8, 4, 2, 1 code. As a result, the many configurations for decimal adders depend upon the technique used to represent numbers (serial, parallel, series-parallel) and the type of binary-coded decimal used.

6 · 16   Positive and negative binary-coded-decimal numbers

The techniques for handling binary-coded-decimal numbers greatly resemble those for handling binary numbers. A sign bit to indicate whether the number is positive or negative is used, and there are three methods of representing negative numbers which must be considered. The first and most obvious method is, of course, to represent a negative number in true magnitude form with the sign bit, so that $-.645$ is represented as 1.645. In this case the handling of numbers is straightforward except that a subtracter for the binary-coded-decimal code group is required in addition to an adder. The other two possibilities are to represent negative numbers in a 9's or a 10's complement form, which forms resemble the binary 1's and 2's complement forms.

6 · 17   Addition and subtraction in the 9's complement system

When decimal numbers are represented in a binary code in which the 9's complement is formed when the number is complemented, the situation is roughly the same as when the 1's complement is used to represent a binary number. Four cases may arise: two positive numbers may be added; a positive and negative number may be added yielding a positive result; a positive and a negative number may be added yielding a negative result; and two negative numbers may be added. As there is no problem when two positive numbers are added, the three latter situations will be illustrated.

Negative and positive number — positive sum:

$$
\begin{array}{ll}
+.692 = & 0.692 \\
-.342 = & 1.657 \\
\hline
+.350 & \llcorner 0.349 \\
& \longrightarrow 1 \\
\hline
& 0.350
\end{array}
$$

Positive and negative number — negative sum:

$$
\begin{array}{ll}
-.631 = & 1.368 \\
+.342 = & 0.342 \\
\hline
-.289 & 1.710 \text{ or } -.289
\end{array}
$$

Two negative numbers:

$$-.248 = 1.751$$
$$-.329 = 1.670$$

$$\begin{array}{r} \underline{-.577} \quad \boxed{1.421} \\ \llcorner\!\!\longrightarrow 1 \\ \overline{1.422} = -.577 \end{array}$$

The rules for handling negative numbers in the 10's complement system are the same as those for the binary 2's complement system in that no carry must be ended around. An arithmetic element may therefore be constructed using only the full decimal adder as the basic component, and all combinations of positive and negative numbers may thus be handled. Notice, however, that the sign bit must be handled differently from the binary groups representing the decimal digits.

In general, a series-parallel arithmetic element resembling that in Fig. 6 · 13 may be used, except that the single accumulator register and single x register must each be replaced by four serial registers operating in parallel, and the amount of gating circuitry must also be increased. The full decimal adder will replace the binary adder in Fig. 6 · 13.

If a complementer which will form the 10's complement directly is used to replace the 2's complement circuit, the operation of the system is just as in Fig. 6 · 13; if a circuit which forms the 9's complement is used, an additional cycle through the adder will be required, during which a 1 is added to the result when the result of an operation is negative.

In order to illustrate the type of circuit which may be used to form complements of the code groups for binary-coded-decimal numbers, a block diagram of a logical circuit which will form the 9's complement of a code group representing a decimal number in 8, 4, 2, 1 binary-coded-decimal form is shown in Fig. 6 · 20. There are four inputs to the circuit, x_1, x_2, x_4, and x_8. Each of these inputs carries a different weight: x_1 has weight 1, x_2 has weight 2, x_4 has weight 4, and x_8 has weight 8. If the inputs represent a decimal digit of the number to be complemented, the outputs will represent the 9's complement of the input digit. For instance, if the input is 0010 (decimal 2), the output will be 0111 (decimal 7), the 9's complement of the input.

There are many types of configurations for decimal machines because of the many choices which can be made: for instance, the type of binary-coded decimal to be used, whether to use 9's or 10's complements or true magnitudes to represent negative numbers, whether

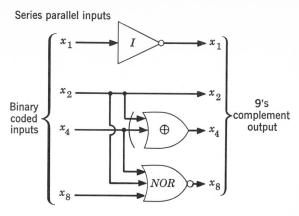

Series parallel inputs

Fig. 6 · 20 Logical circuit for forming 9's complement of 8, 4, 2, 1 binary-coded-decimal digits.

to use a parallel or serial or series-parallel system, etc. The details of each system are determined by the original decisions which are made, and follow almost necessarily after the system has been formulated.

6 · 18   The SHIFT operation

A SHIFT operation is an operation which moves the digits stored in a register to new positions in the register. There are two distinct SHIFT operations: a SHIFT-LEFT operation and a SHIFT-RIGHT operation. A SHIFT-LEFT operation moves each bit of information stored in a register to the left by some specified number of digits. Consider the following six binary digits, 0.00110, which we will assume to be stored in a parallel binary register. If the contents of the register are shifted left one, after the shift the register will contain 0.01100. If a shift right of one is performed on the word 0.00110, after the shift the register will contain 0.00011. The shifting process in a decimal register is similar: if the register contains 0.01234, after a right shift of one the register will contain 0.00123, or after a left shift of one the register will contain 0.12340. The SHIFT operation is used in the MULTIPLY and the DIVIDE instructions of most machines and also is provided as an instruction which may be used by programmers. For instance, a machine may have instructions SHR and SHL, where the letters represent in mnemonic form the order for SHIFT-RIGHT and SHIFT-LEFT instructions.

Block diagrams of logical circuitry for two different types of RIGHT-SHIFT operations for a parallel register are illustrated in Fig. 6 · 21. The first of these, the "broadside" shift, is initiated by a pulse on the SHIFT-RIGHT line. After the pulse, the information

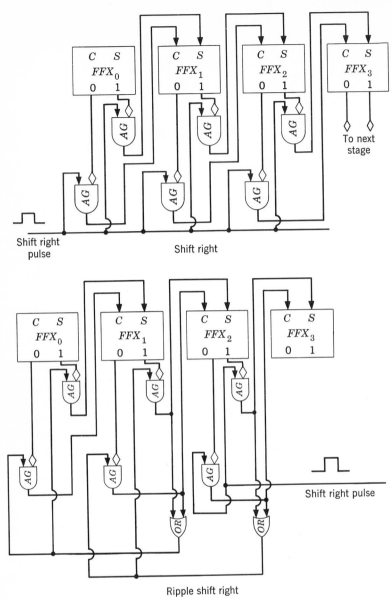

Fig. 6 · 21   The SHIFT-RIGHT operation.

which was stored in each flip-flop will have been moved into the flip-flop immediately to its right in the register (the bit with the next least significance). In the broadside shift right, each bit in the register is shifted simultaneously. The 0 and 1 outputs of each flip-flop in the register, with the exception of the least significant bit, are connected to an AND gate. The output of the gate connected to the 0 output is connected to the RESET input of the next flip-flop to the right, and the 1 output line is conneced, via a gate, to the SET line of the next flip-flop. If a given flip-flop contains a 1, the 0 output line will be a 0 and the SHIFT-RIGHT pulse will be connected to the set input of the next flip-flop only. A SHIFT-LEFT operation requires a set of identical gates except that the gates are connected so that they transfer information to the left instead of the right. Most parallel machines have the ability to shift information to either the right or left.

The problem of timing is important, as information is being read into and out of the flip-flops at the same time. If a given flip-flop contains a 1 and the flip-flops on the right and left both contain 0's, a 0 will be read into the center flip-flop at the same time that a 1 is being read out of it. If the flip-flop containing a 1 changes to a 0 during the pulse, the 0 gate connected to its output would be opened and the 1 gate closed, and the pulse would then attempt to read a 0 into the flip-flop on the right, which would be incorrect. This is another example of the race problem which was discussed in Chap. 4. In the case of the broadside SHIFT-RIGHT operation in Fig. 6 · 21, this problem is generally resolved either by inserting DELAY lines between the gates and the flip-flop inputs, or by using flip-flops which change states only at the trailing edge of the input pulse.

The ripple shift illustrated in Fig. 6 · 21 is also a SHIFT-RIGHT operation which displaces each bit one place to the right. In this case, however, the information is shifted 1 bit at a time, starting at the right end (least significant bit). When the START-RIGHT-SHIFT pulse is applied, one of the two AND gates connected to the flip-flop will be opened and will apply a pulse to the flip-flop immediately on the right, setting it to the value of the flip-flop with the gates connected to its output. An OR gate is also connected to the outputs of the gates, and since one of the gates will transmit a pulse, the OR gate will also pass a pulse which will initiate the operation of the next set of gates on the left. Since each gate will introduce some delay, the pulse will effectively "ripple" from the set of AND gates on the right to the final set of AND gates on the far left. Since the pulse will pass through a total number of gates equal to the number of flip-flops in the register, it is important that either the AND or the OR gates be capable of amplifying the SHIFT pulse lest it be so attenuated as not to be capable of switching the last flip-flop.

6 · 19 Shifting the dynamic register

The shifting of a serial word in a machine is a somewhat different process from the SHIFT operation in a parallel register. Since the serial word is generally stored in some form of dynamic storage, the shift actually consists of a displacement in time of the word to be shifted, relative to the other words of the machine. If the arithmetic element of a machine contains four dynamic registers, the timing will be arranged so that the least significant bit of each word reaches the same point in each register at the same time. A shift right or left for a given register therefore consists of a shift of the location of the bits in the register *relative* to the other words stored in the machine.

It may be seen that this essentially consists of a shift in time of each of the bits stored. If each bit of a word stored in a dynamic register arrives 1 bit time later than in previous cycles through the loop, the register will have been effectively shifted left one place. This may be accomplished by introducing a delay of 1 bit time into the loop; if the time required for a complete word to circulate around the register is normally 30 bit times and the length of the loop is lengthened to 31 bit times for the time it takes a word to circulate, the word stored in the register will be shifted left one place. If the loop remains at the 31-bit-time length for 3 word times, the bits in the word will then be shifted left three places.

In order to shift right, it is necessary to shorten the loop of the register. If the register is a flip-flop shift register, a stage could be by-passed; however, if a dynamic storage register is to be shifted, another technique must be used. Figure 6 · 22 shows a dynamic storage register which has a DELAY line with a delay time of 1 bit time less than the normal word time for the machine. The extra bit time needed is provided by an additional 1-bit-time DELAY line, which may be by-passed. The information stored in this register may be shifted right or left by setting either the shift-left control flip-flop or the shift-right control flip-flop to the 1 state for a period of 1 word time. In the first case, the length of the loop will be shortened by 1 bit time, and in the second case, lengthened by 1 bit time.

6 · 20 Scaling using SHIFT operations

Consider the binary fraction 0.0010 as it would be stored in a register. This is equal to $+\frac{1}{8}$ in the decimal system. If a shift right one is performed, the binary fraction will then be 0.0001 or $\frac{1}{16}$, one-half of the original value. [In the 1's or 2's complement systems, the sign bit is read into the bits to its right, the sign bit remaining unchanged. When a number is shifted left, a 0 (2's complement) or the sign bit (1's complement) is read into the positions which are vacated and the sign bit again remains unchanged.] If the fraction 0.0010 is shifted left once, it will read 0.0100, or $\frac{1}{4}$, and if it is shifted left again, it will become 0.1000 or $\frac{1}{2}$. It may be seen that shifting left one digit results in multiplying the fraction stored by 2. In general, shifting left n

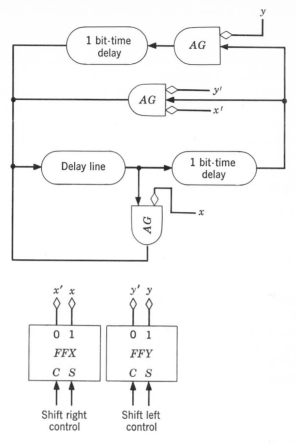

Fig. 6 · 22   Serial SHIFT-LEFT, SHIFT-RIGHT register.

binary digits will effectively multiply the binary fraction stored by 2^n, and shifting right n binary digits will result in multiplying the binary fraction stored by 2^{-n}. Here are three examples:

1   0.0100 (¼ decimal) shifted right two equals 0.0001 (¹⁄₁₆ decimal) by the rule: $\frac{1}{4} \times 2^{-n} = \frac{1}{4} \times 2^{-2} = \frac{1}{4} \times \frac{1}{4} = \frac{1}{16}$.

2   0.0011 (³⁄₁₆ decimal) shifted left one is 0.0110 (⅜ decimal) by the rule: $\frac{3}{16} \times 2^1 = \frac{3}{8}$.

3   1.1011 equals $-\frac{1}{4}$ decimal in the 1's complement system. When this number is shifted right two places, the result is 1.1110 or $-\frac{1}{16}$ by the rule: $-\frac{1}{4} \times 2^{-2} = -\frac{1}{4} \times \frac{1}{4} = -\frac{1}{16}$. (The sign bit is read into the position vacated, the sign bit remaining unchanged.)

The shifts are generally performed by the machine one at a time. Therefore, 6 pulses are required from the control element to shift a number stored in parallel form left or right 6 bits. For serial numbers, a number must be delayed 6 bit times for a shift left of six, and moved forward 6 bit times for a shift right of six. In some instances, facilities are provided for shifting more than 1 bit at a time, but for this purpose extra circuitry is required.

The same principle applies to shifting in a decimal machine, except that the numbers are shifted a complete decimal digit. Shifting the word 0.07640 to the left, for example, will multiply it by 10 and give 0.76400, and shifting to the right will give 0.00764, which is a division by 10. The SHIFT instruction may be used by programmers to move numbers in a register either to avoid overflow in the cases of addition, subtraction, and division, or to maintain precision during computations.

6 · 21　Basic operations

The arithmetic element of a digital computer consists of a number of registers in which information can be stored, and a set of logical circuits which make it possible to perform certain transformations on the information stored in the registers and to perform certain operations between registers.

As we have seen, the data stored in registers may be transformed in the following ways:

1. A register may be cleared.

2. The contents of a register may be complemented to either 1's or 2's complement form for binary, or for decimal to 9's or 10's complement form.

3. The contents of a register may be shifted right or left.

These operations or transformations may be performed regardless of whether the machine handles numbers in a serial, parallel, or series-parallel system. They are therefore basic operations in all systems.

Several operations between registers have also been described. These include:

1. Transferring the contents of one register to another register.

2. Adding to or subtracting from the contents of one register the contents of another register.

The instructions which a computer performs consist of sequenced sets of these two types of operations. For instance, the subtraction of one number from another was seen to consist of several steps: the subtrahend was transferred from a memory register to a y register and then complemented, and the y register was then added to the accumulator. More complicated instructions, such as multiplication and division, require a larger number of these operations, but these instructions may be performed using only sequences of the simple operations already described.

One other important point needs to be made. Certain operations which occur within instructions are *conditional*. That is, a given operation may or may not take place depending on the value of certain bits of the numbers stored. For instance, it may be desirable to multiply using only positive numbers. In this case, the sign bits of the two numbers to be multiplied together will be examined by control circuitry, and if either is a 1, the corresponding number will be complemented before the multiplication begins. This operation, complementing of the register, is a conditional one.

It should also be noted that two or more of the operations may be performed at the same time. For instance, a word may be transferred from memory to some register of the arithmetic element at the same time that the accumulator is shifted right. In order to shorten the time required to perform instructions, it is desirable to perform as many operations as possible in parallel.

Many different sequences of operations will yield the same result. For instance, two numbers could be multiplied together by simply adding the multiplicand to itself the number of times indicated by the multiplier. If this were done with pencil and paper, 369×12 would be performed by adding 369 to itself 12 times. This would be a laborious process compared to the easier algorithm which we have developed for multiplying, but we would get the same result. The same principle applies to machine multiplication. Two numbers could be multiplied together by transferring one of the numbers into a counter which counted downward each time an addition was performed, and then adding the other number to itself until the counter reached zero. This technique has been used, but much faster techniques are also used and will be explained below.

Many algorithms have been used to multiply and divide numbers in digital machines. Division, especially, is a complicated process, and in decimal machines in particular, many different techniques are used. The particular technique used by a machine is generally based on the cost of the machine and the premium on speed for the machine. As in almost all operations, speed is expensive, and a faster division process generally means a more expensive machine.

In order to explain the operations of binary multiplication and division, we will use a block diagram of a generalized binary machine. Figure 6·23 illustrates, in block diagram form, the registers of the arithmetic elements of both parallel and serial machines.[4] The

[4]The dynamic registers would be shift registers as well as delay-line or magnetic-drum registers.

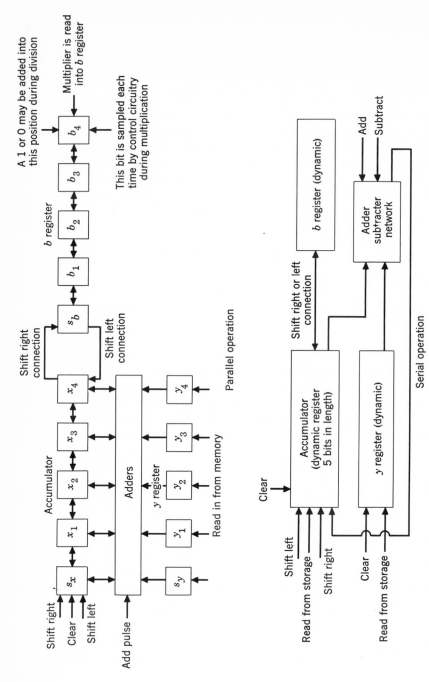

Fig. 6 · 23   Generalized serial or parallel machine.

similarity between the machines is apparent from the figure: both have three basic registers, an accumulator, y register, and b register; and identical operations can be performed on or between the registers of both machines. The operations which can be performed in parallel and binary systems have been described:

1 The accumulator of either machine can be cleared.
2 The contents of the accumulator of either machine can be shifted right or left. Further, the accumulator and b register of either machine may be formed into one long shift register. If we then shift this register right two digits, the two least significant digits of the accumulator will be shifted into the first two places of the b register. Several left shifts will shift the most significant digits of the b register into the accumulator. Since there are 5 bits in the basic machine word, there are five binary storage devices in each register. A right shift of five places will transfer the contents of the accumulator into the b register, and a left shift of five places will shift the contents of the b register into the accumulator.
3 The contents of the y register can be either added to, or subtracted from, the accumulator. The sum or difference will then be stored in the accumulator register.
4 Words from memory may be read into either the accumulator or y register. In the serial machine, the word from memory can be read directly into either the accumulator or y register; for the parallel machine it is necessary first to clear the accumulator and then to read the word from memory into the y register, and then to add the y register to the accumulator.

An arithmetic element which can perform these operations on its registers can be sequenced to perform all arithmetic operations. It is, in fact, possible to construct a machine performing fewer operations than these, but a basic general-purpose computer will generally have an arithmetic element with these capabilities.

In the sections on multiplication and division, no distinction will be made between serial- and parallel-type machines. For example, if we state that "the contents of the y register are added to the accumulator," it may be assumed that this operation may be performed in either machine.

5 · 22   Binary multiplication

The process of multiplying two binary numbers together may be best examined by writing out the multiplication of two binary numbers:

$$.\,1\,0\,0\,1 = \text{multiplicand}$$
$$.\,1\,1\,0\,1 = \text{multiplier}$$

$$
\left.
\begin{array}{l}
1\,0\,0\,1 \\
0\,0\,0\,0 \\
1\,0\,0\,1 \\
1\,0\,0\,1
\end{array}
\right\} \text{partial products}
$$

$$.\,0\,1\,1\,1\,0\,1\,0\,1 = \text{product}$$

The important thing to notice in this process is that there are really only two rules for multiplying a single binary *number* by a binary *digit:* (1) If the multiplier digit is a 1, the multiplicand is simply copied, and (2) if the multiplier digit is a 0, the product is 0. The above example illustrates these rules as follows: the first digit to the right of the multiplier is a 1; therefore the multiplicand is copied as the first partial product. The next digit of the multiplier to the left is a 0; therefore the partial product is a 0. Notice that each time a partial product is formed, it is shifted one place to the left of the previous partial product. Even if the partial product is a 0, the next partial product is placed one place to the left of the previous partial product. This process is continued until all the multiplier digits have been used and then the partial products are summed.

The three operations which the computer must be able to perform in order to multiply in this manner are therefore: (1) the ability to sense whether a multiplier bit is either a 1 or a 0, (2) the ability to shift partial products, and (3) the ability to add the partial products.

It is not necessary to wait until all the partial products have been formed before summing them. They may be summed two at a time just as the adders which have been described form sums. For instance, starting with the first two partial products in the example,

$$
\begin{array}{r}
1\,0\,0\,1 \\
0\,0\,0\,0 \\
\hline
0\,1\,0\,0\,1
\end{array}
$$

The next partial product may then be added to this sum displacing it one position to the left:

$$
\begin{array}{r}
0\,1\,0\,0\,1 \\
1\,0\,0\,1 \\
\hline
1\,0\,1\,1\,0\,1
\end{array}
$$

and finally

$$
\begin{array}{r}
1\,0\,1\,1\,0\,1 \\
1\,0\,0\,1 \\
\hline
1\,1\,1\,0\,1\,0\,1
\end{array}
$$

All that remains is to place the binary point correctly, yielding .01110101.

A multiplier can be constructed in just this fashion. By sampling each bit of the multiplier in turn, adding the multiplicand into some register, and then shifting the multiplicand left each time a new multiplier bit was sampled, a product would be formed of the sum of the partial products. In fact, the process of multiplying in most binary machines is performed in a manner very similar to this. In order to examine the typical technique for multiplying, the generalized arithmetic elements in Fig. 6 · 23 will be used. The multiplication instruction explained will be for a single-address computer, where the contents of the accumulator are multiplied by the contents of the address in storage.

Referring to Fig. 6 · 23, let the multiplier be stored in the accumulator. The multiplicand is then read from storage into the y register. At the same time the multiplier is shifted into the b register so that as the multiplication begins, the multiplier is stored in the b register of the machine, the multiplicand is stored in the y register, and the accumulator contains all 0's. Let us also assume that both multiplier and multiplicand are positive; if either is negative, it must be converted to positive form before the multiplication begins.

The sequence of operations performed is determined by the value of the *rightmost* bit in the b register each time. The control circuitry functions as follows: if the rightmost bit in the b register is a 0, the combined accumulator and b register is shifted right one place; if the rightmost bit in the b register is a 1, the number in the y register is added to the contents of the accumulator, and the combined accumulator and b register is then shifted right one place. The new rightmost bit of the b register is then again examined and the next operation is initiated.

Let us consider the same multiplication which was used in the previous example, that is, .1101 $\times$ .1001, where .1101 is the multiplier. In this case, the accumulator contains 0.0000, the b register 0.1101, and the y register 0.1001.

Since the rightmost bit of the b register contains a 1 (the least significant bit of the multiplier), during the first step the contents of the y register are added to the accumulator, and the combined accumulator and b register is then shifted to the right. The second least significant bit of the multiplier will now occupy the rightmost bit of the b register and will control the next operation.

The y register will still contain the multiplicand 0.1001, the contents of the accumulator will be 0.0100, and the contents of the b register will be 1.0110. The rightmost bit of the b register is a 0, and since it controls the next operation, a shift-right pulse will be initiated and the accumulator and *b* register will be shifted right, giving 0.0010 in the accumulator and 0.1011 in the *b* register. A 1 will now be in the rightmost bit of the *b* register.

The *y* register will therefore again be added to the accumulator, and the combined accumulator–*b*-register will again be shifted right. The least significant bit of the *b* register will be another 1, so the *y* register will again be added to the accumulator and the accumulator shifted right.

After the final shift right, the combined accumulator and *b* register will contain 0.011101010, the correct product. The most significant digits will be stored in the accumulator and the least significant digits in the *b* register.

The product in the accumulator may be "rounded" by examining the sign bit in the *b* register. If this bit is a 1, a 1 should be added to the least significant bit of the left half of the accumulator; and if the bit is a 0, the accumulator should not be changed. Many machines possess multiply instructions which leave the product in the "unrounded" state with the least significant digits in the *b* register, while other machines have multiply-and-round instructions which cause the number in the accumulator to be rounded upward as was described. Still other machines do not use the double-length accumulator and a product with only the number of digits in the accumulator is formed.

The control circuitry is designed to perform the examination of the multiplier bits, then either shift or add-and-shift the correct number of times, and then stop. In this case, the length of the multiplier or *y* register was 4 bits plus a sign bit, so four such steps are performed. The general practice is to examine each bit of the machine word except the sign bit, in turn. For instance, if the basic machine word is 25 bits—that is 24 bits in which the magnitude of a number is stored plus a sign bit—each time a multiplication is performed the machine will examine 24 bits, each in turn, performing the add-and-shift or just the shift operation 24 times. As may be seen, this makes the multiplication operation longer than such operations as add or subtract. Some parallel machines double their normal rate of operation during multiplication: if the machine performs such operations as addition, complement, transfers, etc., at a rate of 1 megacycle per sec for ordinary instructions, the rate will be increased to 2 megacycles for the add-and-shift combinations performed while multiplying. Some machines are able to shift right while adding; that is, the sum of the accumulator and *y* register appears shifted one place to the right each time, and the shift-right operation after each addition may be omitted.

The sign bits of the multiplier and multiplicand may be handled in a number of ways. The sign of the product is generally determined by means of control circuitry before the multiplication procedure is initiated. The sign bit is stored during the multiplication process, after which it is placed into the sign bit of the accumulator, and the accumulator is then complemented, if necessary. Therefore, the sign bits of the multiplier and multiplicand are first examined; if they are both 0's, the sign of the product should be 0; if both are 1's, the sign of the product should be 0; and, if either but not both are 1's, the sign of the product should be 1. This information, retained in a flip-flop while the multiplication is taking place, may be transferred into the sign bit afterward. If the machine handles numbers in the 1 or 2's complement system, both multiplier and multiplicand may be handled as positive magnitudes during the multiplication, and if the sign of either number is negative, the number is complemented to a positive magnitude before the multiplication begins. Sometimes the multiplication is performed on complemented numbers using more complicated algorithms.

6 · 23 Decimal multiplication

Decimal multiplication is a more involved process than binary multiplication. Whereas the product of a binary digit and a binary number is either the number or 0, the product of a decimal digit and decimal number involves the use of a multiplication table plus carrying and adding. For instance,

$$7 \times 24 = (7 \times 4) + (7 \times 20) = 28 + 140 = 168.$$

Even the multiplying of two decimal digits may involve two output digits, for instance, 7×8 equals 56.

Except for simply adding the multiplicand to itself the number of times indicated by the multiplier, a simple but time-consuming process, the simplest method for decimal multiplication involves loading the rightmost digit of the multiplier into a counter which counts downward and then adding the multiplicand to itself and simultaneously indexing the counter until the counter reaches 0. The partial product thus formed may be shifted right one decimal digit and the next multiplier digit loaded into the counter, and the process repeated until all the multiplier digits have been used. This is a relatively slow but straightforward technique.

The process may be speeded up by forming products using the multiplicand and the rightmost digit of the multiplier as in the previous scheme, but by actually forming the left-hand and right-hand partial products obtained when multiplying a digit by a number and then summing them. For instance, 6×7164 would yield 2664 for the right-hand product digits and 4032 for the left-hand product digits. The sum would then be

$$
\begin{array}{r}
2\,6\,6\,4 \\
+\,4\,0\,3\,2 \\
\hline
4\,2\,9\,8\,4
\end{array}
$$

Decimal-machine multiplication is in general a complicated process if speed is desired, and there are almost as many techniques for multiplying binary-coded-decimal numbers as there are types of machines.[5]

6 · 24 Division

The operation of division is the most difficult and time-consuming which the arithmetic element of most general-purpose machines performs. Although division may appear no more difficult than multiplication, there are several problems in connection with the division process which introduce time-consuming extra steps.

Division, using pencil and paper, is a trial-and-error process. For instance, if we are to divide 77 into 4610, we first notice that 77 will not "go" into 46, so we attempt to divide 77 into 461. We may guess that it will go 6 times, however:

$$
\begin{array}{r}
6 \\
77\,\overline{\smash{)}\,4\,6\,1\,0} \\
4\,6\,2 \\
\hline
-\,1
\end{array}
$$

Therefore, we have guessed too high and must reduce the first digit of the quotient which we will develop to 5.

The same problem confronts the machine when it attempts to divide in this manner. It must "try" a subtraction each step of the process and then see if the remainder is negative. Consider the division of 0.01111 by 0.11.

[5]Several machines use table look-up techniques for forming products, where the product of each pair of digits is stored in the memory. These machines are all character addressable machines.

$$
\begin{array}{r}
0.101 \\
.11\overline{\smash{\big)}\,0.01111} \\
011 \\
\hline
0011 \\
0011 \\
\hline
00
\end{array}
$$

It is easy to determine visually at any step of the process whether the quotient is to be a 1 or a 0, but the machine cannot determine this without making a trial subtraction each time. After a trial quotient has been tried and the divisor subtracted, if the result is negative, the current dividend must either be "restored" or some other technique for dividing used.

There are two general techniques or division procedures for binary machines, which are defined as the "restoring" and "nonrestoring" techniques. First, we will examine the restoring technique for division.

The restoring procedure is basically as follows: If a trial division is made, the dividend is destroyed; for instance, if 0.1001 is to be divided into 0.0110, the first step will be to subtract 0.1001 from 0.0110. The result will be -0.0011 or 1.1100 in 1's complement form. This result will then be in the accumulator and the original dividend will be lost. In order to resume the division process, the dividend must be restored by adding back the number which was subtracted (0.1001) to the difference which was obtained. The result of this addition will be the restoration of the original dividend so that the divisor may be tried again.

The restoring technique may be illustrated using the registers in Fig. 6·23 again. Assume the b and y registers to be 5 bits in length (4 bits + sign) and the accumulator 5 bits in length. The dividend will be read into the accumulator and the divisor into the y register. After the division, the quotient will be stored in the b register. The basic procedure will consist of a series of trial divisions, each of which will be made by attempting to subtract the y register from the accumulator. If the result is negative, the divisor will not "go"; a 0 is therefore placed in the rightmost bit of the b register, and the dividend (accumulator) is restored by adding the divisor to the result of the subtraction. The combined b register and accumulator will then be shifted left.

If the result of a trial division is positive, there is no need to restore the partial dividend in the accumulator. A 1 will be placed in the rightmost bit of the b register and the accumulator and b register will both be shifted left. The computer determines whether or not the result of a trial division is positive or negative by examining the sign bit of the accumulator after each subtraction.

Here is an example of the division of 0.1100 by 0.1111. The 2's complement will be used to subtract, using an adder.

ACCUMULATOR	y REGISTER	b REGISTER	REMARKS
0.1100	0.1111	0.0000	Start of division.
0.1100	1.0001	0.0000	y register is 2's complemented and added to accumulator.
1.1101	1.0001	0.0000	Result is negative.
1.1101	0.1111	0.0000	y register is 2's complemented and added to accumulator.
0.1100	0.1111	0.0000	
1.1000	0.1111	0.0000	Accumulator and b register are shifted left.
1.1000	1.0001	0.0000	y register is 2's complemented and added to accumulator.
0.1001	1.0001	0.0000	
1.0010	1.0001	0.0010	Result is positive so 1 is added to right bit of b register and b register and accumulator are shifted left.
0.0011	1.0001	0.0010	y register is added to accumulator.
0.0110	1.0001	0.0110	Result is positive so 1 is added to rightmost bit of b register, and b register and accumulator are shifted left.
1.0111	1.0001	0.0110	y register is added to accumulator.
1.0111	0.1111	0.0110	Result is negative. Accumulator is
0.0110	0.1111	0.0110	restored.
0.1100	0.1111	0.1100	Accumulator and b register are shifted left.

If the machine is to round the quotient, another trial division is performed; and if the result is positive, a 1 is added to the contents of the b register. The steps used in the restoring type of division are time-consuming, therefore nonrestoring division is more generally used. There are several techniques for nonrestoring division, but most are variations of a technique in which the divisor is alternately subtracted and added.

The principle involved here may be explained as follows: let x equal the number stored in the accumulator and y equal the divisor. If the divisor is subtracted, the result is $x - y$. If this result is stored in the accumulator and then shifted left 1 bit, the result will be

$2(x - y)$. If $x - y$ was negative, the divisor is now added to the accumulator, resulting in $2(x - y) + y$ or $2x - y$, which will be correct for this step. The quotient is formed in the same way as in restoring division. If the result of a trial division is positive, a 1 is placed in the rightmost bit of the quotient, and if the result of a trial division is negative, the quotient is left unchanged. After each trial, both the accumulator (the partial dividend) and the quotient are shifted left.

The basic steps required for each trial division are therefore as follows:

1 For the first step the y register is subtracted from the accumulator.
2 If the result is positive, a 1 is placed in the least significant bit of the b register, and the accumulator and b register are shifted left. The next step will be another subtraction.
3 If the result of (1) is negative, a 0 is placed in the least significant bit of the b register, and the accumulator and b register are shifted left. For the next step the y register is added instead of subtracted. If the result is positive, a 1 is placed in the least significant bit of the b register, and the accumulator and b register are shifted left. The next step is to subtract the y register from the accumulator. If the result is negative, a 0 is placed in the least significant bit of the b register, and the accumulator and b register are shifted left. The y register is again added and shifted left until a positive result is yielded, in which case the procedure reverts to the subtract step (1).

Although it is more complicated, fewer steps are required to perform a division by this technique, since the dividend need not be restored at each step. The procedure has, for this reason, often been used.

In some machines the results of the trial division (subtraction) may be examined by the machine without first losing the dividend. In this case it is, of course, not necessary to restore; the result of the trial division which fails may simply be cleared away and the next trial division attempted.

During division, the sign bit is handled in much the same way as during multiplication. Since the first step is to convert both the divisor and dividend to positive magnitude form, the value of the sign bit for the quotient must be stored while the division is taking place. The rule is that if the signs of the dividend and divisor are both either 0's or 1's, the quotient will be positive. If either but not both of their signs is a 1, the quotient will be negative. The relationship of the sign bit of the quotient to the sign bit of the divisor and dividend is therefore the quarter adder or exclusive-OR relationship, that is, $s = xy' + x'y$. The value for the correct sign of the quotient may be read into a storage device while the division is taking place and this value may then be placed in the sign bit of the register containing the quotient after the division of magnitudes has been completed.

6 · 25   Logical operations

In addition to the arithmetic operations, many logical operations are also of value. The branch-type instructions have already been described; more will be said about them in Chap. 9, which describes the control element. Three logical operations will be described here: logical multiplication, logical addition, and *sum modulo* 2 addition (the exclusive-OR operation). Each of these will be operations between registers, where the operation specified will be performed on each of the corresponding digits in the two registers. The result will be stored in one of the registers.

The first operation, logical multiplication, is often referred to as an *extract* or *masking* operation. The rules for logical multiplication have been defined in the chapter on logical algebra. The rules are: $0 \cdot 0 = 0$; $0 \cdot 1 = 0$; $1 \cdot 0 = 0$; and $1 \cdot 1 = 1$. Suppose that the contents of the accumulator register are "logically multiplied" by another register. Let each register be five binary digits in length. If the accumulator contains 01101 and the other register 00111, the contents of the accumulator after the operation will be 00101.

Figure 6 · 24 illustrates circuitry for the logical multiplication operation. The reason that the operation is referred to as "masking" or "extracting" is apparent. If the contents of the accumulator are masked by the contents of a second register, each place in the second register which contains a 0 will place a 0 in the corresponding position in the accumulator, and each position that contains a 1 will leave the accumulator digit unchanged.

The masking or extracting operation is useful in "packaging" computer words. In order to save space in memory and keep associated data together, several pieces of information may be stored in the same word. For instance, a word may contain an item number, wholesale price, and retail price, packaged as follows:

S	$1 \to 6$	$7 \to 15$	$16 \to 24$
	Item no.	Wholesale price	Retail price

If the programmer wishes to extract the retail price, he will simply logically multiply the word above by a word containing 0's in the sign

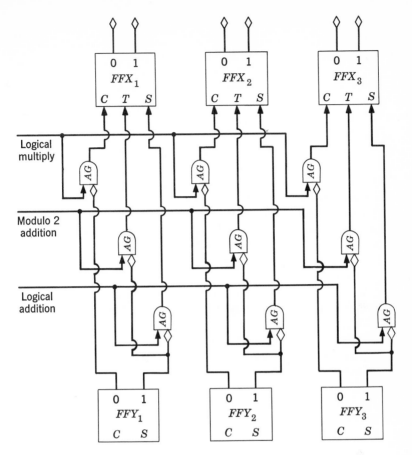

Fig. 6 · 24 Logical operations.

digit through digit 15, and with 1's in positions 16 through 24. After the operation, only the retail price will remain in the word.

The logical addition operation or the *sum modulo* 2 operation may also be performed by pulsing the correct input line in Fig. 6 · 24. The rules for these operations are:

LOGICAL ADDITION	MODULO 2 ADDITION
$0 + 0 = 0$	$0 + 0 = 0$
$0 + 1 = 1$	$0 + 1 = 1$
$1 + 0 = 1$	$1 + 0 = 1$
$1 + 1 = 1$	$1 + 1 = 0$

QUESTIONS

1 Two parallel binary registers, designated as register x and register y, each consists of three flip-flops. Draw a block diagram of the registers and the necessary logical circuitry so that (*a*) register x can be cleared or 1's complemented and (*b*) the contents of register y can be transferred into register x.

2 If we have a register consisting of four flip-flops and if we first clear the register, using the CLEAR-REGISTER operation shown in Fig. 6·1, and then complement the register, using the COM-PLEMENT-REGISTER operation shown in Fig. 6·2, what will be the contents of the register after the COMPLEMENT-REGISTER operation?

3 If a binary machine handles negative numbers in the true magnitude form, how would $-\frac{1}{4}$ be stored in a register with a sign bit and 4 bits representing magnitude? If the same machine stored numbers in the 1's complement system, how would $-\frac{1}{4}$ be stored? In the 2's complement form?

4 If the lower set of flip-flops in Fig. 6·3 contains binary 101 and the upper flip-flops 000, and if we initiate a TRANSFER-AFTER-CLEAR operation as shown in Fig. 6·3 by applying an INPUT pulse on the TRANSFER-PULSE input line and follow this with a COMPLEMENT-REGISTER operation on the upper flip-flops as shown in Fig. 6·2, what will the contents of the three upper flip-flops be after the COMPLEMENT-PULSE input has arrived?

5 The inputs to the full adder in Fig. 6·7 are as follows: $x = 1, y = 1$, and $c = 1$. What will the output on the s and c lines represent?

6 If we load the binary number 1.0011 into the flip-flops in Fig. 6·5, that is, if $X_0 = 1$, $X_1 = 0$, $X_2 = 0$, $X_3 = 1$, and $X_4 = 1$, what will the value of the register be in the 1's complement number system, assuming that we express the number as a binary fraction? Give the answer in decimal. What will the value of this number be if the 2's complement number system is used?

7 Register x contains 0.1100 and register y contains 0.1101 (where the 0's preceding the binary point designate that the number stored is positive). If the two registers are added together, what will the result be?

8 If we store the number 10011 as in the register in Fig. 6·5 in question 6 and then apply a COMPLEMENT-REGISTER operation to the register as in Fig. 6·2, what will the decimal number value be of the number stored in the register before and after the COMPLEMENT operation in 1's complement notation and in 2's complement notation?

9 If negative numbers are stored in true magnitude form, can you think

of any reason why it might be convenient to have the sign bit precede the magnitude of binary numbers represented in a serial system using both a full adder and full subtracter?

10 Notice that a number which is positive in 1's complement notation has the same magnitude as its digit-by-digit complement, so that for instance in Question 8 we have simply changed the value of the number from negative to positive by complementing the register. However, the 2's complement number was changed in magnitude when we complemented the register. What must we do to restore the magnitude of the 2's complement number?

11 A binary register consists of five binary storage devices; one stores the sign bit and the other four store the magnitude bits. If the number stored is 0.0100 and this number is then shifted right one binary place, what will be the result?

12 Design a half adder using only NOR gates.

13 A 5-bit binary register contains 1.1001. The number is stored in the 1's complement system, and the 1 preceding the binary point indicates the number stored is negative. What will the number stored be after a shift left of one? After a shift right of one? After a shift right of two? Convert the numbers stored after each shift into decimal fractions.

14 Design a full adder using only NAND gates.

15 Design a half adder using only NOR gates.

16 Design a half subtracter using only NAND gates.

17 Can an overflow occur during multiplication in a machine which expresses numbers in fixed-point binary-fraction form? Can an overflow occur during division in this type of machine? Explain and give examples.

18 Draw the waveforms which represent the binary number 1.1100 in a serial number system as in Fig. 6 · 12. Draw both the input and 2's complement output waveforms for this particular bit pattern, and then show that this circuit will complement both positive and negative 2's complement's numbers by expressing $+\frac{3}{4}$ and $-\frac{3}{4}$ as a sign digit plus four magnitude digits in the 2's complement system. Show the input and output waveforms for these binary numbers.

19 If a register containing 0.110011 is logically added to a register containing 0.101010, what will the result be? What will be the result if the registers are logically multiplied? If the registers are exclusive-ORed together?

20 Referring to Fig. 6 · 24, show that a logical multiply followed by a logical addition will transfer the contents of Y into X.

21 Demonstrate by means of a truth table of combinations that two half adders plus an OR gate do make a full adder as shown in Fig. 6 · 8.

22 Draw the logic symbol diagram or block diagram for a full subtracter using NAND gates only.

23 Draw the block diagram for a full subtracter using NOR gates only.

24 When addition is performed in a binary machine using the 2's complement number system to represent negative numbers, an overflow may occur in a register only when two positive numbers are added or when two negative numbers are added. Show that the addition of a positive number and a negative number cannot result in an overflow condition.

25 When the 2's complement number system is used and addition is performed, let us designate the carry-out of the full adder connected into the full adder for the sign digits as C_1 (refer to Fig. 6 · 5). The rule for overflow is that two numbers cause an overflow when they are added if both numbers are positive and C_1 equals a 1 or if both numbers are negative and C_1 does not equal a 1. Therefore, by examining the sign digits of the two numbers being added and the carry-out of the full adder which adds the two most significant digits of the magnitude of the numbers being added, we can form a logic network the output of which will be a 1 when an overflow condition arises and 0 if the addition is legitimate. Let X_0 store the sign digit of the addend, Y_0 store the sign digit of the augend, and C_1 again be the carry-out of the full adders connected to the X_1 and Y_1 flip-flops as in Fig. 6 · 9. Show that the logic equation for an overflow condition is $X_1 Y_1 C_1' + X_0' Y_0' C_1 =$ overflow.

26 The Boolean algebraic expressions on the output lines from the NOR gates in Fig. 6 · 15 are not completely filled in. Redraw Fig. 6 · 15 and write in the Boolean algebraic expressions for the outputs of each of the nine NOR gates in the figure. Finally, develop the Boolean algebraic expressions for the S and C outputs from the network.

27 If we add two 20-digit binary numbers using the full adder shown in Fig. 6 · 15 and if 10 nsec is required for a signal to pass through a NOR gate in Fig. 6 · 15, what is the maximum time it will require a CARRY signal to propagate from the lowest order bits to the highest order bits, assuming a full adder which is parallel as in Fig. 6 · 9? Notice that the time required to form the carry in the first full adder and that the time for a carry in the leftmost full adder to be made into a sum are not the same as the time required for a CARRY signal to pass through a given full adder circuit.

28 Show that when we add 7 plus 9 in the binary-coded-decimal system using the series-parallel binary-coded-decimal adder in Fig. 6 · 19, the answer will be correct. Do this by tracing the outputs of the circuit filling in the binary value for each C and S shown in the figure and also by showing the values of z_8, z_4, z_2, and z_1.

29 If we have a seven-digit register which stores binary numbers and

shift this register right two digits, what will the contents of the register be if numbers are stored in 2's complement form and the original number in the register was:

a. 1.000111   b. 0.000111   c. 1.001100   d. 0.0010011

30 For parts a, b, c, and d of question 29, suppose that the numbers are stored in 1's complement form. What number will be stored in the register if each of the above numbers is shifted right two places?

31 Again using the numbers in the Question 29, what will the results be if numbers are stored in 2's complement form and we shift the register left two? Suppose that numbers are stored in 1's complement form and we shift the register left two places.

32 Explain the following statement: When two numbers represented in the 1's complement number system are multiplied together, an overflow never occurs; for if two fractions each of which are less than 1 are multiplied together, the product must be of magnitude less than 1. However, if two numbers stored in binary 2's complement notation are multiplied together, it is possible for a number which is not representable in the number's system to occur.

33 What is the binary number which represents -1 in the 2's complement number system if we represent the number using a sign digit plus four magnitude digits?

34 Using the 8, 4, 2, 1 binary-coded-decimal system, write in binary form the following decimal numbers. Use a single digit for the sign digit and express the numbers as magnitude plus sign.

a. $+0042$ b. -0122 c. $+1034$ d. -1097

35 Express each of the numbers in the preceding question using the 9's complement and the 8, 4, 2, 1 binary-coded-decimal system. Example:

$$-0.1024 = 1.1000\ 1001\ 0111\ 0101$$

36 Write the decimal numbers in Question 34 using the 10's complement number system and again the 8, 4, 2, 1 binary-coded-decimal system to represent these numbers. For example:

$$0.1420 = 1.1000\ 0101\ 1000\ 0000$$

7

The memory

element

One of the most basic functions which a digital computer must perform is that of storing information. It is only natural that the development of the high-speed electronic computer has progressed in parallel with the development of adequate memory systems.

The memory of a large computer is not actually concentrated in one place, but storage devices are scattered throughout the machine. For instance, the basic storage devices for a machine consist of the *operation registers*, which comprise the storage devices used in the arithmetic and control elements of the computer. The actual calculations on data take place in these registers. For instance, additions, multiplications, shifts, etc., are all performed in these registers of the machine. The actual processing of information is performed in and at the direction of these registers.

Looking outward, the next category of storage device which is encountered is the *inner memory*. This section of the computer's memory consists of a set of storage registers, each of which is identified with an address which enables the control unit either to write into or read from a particular register.

It is desirable that the operating speed of this section of the computer's memory be as high as possible, for most of the transfers of data to and from the information processing section of the machine will be via the inner memory. For this reason, storage devices with very fast access times are generally chosen for the inner memory; unfortunately the presently available devices which are fast enough to perform this function satisfactorily do not possess the storage capacity which is sometimes required. As a result, an additional memory, which we will define as the *auxiliary memory*, is added to most large computers. This section of the computer's memory is characterized by low cost per digit stored, but it generally has an operating speed far lower than that of either the operation registers or the inner memory. This section of the memory is sometimes designated the "back-up store," for its function is to handle quantities of data in excess of those which may be stored in the inner memory.

The final and outermost storage devices are those which are used to introduce information into the computer from the "outside world." The storage media in this case generally consist of such input media as punched cards or perforated paper tape, and the outputs from the machine generally consist of printed characters. Again, the cost per bit is very low, but the operating speeds of the tape and card readers, printers, etc., are liable to be on the order of one thousand times slower than the speeds of the operation registers. These devices will be described in Chap. 8 under the heading of "Input-Output Devices." This chapter will be limited to the *internal storage* of the machine, which is defined as those storage devices which form an integral part of the machine and are directly controlled by the machine.

There are certain characteristics possessed by each of the divisions of memory. For instance, the premium on speed is very high for the operation registers. These registers must generally perform operations at several times the speed of the inner memory. The inner memory also requires high operating speeds, but because it is desirable to store large quantities of data in this section of the memory, a compromise between cost and speed must generally be made. Flip-flop registers could, for instance, be used to construct an "ideal" inner memory; however, since the storage capacity of the average inner memory is liable to be in the region from 10^5 to 10^6 binary bits, the cost would be prohibitive. The same sort of compromise must often be made in the case of the auxiliary memory. In a large machine the auxiliary memory may have to store from 10^6 through 10^{11} binary digits, and in these instances, it might prove too expensive to use devices such as those used in the inner memory.

An important point to notice when considering operating speed is that before a word can be read, it is necessary to locate it. The procedures for locating information may be divided into two classes, random access and sequential access. A random-access storage device is one in which any location in the device may be selected at random, and access to the information stored is direct. A flip-flop register is an example of a random-access storage device, as is the magnetic-core memory system which will be described. A sequential-access device is one in which the arrival at the location desired may be preceded by sequencing through other locations. For instance, if we try to read a word stored on a reel of magnetic tape and the piece of tape on which the word is stored is near the center of the reel, it will be necessary to sequence through all the intervening tape before the word may be read.

Another way to subdivide storage devices is according to whether they are *static* storage devices or *dynamic* storage devices. A static storage device is one in which the information does not change positions; flip-flop registers, magnetic-core registers, or even punched cards or tape are examples of static storage devices. Dynamic storage devices, on the other hand, are devices in which the information stored is continually changing position. Circulating registers utilizing delay lines are examples of dynamic storage devices, as are magnetic drums and magnetic disks.

Another characteristic to be considered is whether the information stored in a given storage device is *erasable*. Certainly the information stored in dynamic registers, flip-flop registers, and the core memory, magnetic drum, and tape devices is erasable. On the other hand, the information stored in punched cards and on paper tape is not readily erasable. Several types of nonerasable storage media have been worked on; for instance, developmental work has been done on photographic means for storing digital information.

This chapter will concentrate on the three most frequently used devices for storing digital information in the internal memory sections of computers. These are: (1) magnetic-core and thin-film memories, which are random-access, static, erasable devices used principally in the inner memory because of their high operating speeds and moderate cost per bit; (2) magnetic-drum and disk memories, which are sequential-access, dynamic storage devices used for auxiliary storage in very large and high-speed computers and also as the inner memory, and sometimes even to form the operation registers of medium and lower-speed computers; and (3) magnetic-tape and card memories, which are used exclusively as an auxiliary or back-up storage, but which are capable of storing large quantities of information at low cost. Following the sections on magnetic-drum and tape devices, the techniques used to record digital information on a magnetic surface will be described. Then we will study read-only memories and tunnel-diode memories, which are special types of newer memory devices.

7 · 1   Magnetic-core storage

The basic storage device in a magnetic-core memory consists of a small toroidal (ring-shaped) piece of magnetic material called a magnetic core. The magnetic core may be a solid piece of ferromagnetic ceramic material or may consist of a length of thin ferromag-

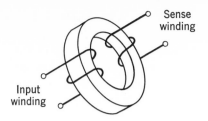

Fig. 7 · 1   Magnetic core.

netic metal tape either coiled or wound around a bobbin. Figure 7 · 1 illustrates a ceramic magnetic core, many times actual size. Each magnetic core in the memory is capable of storing 1 bit of digital information. An input winding is shown on this core; if current is passed through this winding, magnetic flux will be produced, with a direction dependent on the direction of the current through the winding. The core is ring-shaped and formed of material with a high permeability, so that it will present a low reluctance path for the magnetic flux. Depending on the direction of the current through the input winding, the core will become magnetized in either a clockwise or counterclockwise direction. The retentivity of the material used in the core is such that when the magnetizing force is removed, the core remains magnetized, retaining a large part of its flux.

The characteristics of a given type of magnetic core are generally studied by means of a graph, with the magnetizing force H produced by the winding current plotted along the abscissa, and the resulting flux density B through the core along the ordinate (Fig. 7 · 2). If a cyclical current which is alternately positive and negative is applied to the input winding, for each value of the input current there will be a magnetizing force H applied to the core. If the flux density B in the core is then plotted against this magnetizing force, the resulting curve is called a *hysteresis loop*. In Fig. 7 · 2, the force H applied is sufficient to saturate the core material at both the positive and negative extremities of the input current. The maximum flux density through the core when the core is saturated with a positive value of H is designated as $+B_m$, and for the corresponding negative value of H is denoted $-B_m$.

Notice that for each value of magnetizing force there are two values of flux density. One occurs when the magnetizing force is increasing and the other when the magnetizing force is decreasing. If the magnetizing force is varied from $-H_m$ to $+H_m$, the flux density will move along the lower part of the curve, and if the magnetizing force is moved from $+H_m$ to $-H_m$, the flux density will move along the upper part of the curve, again following the arrows, to point $-B_m$.

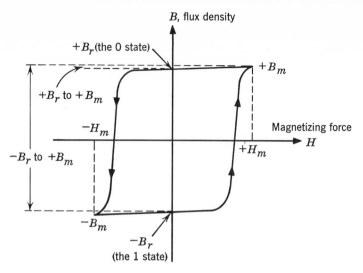

B, flux density

$+B_r$ (the 0 state)

$+B_m$

$+B_r$ to $+B_m$

$-H_m$

Magnetizing force
H

$+H_m$

$-B_r$ to $+B_m$

$-B_m$

$-B_r$
(the 1 state)

Fig. 7 · 2   Hysteresis loop for a magnetic material.

If a current sufficient to cause the core to be saturated is applied at the input winding and then removed, the flux density through the core will revert to either point $+B_r$ or to point $-B_r$, depending on the polarity of the current. These two operating points are called the *remanent* points, and when the flux through the core is at either of these points, the core resembles a small permanent magnet. If a core is at the $+B_r$ point of the graph and a current of sufficient amplitude to cause a force of $-H_m$ is applied, the flux produced will be in opposition to the remanent flux in the core, $+B_r$, and the flux through the core will be reversed, moving the operating point to $-B_m$. After the current has been removed, the majority of the flux will remain, and the flux density in the core will be at the $-B_r$ point of the curve. The fact that the core can be in either one of two unique states of magnetization makes it possible to consider one state as representing a 1 ($-B_r$ in the figure) and the other state as a 0 ($+B_r$ in the figure).

Another winding, called a *sense winding* (Fig. 7 · 1), is used to determine whether a core contains a 0 or a 1. In order to sense the state of the core, a current sufficient to produce a magnetizing force $+H_m$ is applied to the input winding. If the core was at $-B_r$, the operating point will be moved upward along the arrows in Fig. 7 · 2 to the $+B_m$ point. If the core was at the $+B_r$ point, the operating point will be moved horizontally to $+B_m$. The amount of change in flux in the core will be quite different for each of these cases. If the core was initially in the 1 state (at point $-B_r$ on the hysteresis curve), the direction of magnetization of the core will be changed and the flux through the core will change from $-B_r$ to $+B_m$. The magnitude of this change in the magnetization of the core is indicated as $-B_r$ to $+B_m$ on the figure. If, however, the core was originally in the 0 state at $+B_r$ on the curve, the change in magnetization will be small, only from $+B_r$ to $+B_m$, and the magnitude of this change in flux is indicated as $+B_r$ to $+B_m$ on the figure. A change in the flux density through the core will induce a voltage in the sense winding which is proportional to the rate of change of flux. If the core was originally in the 0 state, the change and rate of change in flux will be small, and therefore the voltage induced in the sense winding will be small. If the core was originally in the 1 state, the amount of change and rate of change in flux will be large, and consequently the voltage induced in the sense winding will be large. A small output from the sense winding will therefore indicate that the core originally contained a 0, and a large output will indicate that the core originally contained a 1.

The difficulty in the use of this technique for sensing the state of a core is that the core is always reset to the 0 state. This readout technique is therefore "destructive" in that the core no longer contains the information which was previously stored in it. It is generally desirable to retain information in storage after it has been read. Since reading from a core is destructive, it is necessary to write the original state of the core back into it. By detecting and amplifying the output of the sense winding when the core's state is sensed, it is possible to use the signal to set a flip-flop or other temporary, erasable storage device. The contents of the flip-flop may then be written back into the core via the input winding, returning the core to its original state.

7 · 2 Storage of information in magnetic cores in a two-dimensional array

The previous discussion showed how a single bit of information may be stored in and read from a single core. In digital computer systems, however, it is necessary to store many bits of information; some of the larger computers have core memories with over a million cores. In order to utilize these cores, the computer must be able to write information into any given core and also to read from any given core. Techniques for writing or reading information into or from a selected core or group of cores in a memory are known as *selection techniques*. The selection technique which will be explained is one of a number of techniques which have been used. All these techniques follow from the basic magnetic-core properties. The selection technique which will be described is called the *coincident-current technique* and it is the most commonly used one in large computer systems.

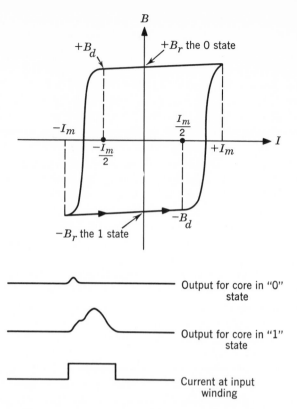

Fig. 7 · 3   Current versus flux-density hysteresis loop for a magnetic core.

Figure 7 · 3 plots the values of flux density for a magnetic core versus current I through the input winding of a core. If the current reaches a value of $+I_m$, which is sufficient to saturate the core, and is then removed, the core will be placed in the $+B_r$ or 0 state. If the operating point on the curve is at $+B_r$ with no input current through the winding, and a negative pulse of current with amplitude $-I_m$ is applied, the core will be switched to the 1 state. The important thing to notice in Fig. 7 · 3 is that if the core is in the 0 state and a current of only $-I_m/2$ is applied and then removed, the state of the core will not be changed. Instead, the operating point will move from $+B_r$ to $+B_d$, and when the current is removed, will move back to approximately $+B_r$. The same principle applies if the core is in the 1 state at point $-B_r$ on the curve. A current of $+I_m$ will switch the core to the 0 state, but a current of $+I_m/2$ will only move the operating point to $-B_d$, and when the current is removed, the core will return to point $-B_r$.

Figure 7·4 shows nine cores arranged in a square array. Each core has two input windings, one from a set of X input lines and one from a set of Y input lines. Assume that all of the cores are in the 0 state and a 1 is to be written into core x_2y_2. If a current with an amplitude of $-I_m$ is applied on the X_2 line, core x_2y_2 will be switched to the 1 state; however, all the cores connected to the X_2 input line will also be switched to the 1 state. The same holds true if a current of $-I_m$ is applied to input line Y_2, in which case all the cores connected to this Y input line would be switched to the 1 state.

If, however, currents of $-I_m/2$ are applied to both the X_2 line and the Y_2 line at the same time, only core x_2y_2 will receive a total current of $-I_m$ (Fig. 7·4). Each of the other cores along the Y_2 input line will receive a current of $-I_m/2$, as will each of the cores along the X_2 input line. Since these cores will have started at point $+B_r$ on the graph and will receive a current of $-I_m/2$, their operating point will be moved as far as $+B_d$ on the curve; however, the operating point will not be moved as far as the steep incline which leads to the $-B_r$ section of the graph. When the current is removed, these cores, with the exception of x_2y_2, will return to the $+B_r$ point and will be in the 0 state. Therefore, only core x_2y_2 will receive a total current of $-I_m$ and will be switched into the 1 state.

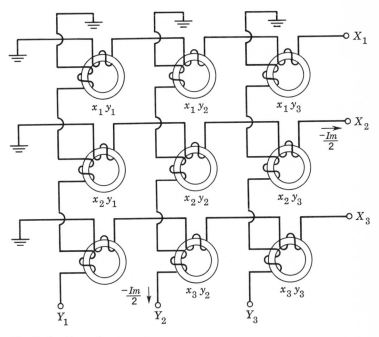

Fig. 7·4   Magnetic-core array.

By this technique, any given core can be selected from the array. For instance, core x_1y_3 can be selected by applying currents of $-I_m/2$ to the X_1 and the Y_3 input lines at the same time. This is known as the *coincident-current selection* technique. The core which receives a full $-I_m$ current is known as a *fully selected* core and all the cores which receive a current of $-I_m/2$ are known as *half-selected* cores. For instance, if a current of $-I_m/2$ is connected to input lines X_1 and Y_3, core x_1y_3 will be fully selected, and cores x_1y_1, x_1y_2, x_2y_3, and x_3y_3 will be half selected.

Notice that regardless of the previous state of each of the cores in the array, a current of $-I_m/2$ applied to one X and one Y input line will result in sufficient current to switch only one core of the array. If cores in the 0 state are half selected, they will remain in the 0 state; and, if cores in the 1 state are half selected, they will remain in the 1 state.

The state of any given core can be sensed using the same technique. If currents of $+I_m/2$ are applied to input lines X_2 and Y_2, a full $+I_m$ current will be applied to core x_2y_2, causing it to change states if it contained a 1, and remain in the same state if it contained a 0. The fully selected core will be the only core which can change states and therefore the only core which is capable of causing an appreciable output on a sense winding. The sense winding is therefore threaded through all the cores; if a certain core is selected, the output at the sense winding will represent the state of that core only.

It may be seen that there are two separate operations involved: first, the writing of information into a core, and second, the reading of information which has been stored in a core. A 0 or a 1 may be written into any core in the array by applying a current of either $+I_m/2$ or $-I_m/2$ to the correct pair of input lines, and the state of any core may be sensed by applying a current of $+I_m/2$ to the correct pair of input lines and sensing the magnitude of the output voltage on the sense winding.

7 · 3 Assembly of core planes into a core memory

Figure 7 · 5 illustrates a small *core-memory plane*. Any core in this plane may be selected, and a 0 or 1 written into the core, or the state of any core may be sensed, by applying the correct currents to one of the X input lines and one of the Y input lines simultaneously. A complete core memory consists of a number of such planes, stacked in a rectangular array. The X windings of each plane are connected in series, so that a pulse connected to the X_1 winding of the first plane must travel through the X_1 winding of the second plane, and so on, until it passes through the X_1 winding for the last plane in the array.

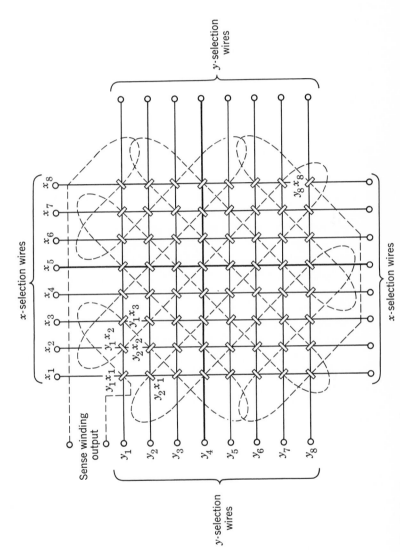

Fig. 7 · 5   Core-memory plane.

If the plane illustrated in Fig. $7 \cdot 5$ were connected in an array, the X_1 winding at the top left of the drawing would be connected to one end of the X_1 winding from the preceding core plane, and the X_1 winding at the bottom left would be connected to the X_1 connection of the following core plane. If 10 core planes of the size in Fig. $7 \cdot 5$ were stacked in this manner, a pulse on the X_1 input line would have to travel through 80 cores. The Y windings are connected in the same manner. Each plane has its own sense winding, however, and the sense windings for the planes are not connected together in any way; instead, a sense amplifier is connected to the sense-winding output from each plane.

It may be seen that a WRITE 1 pulse on a selected Y line and X line will write a 1 into a single core in the same relative position in each of the planes. For instance, if the X_3 and Y_4 input lines are pulsed with a current of $-I_m/2$, the $x_3 y_4$ core in each plane will receive a $-I_m$ current. If a $+I_m/2$ pulse is then applied to the same X and Y selection lines, an output will be sensed on the sense winding[1] of each plane.

In general, there will be as many core planes in the array as bits in the word length of the computer in which the array is used. If the word length is 15 bits, there will be 15 planes in the array; if the word length is 35 bits, 35 planes. There will be a sense winding for each plane, so that the output from each core which is selected will be sensed.

One problem still remains; a WRITE 1 $(-I_m/2)$ pulse on a pair of X and Y input lines will write a 1 into the core in the same relative position of each plane, and therefore into every position of the word, and it may be necessary to write 0's into some cores and 1's into others. A fourth winding through each core is therefore added. This winding is called the *digit winding* or the INHIBIT *winding* and is used to inhibit the writing of a 1 into a given selected core in a plane. A separate INHIBIT winding is threaded through each core in a single plane, so that a current of $+I_m/2$ on the winding will oppose the WRITE 1 current. There are therefore as many INHIBIT windings as core planes. There is also a single driver for each INHIBIT winding, which can be gated on or off, depending on whether a 1 or a 0 is to be written into the selected core of the plane. The amplitude of the current through the INHIBIT winding is the same as the $+I_m/2$ current used in the X and Y selection lines. The INHIBIT winding is threaded through the cores so that the magnetizing force

---

[1]The sense windings are threaded through the cores diagonal to the other windings to reduce the coupling between drive and sense windings (Fig. $7 \cdot 5$) and to cancel the output signals from half-selected cores caused during a READ pulse.

from the current through the inhibit winding always opposes the magnetizing force of the WRITE 1 currents.

Since the WRITE 1 pulse from the x and y drivers is of $-I_m/2$ amplitude and the pulse from the INHIBIT driver is of $+I_m/2$ amplitude, if a WRITE 1 pulse is applied from a given pair of x and y drivers at the same time as an INHIBIT pulse is applied, the total current through the selected core will be $(-I_m/2) + (-I_m/2) + (+I_m/2) = -I_m/2$, which is not sufficient to switch the core to a 1. A 1 or 0 may therefore be written into the selected core of a given plane by first clearing the cores with a $+I_m/2$ pulse on the correct pair of X and Y select lines, and then turning the INHIBIT driver on for each plane where a 0 is desired and off for each plane where a 1 is desired, while applying a WRITE 1 pulse to the X and Y select lines.

7 · 4   Timing sequence

The same timing sequence is generally used whether the computer is to write information into the core memory or to read information from the core memory. The total time taken by the entire timing sequence is called a *memory cycle*, and is one of the principal speed-determining factors for a machine. Each memory cycle consists of two periods, the first of which is called the READ *time* and the second of which is called the WRITE *time*. Figure 7 · 6 shows the sequence of pulses for a complete memory cycle. The operation of writing a word into the memory will be examined first, then the READ operation. Assume that there are five core planes in the total array and that each core plane contains 64 cores as in Fig. 7 · 5.

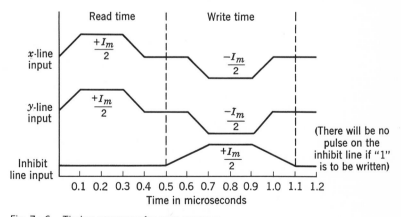

Fig. 7 · 6   Timing sequence for core memory.

1   *The WRITE Operation.* The binary number 10100 is to be written into core location x_3y_4 of the memory. Zeros are therefore to be written into the selected cores of planes 2, 4, and 5, so that the INHIBIT drivers for each of these planes are enabled; that is, when the WRITE time begins (Fig. 7·6), the drivers connected to the INHIBIT windings of planes 2, 4, and 5 will drive current through the INHIBIT windings of these core planes.

First the correct drivers are selected; since core x_3y_4 in each plane is to be written into, the drivers connected to the X_3 line are enabled as are the drivers connected to the Y_4 line of the array. When the READ pulses are applied, 0's are written into the x_3y_4 core in each of the five planes; after 0.4 μsec, each of the selected cores will contain a 0. At 0.5 μsec after the sequence is initiated, the INHIBIT drivers connected to planes 2, 4, and 5 are turned on; in addition, the WRITE time begins. A 1 will then be written into the selected core in planes 1 and 3, and the subtraction of the INHIBIT current from the coincident current through the selected cores in planes 2, 4, and 5 will result in the selected cores in these planes remaining in the 0 state. After the sequence of pulses, the selected cores in planes 1 and 3 will contain 1's, the selected cores in planes 2, 4, and 5 will contain 0's, and the computer word 10100 will have been stored in the memory in location x_3y_4.

2   *Reading from Cores.* Assume that at a later time the location x_3y_4, which was written into in the WRITE sequence above, is to be read from. The timing sequence illustrated in Fig. 7·6 still applies, although there are several differences in operation. First, the READ currents are applied to the selected cores (from 0 time to 0.5 μsec in Fig. 7·6). If a large signal is received at the sense amplifier connected to a given plane during this period, the selected core in that plane contained a 1; if a small signal is received, the selected core in the plane contained a 0. The sense windings connected to planes 1 and 3 will therefore produce signals indicating 1's and the sense windings connected to planes 2, 4, and 5 will produce small signals, indicating 0's. The word stored was therefore 10100. This word must now be written back into the memory array. The output of each sense winding is amplified and used to set a storage device to the 0 or 1 state during the READ period, and the contents of each of these storage devices is then used to control the INHIBIT winding drivers during the WRITE time. Only the INHIBIT drivers connected to planes 2, 4, and 5 will therefore be enabled by signals from the respective storage devices and conduct during the WRITE time, and the selected cores in these planes will remain in the 0 state. After the WRITE time, the selected cores will again contain 10100, just as before the READ operation.

7 · 5   Characteristics of core-memory array

Each core of a core memory of the type described is threaded by four windings. Although some memories use windings such as those in Figs. 7 · 1 and 7 · 4, generally the windings are only threaded through the cores as in Fig. 7 · 5.[2] Since the cores are generally quite small, perhaps 20 to 50 thousandths of an inch outer diameter, the total size of the arrays can be made quite small. Each plane of one of the memories used in the TX-2 computer at Lincoln Laboratory is a 64 × 64-core plane and therefore contains 4,096 cores; there are 37 planes in the array and therefore a total of 151,552 cores in the complete array. This array is about the size of a 5-in. cube. There are 64 X-selection winding inputs to the array and 64 Y-selection inputs, 37 sense windings, and 37 inhibit windings.

Some general characteristics of coincident-current core memories are evident from this: the number of planes used generally equals the number of bits in the computer word; the number of X input lines times the number of Y input lines equals the number of words which can be stored in the array.

Not all core memories consist of individual cores assembled and individually threaded. Some memories utilize apertured ferrite plates which consist of a ferrite plate with a number of holes through which the X and Y selection lines, sense windings, and inhibit windings may be threaded. The plate is constructed so that each of the areas around the apertures acts as a single core; the plate has similar characteristics to a plane of cores.

7 · 6   Memory address and memory buffer registers

The computer communicates with the core memory through two registers: (1) the *memory address register* which contains the address of the word which is to be read from or written into, and (2) the *memory buffer register* which contains the word which was read from the memory (after a READ cycle) or the word which is to be written into memory. In order to locate a word in memory, the address of the word is first loaded into the memory address register. If the memory is to be read from, the states of the cores at the address specified will be sensed and written into the memory buffer register. The computer can then read the word which was looked up from the memory buffer register. If a word is to be written into the memory, the

---

[2]The windings shown in Fig. 7 · 5 are in a commonly used form. It has the advantages of minimum coupling from drive to sense windings, optimum cancellation of half-select noises, and uniform distribution of driving circuits and terminals about the memory plane.

address to be written into is loaded into the memory address register, and the word to be written into the memory is loaded in the memory buffer register. After the memory cycle, the word will be stored in the memory at the address specified.

7 · 7 Driving the X and Y selection lines

Flip-flops are generally used as the storage devices for both the memory address register and memory buffer register. Fig. 7 · 7 illustrates, in block diagram form, the operation of a selection system for a core memory with each plane the size of the plane illustrated in Fig. 7 · 5. Since there are eight X selection lines and eight Y selection

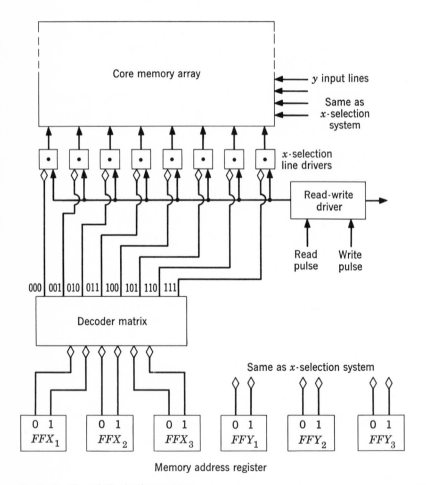

Fig. 7 · 7 X- and Y-selection system.

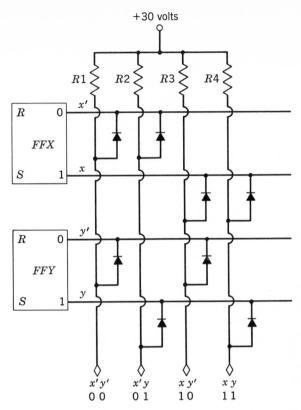

+30 volts

$R1$ $R2$ $R3$ $R4$

R 0 x'

FFX

S 1 x

R 0 y'

FFY

S 1 y

| $x'y'$ | $x'y$ | xy' | xy |
| 0 0 | 0 1 | 1 0 | 1 1 |

Fig. 7 · 8   Diode decoder matrix.

lines, three flip-flops will be required to select an X line and three more to select a Y line. There are therefore six flip-flops in the memory address register so that any one of the 64 (2^6) locations in each plane may be selected. The flip-flops in the register illustrated have been designated X_1, X_2, X_3 and Y_1, Y_2, Y_3, to indicate that the first three are used to select the X winding and the second three to select the Y winding.

1   *Decoder Matrix.* The outputs of the X_1, X_2, and X_3 flip-flops in Fig. 7 · 7 are connected to a decoder matrix. This is a frequently used configuration which has several input and output lines, and the characteristic that for each combination of input values, only one output line will represent a 1. Figure 7 · 8 illustrates a decoder matrix constructed of diodes. There are four input lines to the matrix: two from a flip-flop designated as X, and two from a flip-flop designated Y. The two flip-flops may be in any one of four possible states. For instance, flip-flop X may contain a 0 and Y a 1, in which case the x'

input will be "high" and the y input will be "high." In this case the $x'y$ output line will be high (representing a 1) and the other three output lines will be "low."

This type of decoder matrix is often referred to as a "many-to-one decoder" because the inputs to the matrix effectively select one of the output lines. If we have inputs from three flip-flops, as in Fig. 7 · 7, and designate the flip-flops as FFX_1, FFX_2, FFX_3, the states of the flip-flops may be written as a binary number such as 011, meaning FFX_1 contains a 0, FFX_2 a 1, and FFX_3 a 1. We may then designate each output line with a binary number (Figs. 7 · 7 and 7 · 8) and the output line which will be high will correspond to the input number represented by the state of the input flip-flops.

Since there are three X flip-flops, the flip-flops may take any one of eight states, representing from 000 to 111. For each input state, only one of the outputs from the decoder matrix will be high and therefore only one of the X-selection line drivers (Fig. 7 · 7) will be enabled.

Decoder matrices may also be constructed of transistors, or sometimes of magnetic cores similar to those used in the magnetic-core memory. If the decoder matrix is large, it may be more economical to use other configurations than that shown, but the function of these decoder matrices is the same, one output line is selected for each input state.

2 *X-selection Line Drivers.* There are eight X-selection line drivers in Fig. 7 · 7, each of which has two inputs, one from the decoder matrix and one from the READ-WRITE driver. The output currents from the READ-WRITE driver may be either negative or positive; the X-selection line drivers are therefore capable of passing current in either direction. The X-selection line drivers also function as AND gates, for they will only pass current when the input signal from the decoder matrix represents a 1. Only one of the X-selection line drivers will be enabled by the decoder matrix at any given time. If the X flip-flops in the memory address register contain 000, only the leftmost driver in the illustration will be enabled. All of the X-selection line drivers will receive a READ- and then a WRITE-current pulse (of opposite polarity) from the "READ-WRITE driver." Since only one X-selection line driver is enabled by a 1 signal from the decoder matrix, only one of the X windings in the array will receive the drive currents. The same holds true for the Y-selection line system, which is identical to the X system. Since only one X line and only one Y line are pulsed during each memory cycle, only one core in each plane will receive a full-select READ and WRITE pulse.

3 *READ-WRITE Driver.* The READ-WRITE driver receives two clock pulses each memory cycle. The first is the READ pulse, which causes the READ-WRITE driver to deliver a positive HALF-

SELECT pulse of current to both the X- and Y-selection line drivers. The second input pulse to the READ-WRITE driver is the WRITE pulse, which initiates a negative pulse of current to the X- and Y-selection line drivers. The current supplied by the READ-WRITE drivers is generally on the order of 0.1 to 1 amp.

The operation of the memory address register and its associated circuitry causes a single core in each plane of the memory to receive a FULL-READ and then a FULL-WRITE current pulse. The memory address register is generally loaded directly from the instruction which is being interpreted by the machine. That is, the address section of the word is read directly into the memory address register. (This will be described in Chap. 9.)

7·8   Memory buffer register and associated circuitry

The memory buffer register consists of a flip-flop register which contains one flip-flop for each plane in the array. The number of planes in the array, and hence the length of the memory buffer register, is equal to the number of bits in the basic computer word. The arithmetic element and control element of the machine generally communicate directly with the memory buffer, either loading the word to be written in storage into it or reading from it.

Figure 7·9 illustrates two flip-flops of a memory buffer register along with their associated circuitry. Each bit in the memory buffer register has identical circuitry. There are two distinct sequences which may occur; the first involves the reading of a word from memory and the second the writing of a word into the memory.

1   *Reading from Memory.* The location of the word to be read from the memory is first loaded into the memory address register (Fig. 7·7). The memory buffer register is then cleared. During the READ time (Fig. 7·6) the selected core in each plane receives a full current pulse and is set to 0. If the selected core in a given plane contained a 1, a pulse is received on the sense winding. This is amplified by the sense amplifier and then used to set a 1 into the memory buffer flip-flop used to control the INHIBIT driver for the core plane. If the selected core in the plane contained a 0, the signal received by the sense amplifier will be small, and no pulse will appear at the output of the sense amplifier, and the flip-flop will remain in the 0 state.

The sense amplifier is "strobed" (Fig. 7·9) with a narrow pulse because, despite that fact that a core containing a 0 will produce a small signal when "sensed," many of the cores in each plane will receive HALF-SELECT pulses and each will generate a small amount of noise on the sense winding. If this noise is additive, it may

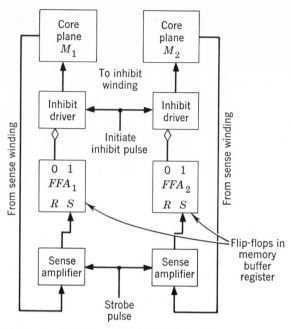

Fig. 7 · 9   Operation of memory buffer register.

approach the signal from a core whose polarity is reversed. It has been found that the noise generated by the half-selected cores dies out shortly after the HALF-SELECT pulses are started; therefore, the sense amplifier is strobed during the latter part of the READ time, when the output from a selected core reversing states is highest in proportion to the noise from half-selected cores. Only the output signal during the strobe pulse is gated into the SET line of the flip-flop.

During the WRITE time (Fig. 7 · 6), each of the selected cores receives a FULL-SELECT current from the *x* and *y* selection system. As a result of the reading operation, all of these cores have previously been set in the 0 state; however, the memory buffer flip-flops now contain 1's for each plane in which a 1 was stored in the full-selected core. The outputs from these flip-flops are used to enable the INHIBIT drivers for each plane in which a 0 is to remain. All other full-selected cores will be set to the 1 state. The 0 output from each flip-flop is therefore used to enable the INHIBIT driver for the plane associated with the flip-flop. After the WRITE time, the selected core in each plane will be in its original state.

2   *Writing into Core Memory.* The X- and Y-selection system goes through the same timing sequence when a word is to be written into

memory as when a word is read from memory. The operation of the memory buffer register differs however. The word to be written into the selected location is loaded into the memory buffer register, and the address in memory to be written into is loaded into the memory address register. During the READ time the sense amplifier is not strobed, so the memory buffer register is not disturbed.

After the READ time, all the selected cores will have been set to 0. During the WRITE time, the same cores all receive full-current WRITE pulses from the X- and Y-selection system; however, the planes in which 0's are to remain have their inhibit drivers enabled by the memory buffer flip-flops (Figs. 7·7 and 7·9), and the half-current pulses from these drivers cancel the selection current, leaving the full-selected cores in the 0 state. All other full-selected cores are set to 1.

After the WRITE time, the word in the memory buffer register will have been written into the cores.

7·9   Characteristics of core memories

The small memory described is typical of the random-access memories now used, except for its size. Memories are now in use which contain over a million cores. While the fundamentals of such memories are the same, the circuitry will of necessity differ in details.

The memory-cycle times vary with different machines, but most commercial machines have memory-cycle times in the 1 to 8 μsec region. Some faster machines have times of less than 1 μsec, and several newer memories may be operated in the 0.1 to 0.3 μsec region. *Reading access time* is defined as the duration of the delay before a word may be used during the reading process. This is less than the memory-cycle time, because the READ time occurs first, and the word may be used as soon as the sense amplifier is strobed and the word loaded into the memory buffer register. The access time for some high-speed memories is less than 0.1 μsec.

·10   Magnetic-core logical elements

The characteristics which make magnetic cores desirable for the storage of digital information also make them appear to be ideal for use as logical elements. As a result, a great deal of research has gone into the development of both magnetic storage and logical devices.

An example of the use of magnetic cores in other than a large computer memory may be seen in Fig. 7·10, which shows a magnetic-core shift register. This register operates in a manner similar to that

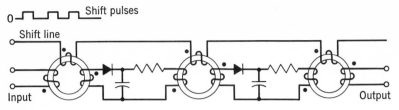

Fig. 7 · 10   Magnetic-core shift register.

of the flip-flop shift register in Chap. 4, in that each time a SHIFT pulse is applied, each bit in the register is shifted one place to the right. New information may be read in via the input line and the signals appearing on the output line will represent the number stored in the register in serial form.

The operation of the circuitry is dependent on the cores used having a hysteresis loop similar to that shown in Figs. 7 · 2 and 7 · 3. The SHIFT winding is arranged so that a SHIFT pulse will reset all the cores to the 0 state. If a given core in the register contains a 1 when the SHIFT pulse is applied, the core will be switched to the 0 state, but in switching it will develop a signal across its output winding which is connected to the next core to the right in the figure. The signal developed will be stored by the capacitor, and when the output signal from the core which was switched has decayed, the capacitor will begin to discharge. The diode will prevent the capacitor from discharging through the winding to the left and therefore the capacitor will discharge through the winding of the core on the right, setting it to the 1 state. If a core is in the 0 state when a SHIFT pulse is applied, the core will not change state, and since no output pulse will be developed, the core to the right will remain in the 0 state. Transistors are sometimes used instead of the diodes in the circuit in Fig. 7 · 10.

While there are many obvious advantages in the use of magnetic switching devices, there are also disadvantages. At present, magnetic elements cannot match the speeds of solid-state circuitry. Also, the switching currents used in most magnetic-element circuits must be accurately regulated, and there are also problems in the timing of the operation of present circuitry. Nevertheless there is little doubt of the future of magnetic logical devices, and several small computers now use them. In the long run, the advantages of magnetic logical elements may more than offset the disadvantages, and a far greater use of magnetic elements could then be anticipated.

Notice that the magnetic-core register in Fig. 7 · 10 must be shifted in order to sense the state of the cores in the register. While the series of SHIFT pulses may be interrupted and the information stored in the register will not be lost, the cores must be switched to sense their states.

7 · 11   Selections systems

An important part of the system which selected the cores to be read from and written into in a coincidence-current memory is the decoder matrix shown in Fig. 7 · 8. This particular circuit is called a many-to-one decoder or simply a decoder, and has the characteristic that for each of the possible 2^n binary input numbers corresponding to n input cells, the matrix will have a unique one of its 2^n output lines selected. A decoder network generally has $2n$ input lines (n is the number of memory cells which are being decoded) because for each input device or cell the decoder will require both the output of the device and its complement.

Figure 7 · 11 shows a decoder which is completely parallel in construction and is designed to decode three binary cells or flip-flops. In this case, there are six input lines to the network (X_1, X_1', X_2, X_2', X_3, and X_3'). There are then $2^3 = 8$ output lines, and for each of the 8 states which the three flip-flops may take, a unique output line will be selected. As may be seen, when a decoder network of this type is constructed, the number of diodes per AND gate is equal to the num-

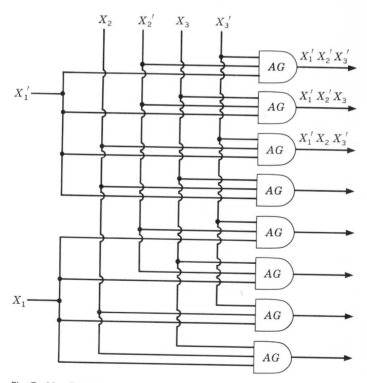

Fig. 7 · 11   Parallel decoder.

ber of inputs to each AND gate, and this is equal to the number of flip-flops which are being decoded. Further, the number of AND gates is equal to the number of output lines, which is equal to 2^n (n is the number of flip-flops being decoded). The total number of diodes is therefore equal to $n \times 2^n$, and for the binary-decoding matrix in Fig. 7 · 11, 24 diodes are required to construct the network. As may be seen, the number of diodes required goes up sharply with the number of inputs to the network. For instance, in order to decode an eight flip-flop register, we would require $8 \times 2^8 = 2{,}048$ diodes if the decoder was constructed in this manner.

As a result, there are several other types of structures which are often used in building decoder networks. One such structure is shown in Fig. 7 · 12 and is called a *tree-type decoding network*. The particular tree network shown in Fig. 7 · 12 decodes four flip-flops, and therefore has $2^4 = 16$ output lines, a unique one of which is selected for each state of the flip-flops. An examination will show that 56 diodes are required to build this particular network, while $2^4 \times 4 = 64$ diodes would be required to build the parallel decoder type shown in Fig. 7 · 11.

Still another type of decoder network is shown in Fig. 7 · 13, and this network is called a *balanced multiplicative decoder network*. Notice that this particular network requires only 48 diodes. It can be shown that the type of decoder network shown in Fig. 7 · 13 requires the minimum number of diodes for a complete decoder network, and the difference in the number of diodes or decoding elements to construct a network such as shown in Fig. 7 · 13, compared with that in 7 · 12 and 7 · 11, becomes more significant as the number of flip-flops to be decoded increases. The type of network shown in Fig. 7 · 11, however, has the advantage of being the fastest of the three types of networks. This is counterbalanced by the fact that it is the most costly. The tree network shown in Fig. 7 · 12 is quite often used, this being a compromise between the number of diodes or logical elements used and the speed of decoding, which is dependent upon the maximum number of gates a signal must pass through.

Having studied the three types of decoding matrices which are now used in digital machines, we will simply draw the decoder networks as a box with n inputs and 2^n outputs, with the understanding that one of the three types of circuits shown in Figs. 7 · 11, 7 · 12, and 7 · 13 will be used in the box.

The complexity of selecting a word in a large memory which is to be written into or read from generally involves one or more decoders similar to those just described, plus what is called the *number of dimensions* or the *number of coordinates* into which the memory is organized. For instance, for core memories it is also possible to select

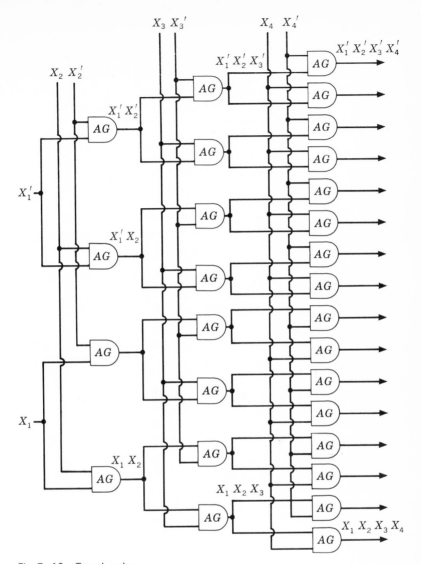

Fig. 7 · 12   Tree decoder.

a word in the memory using a single word winding as well as using the technique already described, so that we have a particular word winding corresponding to each word in the memory. Figure 7 · 14*b* shows a selection technique where all of the flip-flops in the memory address register are decoded by a single decoder matrix, which then selects a given word from the memory. A selection system of this type is called a *word-organized* or *linear-selection* memory. The selection

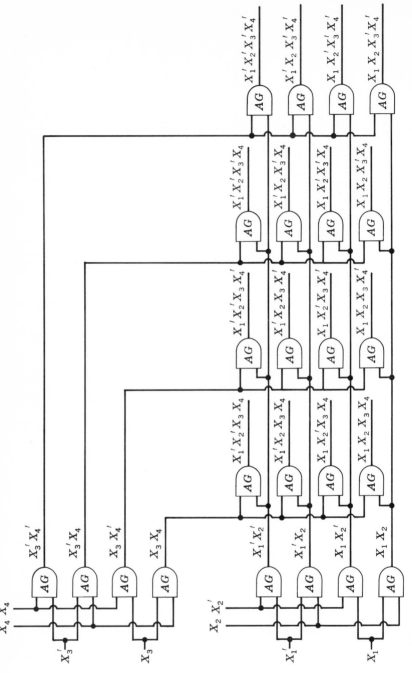

Fig 7 · 13 A balanced decoder

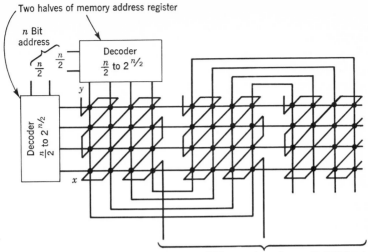

(a) Coincident-current or two-dimensional selection system

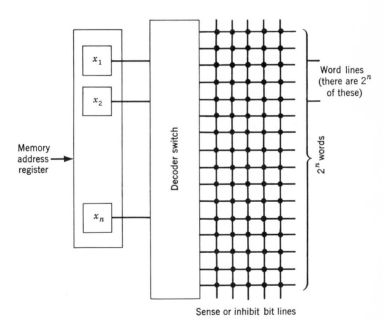

Sense or inhibit bit lines

(b) Word-organized or linear-select memory which is one dimensional

Fig. 7 · 14   Memory selection system techniques.

scheme for this memory is said to be *single dimensional* or *one coordinate*. Figure 7·14a shows a *coincident-current* memory, and a memory of this type can be seen to select words using a two-dimensional or two-coordinate system.

Notice that the complexity of the decoder network is significantly reduced for a coincident-current memory system over that of a linear-selection or word-organized memory system. If we use a linear-selection or word-organized system in order to build a 4,096-word memory, we shall require, using the decoder matrix type shown in Fig. 7·11, $12 \times 2^{12} = 49,352$ diodes to construct the selection matrix. If, however, we use a coincident-current memory, we need two decoder matrices, each for six binary digits or flip-flops, so that $6 \times 2^6 = 384$ diodes are required for each decoder matrix. Since two decoding matrices are required, we shall need a total of 768 diodes for the two decoders required.

The advantages of the word-organized scheme are that greater currents can be used and that the greater tolerance of variations in output currents is provided with regard to the memory cell drivers. Since only the selected word in the memory receives current through the selection-coded matrix in the word-organized memory, we can drive the cores deep into saturation when reading or writing, and that will permit us to operate the memory much faster. The output signals will also be somewhat cleaner since none of the cores will be half selected, as only the particular word selected will receive input current. Nevertheless, because of the simplicity of the decoding matrices, the coincident-current memory remains the prevalent type of core memory used in modern digital machines. We shall see in subsequent sections, however, that there are many memories which are word organized; this particular scheme is necessary or advantageous to many of the memory types which are now in use.

7·12 Magnetic film memories

In the search for higher speeds, a type of memory called the *thin-film memory* has been produced. This type of memory is faster but, at present, more expensive than the core type for large memories and is therefore less frequently used. The basic memory cell in a thin-film memory is a thin circle or rectangle of magnetic material deposited on a glass substrate (refer to Fig. 7·15). If a thin-film dot of magnetic material such as a nickel-iron alloy is deposited in the presence of a high magnetic field, when the field is removed the thin dots (about 1,000 angstroms is usual) will behave as small magnets, with a direc-

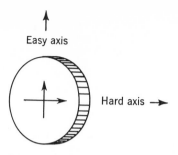

Fig. 7 · 15   Thin-film memory element or dot.

tion of hard magnetization and a direction of easy magnetization. In Fig. 7 · 15, a hard axis and an easy axis are shown. The film acts as a small magnet with a north pole and a south pole aligned in the easy direction, provided no magnetic field is applied externally. We shall adopt the convention that when the north pole is up on the page (and the south pole down) a given dot stores a 1; when the north pole is down, the dot stores a 0. If the dot has its north pole up and we spin the field so the north pole is down by using an externally applied field, this direction of magnetization will remain after the field is removed. We can therefore store a binary digit in such a thin-film dot.

Further, if we force the direction of magnetization to the hard direction using an externally applied field, the direction of magnetization will spin to the easy direction which is closest when this field is removed.

Figure 7 · 16 shows a typical rectangular dot (many times normal size) in a thin-film memory and a *word-line* conductor, a *bit-line* conductor, and a *sense-line* conductor. The word line is used to select the film dot to be read or written into; the bit line is used to write a 0 or a 1 (current can be driven in either direction through the bit line); and the sense line is used to sense whether a given film dot stores a 0 or 1 when we read from the memory. (These conductors are not necessarily wires in the conventional sense, but are generally strips of conductor deposited on some nonconducting substrate. The memory plane containing the thin-film dots is then sandwiched between the conductor substrates.)

If an electric current is applied downward through the word-line conductor in Fig. 7 · 16, the magnetization of the film will be spun to the hard direction as shown in Fig. 7 · 16; and, if a current on the bit line in the 1 direction (which is from left to right) is then applied, the direction of magnetization will be spun slightly counterclockwise. If the word-line current is removed followed by the bit-line current,

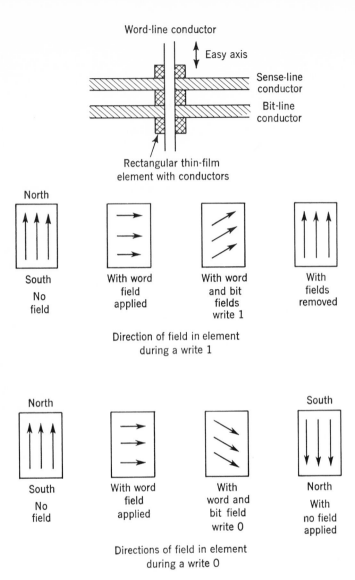

Fig. 7·16 Conductors and field directions for a thin-film magnetic element.

the direction of magnetization of the film will "fall" to the easy direction with a polarity of north up, representing a 1.

If a current is now applied to the word conductor,[3] the magnetic field in the dot will be spun in a clockwise direction and a positive

[3]Notice that the current through the word-line conductor is always in the same direction, while the current drivers for the bit line must drive current in both directions.

pulse will be induced in the sense winding, which indicates a 1 was stored in the thin-film dot.

We can magnetize the dot in the 0 direction (north down) by applying a current on the word line while applying a current on the bit line in the 0 direction, which is from right to left on the page, and then removing the word-line current followed by the bit-line current.

If we again apply the word-line current, the magnetization of the thin-film dot will be spun in a counterclockwise direction, causing a negative signal to be induced on the sense line. In this manner, we can write the direction of magnetization representing a 0 or a 1 into a given selected film dot. This direction of magnetization will remain until we interrogate the dot by applying a current on the word line, at which time we can tell whether we stored a 1 or a 0 in the film dot by whether a positive or negative signal is induced in the sense line.

Figure 7 · 17 shows a typical sequence of signals on the word, bit, and sense lines. Notice that while for the core memory a 1 or a 0 is

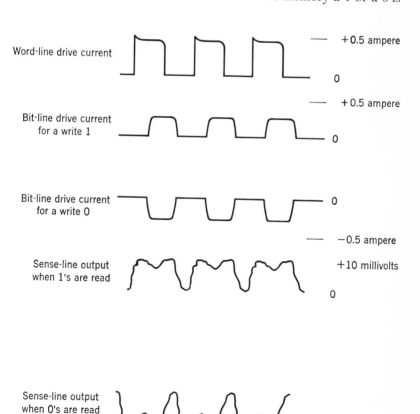

Fig. 7 · 17   Waveforms for a thin-film memory system.

Note: Memory buffer register can be loaded from the sense amplifier outputs when we read or from an external set of lines when we write into the memory

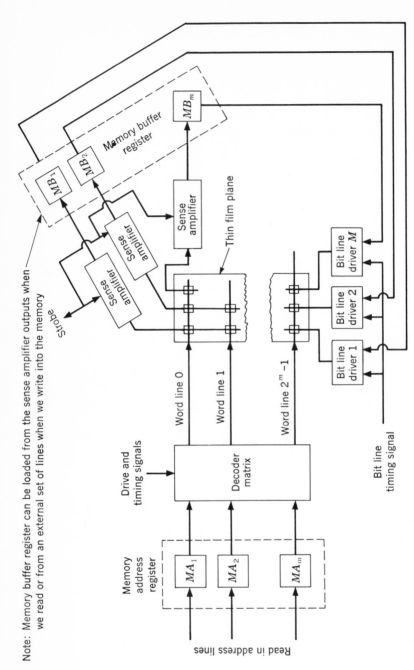

Fig. 7 · 18   Block diagram of thin-film memory.

represented by signal and no signal respectively, and polarity of signal in the sense does not matter, the film memories' 1's are distinguished from 0's by the polarity of the signal on the sense line.

A block diagram for a thin-film memory is shown in Fig. 7 · 18. Thin-film memories are generally not coincident-current, but rather *linear-selection* or *word-organized* memories; in their simplest form, the number of drives or word lines is equal to the number of words in the memory. This means that for a 4,096-word memory, a 12-input–4,096-output selection circuit is required. There are selection-system tricks to alleviate this problem, but basically a linear-selection memory always requires more equipment than the coincident-current system. This becomes an important factor in the price of the memory.

A typical trick for reducing the number of components required to select a word in a thin-film memory is shown in Fig. 7 · 19. Only the thin-film word line connected at the intersection of the X and Y drivers which are selected will conduct current for this circuit. Notice that the selected X driver is turned on and the selected Y driver is turned off. All other combinations of drivers are either on to on, which leads to zero current, or if an X driver is off and a Y driver on, current will be prevented from flowing by the diode in series with the thin-film line. This technique requires one diode per word and one transistor per output of the selection matrices.

Another selection technique using one transistor per word is shown in Fig. 7 · 20. In this scheme the only transistor with its base forward biased with regard to its emitter is at the intersection of the lines which are labeled.

Thin-film dots have been made to switch or rotate in a few nanoseconds, but most thin-film memories operate with cycle times of from 0.1 μ to 0.5 μsec.

The basic operating sequence of the thin-film memory is much the same as for a magnetic-core memory. The address register contains the address of the word to be read or written into; during the read portion of the memory cycle the film dots constituting this word are read by spinning their direction of magnetization in the hard direction. Flip-flops are set by the polarity of the output signals on the sense lines if information is being read, and these flip-flops determine the direction of current through each bit line. If new information is being read in, the flip-flops control the direction of current through the bit lines just as flip-flops control the flow or absence of current through the inhibit lines in a coincident-current memory.

There are as many word lines as words in the thin-film memory—a memory plane and a bit line for each bit in the basic word, and a sense line and sense amplifier for each bit in the basic word. A 2,048-word–

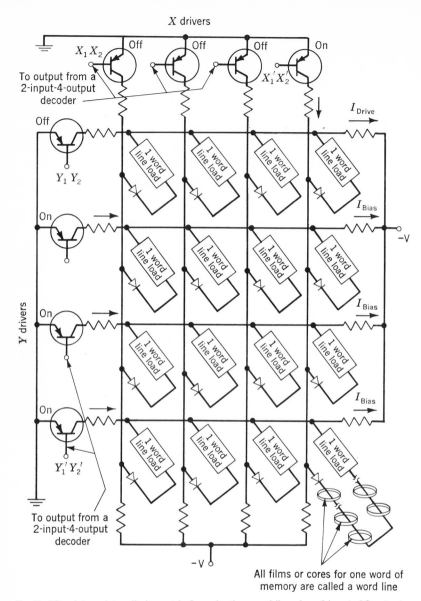

Fig. 7 · 19   A transistor-diode matrix for selecting word lines in a 4-input–16-output decoder.

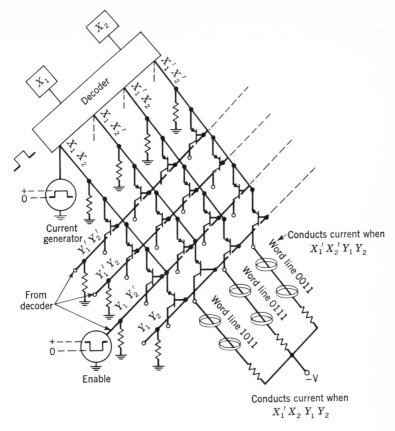

Fig. 7 · 20   An all-transistor switch for a decoder.

35-bit-per-word memory would consist of 35 planes, 2,048 word lines, 11 flip-flop address registers, 35 sense amplifiers, and 35 memory buffer flip-flops.[4]

7 · 13   Magnetic-drum storage

The storage devices which have been described utilize the principle of setting a device which is essentially bistable into one of its two states. Access to the devices was essentially random—once addressed a core is immediately available and a flip-flop continuously produces an indication of its state. The limitations on this type of storage are

[4]Sometimes thin-film memories use cylindrical films rather than flat dots. The memory cells then consist of plated wires. These memories have, in general, longer output signals, can be made coincident current, but are somewhat slower. They are often referred to as "plated wire" or "rod" memories because of their construction.

based on the complexity, and therefore the cost and reliability, of storing a large number of bits. While core memories have been constructed which can store a million bits, some large machines require the storage of as many as 10^{12} bits. This would require 10,000 core memories. The high speed of core-memory storage is therefore paid for in the complexity and cost of the storage.

Magnetic drums provide a relatively inexpensive means of storing information and have reasonably short access times.

A magnetic drum consists basically of a rotating cylinder coated with a thin layer of magnetic material which possesses a hysteresis loop similar to that of the material used in magnetic cores (Fig. 7·2). A number of recording heads (Fig. 7·21) are mounted along the surface of the drum. These are used to write and read information from the surface of the drum by magnetizing small areas, or sensing the magnetization of the areas on which information has been recorded. While Fig. 7·21 shows only a few heads, some magnetic drums have several hundred recording heads scattered about their periphery.

As the drum rotates, a small area continually passes under each of the heads. This area is known as a *track* (Fig. 7·21). Each track is subdivided into cells, each of which can store 1 binary bit. All the cells which are under a set of heads at the same time are called a *slot*.

Generally one of the tracks is used to provide the timing for the drum. A series of timing signals is permanently recorded around this timing track, and each signal defines a *time unit* for the drum system. The timing track is then used to determine the location of each set of storage cells around the tracks. For instance, if the timing track is 60 in. in length and timing pulses are recorded at a density of 100

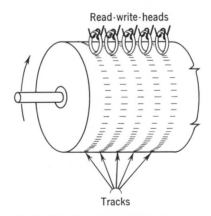

Fig. 7·21   Magnetic-drum storage.

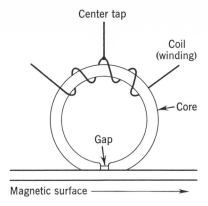

Center tap

Coil
(winding)

Core

Gap

Magnetic surface

Fig. 7 · 22   Magnetic recording head.

per in., there will be 6,000 locations for bits (cells) around each of the tracks. If the drum has 30 tracks plus the timing track, the drum will have the capacity to store a total of 180,000 bits.

Information is written onto the drum by passing current through a winding on the WRITE heads. This current causes flux to be created through the core material of the head. Figure 7 · 12 illustrates a ring-type head for writing or reading information from a drum. Some drum systems use separate heads for reading and writing, and others use combined READ-WRITE heads. The head in Fig. 7 · 22 consists of a ring formed of high-permeability material around which a coil is wound. When information is to be written on the surface of the drum, pulses of current are driven through the winding. The direction of flux through the head, and in turn the polarization of the magnetic field recorded on the surface of the drum, depends upon the direction of current through the coil.

The gap in the core presents a relatively high-reluctance path to the flux generated by the current through the coil. Since the magnetic material on the surface of the drum is passing near the gap, some of the flux passes through this material. This causes a small area of the drum surface to be magnetized, and since the material used to coat the surface of the drum has a relatively high retentivity, the magnetic field remains after the area has passed from under the head, or the current through the coil is discontinued. It should be noted that the head does not actually touch the surface of the drum. Instead, to prevent wear, the heads are located very close to the drum surface but not touching it. The drum must therefore be of very constant diameter in order to keep the heads at a constant distance. If the head moves farther from the surface of the drum, the signals recorded will become weaker.

The signals recorded on the surface of the drum are read in a similar manner. When the areas which have been magnetized pass under the head, some of the magnetic flux is coupled into the head and changes in this flux induce signals in the winding. These signals are then amplified and interpreted. A description of the recording techniques used will be found in the last section of this chapter.

The sizes and storage capacities of magnetic drums vary greatly. Small drums with capacities of less than 25,000 bits have been constructed. Drums of this size generally have from 15 to 25 tracks and from 15 to 50 heads. In order to decrease access time, heads are sometimes located in sets around the periphery of the drum, so that a drum with 15 tracks may have 30 heads divided into two sets of 15 heads, each set located 180° from the other. For very fast access time, there may be even more than two sets of heads.[5]

Much larger drums can store up to 15,000,000 bits and may have from 300 to 400 tracks. The larger drums are generally rotated much more slowly than small drums, and speeds vary from 120 rpm (for laboratory models) up to 75,000 rpm. The access times obviously decrease as the drum speeds increase; however, there is another important factor: the packing density along a track. Most present-day drums have a packing density of from 200 to 300 bits per in., although by maintaining the heads very close to the drum surface and rotating the drum slowly, packing densities in excess of 1,000 bits per in. may be achieved.

7 · 14   Parallel operation of a magnetic drum

It is possible to operate a drum in either a serial or parallel mode. For parallel operation, all the bits of a word may be written simultaneously, and read in the same manner. If the basic computer word contains 40 bits, the drum might read from 41 tracks (one for timing) simultaneously, thus reading an entire computer word in one bit time. When the drum is read from and written into in parallel, a separate READ and WRITE amplifier is required for each track that is used simultaneously, so that to read a 40-bit word in a bit time, 40 READ amplifiers are required. The correct set of heads is then selected and the drum system locates the selected set of cells.

Notice that words in a parallel system may be located by means of a timing track. If each track contains 8,192 bits, a 13-bit counter may be set to zero at the same position each time the drum revolves, and

[5]The actual access time can be reduced by clever coding of the computer program. If the computer only writes into or reads words near the reading or writing heads when the instruction is initiated, the access time may be minimized.

stepped by one each time a timing pulse appears. In this way, the location 1,096 will be the 1,096th slot around the track from the 0 location. If the address of the word to be read is loaded into a register, the signals from the drum can be gated into the computer when the counter agrees with the register's contents. In this way words may be located on the drum.

· 15 Serial operation of magnetic drum

A magnetic drum may also be operated in a serial mode. In this case only one track will be read from or written into at a given time. Since there are a number of tracks for each drum, the correct READ-WRITE head as well as the location of the desired bits around the track must be selected.

Each track is therefore assigned a number. In addition, each track is divided into *sectors*, each sector containing one full computer word. For instance, if the basic computer word is 20 bits in length[6] and 640 bits can be recorded around each track of the drum, each track will be divided into 32 sectors. Each sector will then contain one 20-bit computer word.

In order to specify the address of a word on a magnetic drum operated serially, both the track number and sector number must be given. Consider a drum with 32 tracks plus a timing track, and 32 words (sectors) around each track. The address of a word on the drum in a binary machine will consist of 10 bits, 5 bits to specify the track and 5 bits the sector. When written as the address section of a computer instruction word (refer to Chap. 2), the address will contain 10 bits. The first 5 bits may be used to designate the track number and the second 5 bits the sector number.

The five flip-flops containing the track number may be connected to a *decoder matrix* similar to that in Fig. 7 · 8, which will then select the correct READ-WRITE head.

Several techniques involving the timing tracks may be used to locate the selected sector. One technique involves the use of several

[6]Sometimes a space bit is left between the end of one word and the beginning of the next.

timing tracks instead of one. Figure 7 · 23 shows a technique utilizing three timing tracks. One of the tracks contains a set of signals indicating the location of each bit around the tracks. The second track contains a set of pulses with a pulse at the beginning of each word time. (The word-time signals illustrated are 12 bits apart so the basic word would be 11 or 12 bits in length.) In addition, the *sector number* of the *next* word around the drum is recorded around a third timing track. The computer reads sector numbers from this track, and when the number read agrees with the sector number in the address, the computer can then read the selected word from the next sector beginning with the next word-time pulse.

When a magnetic drum is used as the principle storage device for a computer, the registers of the computer may consist of dynamic registers similar to those described in Chap. 4. By locating reading and writing heads displaced about the surface of the drum as shown in Fig. 7 · 24, dynamic registers may be formed using the surface of the drum as the delay medium. The operation of a system of this sort is serial; the words are read from a track and re-recorded on the same track, displaced by some number of cells which is determined by the spacing of the heads. By using a pair of heads and a track for the accumulator, and another pair of heads and a track for the other registers of the arithmetic and control sections of the computer, an arithmetic element consisting basically of dynamic registers of this type may be constructed.

A drum may also be operated in series-parallel. If the system is constructed using a binary-coded decimal to represent decimal digits and the decimal register consists of four binary serial registers each circulating in parallel, the registers may be formed by operating four READ-WRITE heads in parallel. Four tracks will thus form a register in the machine. (The group of four tracks forming a register is sometimes called a *band.*)

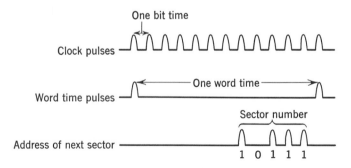

Fig. 7 · 23 Timing signals for a magnetic drum.

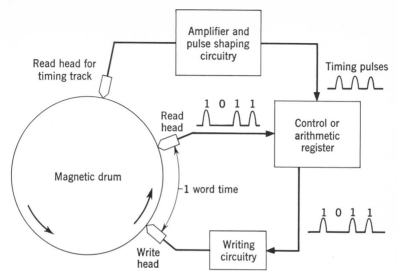

Fig. 7 · 24 Magnetic-drum circulating or dynamic register.

· 16 Magnetic-disk memories

Another type of memory, called a *magnetic-disk memory*, greatly resembles the magnetic-drum memory in operation. The magnetic-disk memory provides very large storage capabilities with moderate operating speeds. In this respect, the magnetic-disk memory falls somewhere between the magnetic drum and magnetic tape; the cost per bit and the speed are somewhat lower than those of magnetic drums and somewhat higher than those of magnetic tape. There are quite a large number of different types of magnetic-disk memories now on the market. While differing in specific details, all of them are based on the same principles of operation.

In appearance, a magnetic-disk memory resembles the coin-operated automatic record player or "juke box." A number of rotating disks coated with a magnetic material are stacked with space between each disk (refer to Fig. 7 · 25). Information is recorded on the surface of the rotating disks by magnetic heads which are positioned against the disks. (Information is recorded in bands rather than on a spiral.) Each band of information around a given disk is called a "track." On one side of a typical disc there may be from one hundred to several hundred of these data tracks. Bits are recorded along a track at a density of from perhaps 500 to 1,000 bits per in. In most systems, the outer tracks contain more bits than the inner tracks, because the circumference of an outer track is obviously greater than that of an inner track. The speed at which the disks rotate

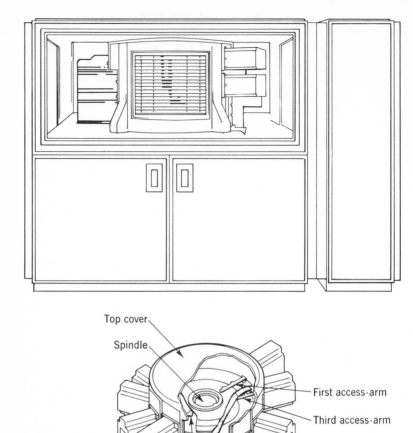

Fig. 7 · 25   A magnetic-disk memory system. (Data Products Corporation, Culver City, Calif.)

varys, of course, with the manufacturer, but typical speeds are on the order of 1,000/rpm.

Since each disk contains a number of tracks of information and since there are a number of disks in a given memory, several techniques have evolved for placing the magnetic READ and WRITE head in the correct position on a selected track. Since the same head is generally used for reading and for writing, the problem becomes that of placing this head accurately and quickly on a track selected at random and on a disk selected at random. Some disk memories have one READ-WRITE head for each surface of each disk. Others have one READ-WRITE head for each pair of adjacent surfaces (because information is generally written on both the top and bottom of each disk). These memories have an arm which can be moved up and down and in and out with a READ-WRITE head positioned on the top and bottom of the arm between each pair of surfaces used. Other systems have only one pair of READ-WRITE heads for the entire memory. In these systems, the two recording heads are positioned on an arm which is first moved between the correct pair of disks, then selects the correct surface of the adjacent surfaces (again because information is written on both the top and bottom of each disk), and finally is placed upon the correct selected track of the disk.

The positioning of the heads by means of the mechanical movement of arms is a difficult and tricky business, particularly since the tracks are generally recorded several one-hundredths of an inch apart on the disk. It should be apparent that disk-file memories with a number of heads can locate and record or read from a given track faster than ones with only a single pair of heads, since the amount of mechanical movement before the track is reached will be less for the multihead system.

The READ and WRITE heads used on magnetic-disk memories are almost invariably of a type called *flying heads*. A simplified diagram of a flying head is shown in Fig. 7·26. When a disk rotates at a high speed, a thin but resilient boundary layer of air rotates with the disk. The head is so shaped that it rides on this layer of rotating air,

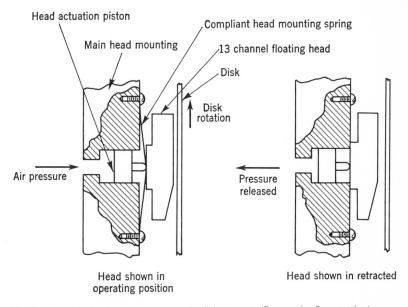

Fig. 7·26 A flying head for a magnetic-disk system. (Burroughs Corporation)

Fig. 7 · 27   Changeable disk pack for IBM 1311 disk-storage system.

which causes the disk to maintain separation from the head, thus preventing wear on the surface of the disk. In effect, the layer of air rotating with the disk acts like a spring with a stiffness exceeding several thousand pounds per inch, thus forcing the head away from the surface of the disk. In order to force the head into the correct proximity with the disk, a number of mechanisms have been used. Often, compressed air is simply blown into a mechanism which forces the head toward the surface of the disk, using a pistonlike arrangement as is shown in Fig. 7 · 26.

Some manufacturers make disk memories which have changeable disk packs. Each disk pack contains a set of disks which rotate together. The IBM 1311 changeable disk pack, for instance, contains 10 recording disk surfaces consisting of six disks (refer to Fig. 7 · 27). (In this particular configuration the top of the top disk and the bottom of the bottom disk are not used.) There are 10 heads used, one for each surface on which information is recorded. The disks revolve at a speed of 1,500 rpm. Each disk surface is divided into 100 concentric magnetic tracks so that tracks are spaced 50 per in., and each track contains 18,000 bits. The actual packing density of bits on the surface area of these disks is about 50,000 bits per sq in.

As a further example, one of the magnetic-disk memories made by Data Product Corporation contains 32 oxide-coated disks, each 31 in. in diameter and ⅛ in. thick. These are rotated at a rate of 1,200 rpm. Each disk is accessed by eight READ-WRITE heads. Each disk has 256 tracks on the top surface and 256 tracks on the bottom surface. The distance between these tracks is about 0.025 in. The nominal recording density is about 600 bits per in. Each disk is divided into an inner and outer area, each consisting of a set of tracks. The outer tracks contain 34,840 bits, while the inner tracks contain about 20,904. A given head may be moved into a reading or writing position on a selected track in about 20 to 30 msec. The disks rotate at a rate of 1,200 rpm.

There are many sizes and speeds for disk memories. Some disks are quite large, running up to 4 ft in diameter. Others are smaller, rotate faster, are changeable, etc. Because of the large market for these memories and the seemingly infinite variety of configurations in which they can be manufactured, the system user is afforded considerable freedom in his selection.

Because of the relative inexpensiveness per bit of information stored in disk memories and because of the relatively low access times and the high transfer rates attainable when reading or writing data from or into a disk file, magnetic-disk memories have become one of the most important storage devices in modern digital computers. The ability to store hundreds of millions of binary digits in a given disk-file system at a cost of some fractions of a cent per bit has made the disk memory second only to magnetic tape in its use for storing large quantities of digital information.

7 · 17 Magnetic tape

At present, the most popular medium for storing very large quantities of information is magnetic tape. While, because of its long access time, magnetic tape is not a desirable medium for the main high-speed storage of a computer, modern mass-production techniques have made the cost of tape very low, so that vast quantities of information may be stored cheaply. Furthermore, since it is possible to erase and rewrite information on tape, the same tape may be used again and again. Another advantage of magnetic tape is that the information stored does not "fade away," and therefore data or programs stored one month may be used again the next.

Another advantage of using magnetic tape for storing large quantities of data derives from the fact that the reels of tape on a tape mechanism may be changed. In this way the same magnetic-tape handling mechanism and its associated circuitry may be used with many different reels of tape, each reel containing different data.

There are four basic parts of a digital magnetic tape system:

1 *Magnetic Tape.* This is generally a flexible plastic tape with a thin coating of some ferromagnetic material along the surface. Some tapes are sandwiched; that is, the magnetic material is located between two layers of plastic. Plated metallic tapes have also been used.

2 *The Tape Transport.* This consists of a mechanism designed to move the tape past the recording heads at the command of the computer. Included are the heads themselves and the storage facilities for the tape being used, such as the reels on which the tape is wound.

3 *The Reading and Writing System.* This part of the system includes the reading and writing amplifiers and the "translators" which convert the signals from the tape to signals which may be used in the central computing system.

4 *The Switching and Buffering Equipment.* This section consists of the

equipment necessary to select the correct tape mechanism if there are several, to store information from the tape and also information to be read onto the tape (provide buffering), and to provide such facilities as manually directed rewinding of the tape.

The tape transports used in digital systems have two unique characteristics: (1) the ability to start and stop very quickly, and (2) a high tape speed. The ability to start and stop the tape very quickly is important for two reasons. Since the writing or reading process cannot begin until the tape is moving at a sufficient speed, a delay is introduced until the tape gains speed. Secondly, information is generally recorded on magnetic tape in "blocks." Since the tape may be stopped between blocks of information, the tape which passes under the heads during the stopping and starting processes is wasted. Fast starting and stopping conserves tape.

In order to accelerate and decelerate the tape very quickly, an effort

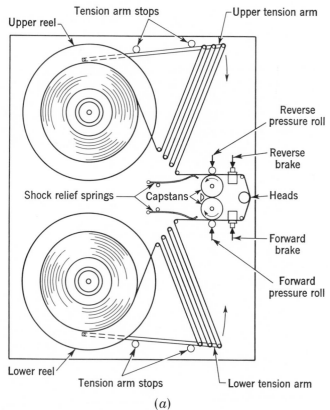

(a)

Fig. 7 · 28   High-speed start-stop tape systems.

is made to isolate the tape reels, which have a high inertia, from the mechanism which moves the tape past the recording heads. Figure 7·28a shows a high-speed start-stop tape mechanism which uses a set of tension arms around which the tape is laced. The upper and

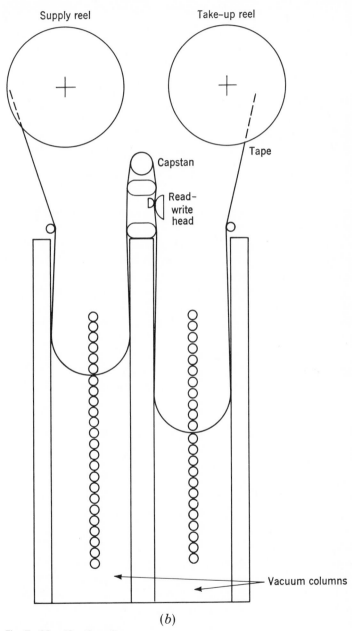

Supply reel

Take-up reel

Tape

Capstan

Read–
write
head

Vacuum columns

(b)

Fig. 7·28 (Continued)

lower tension arms in Fig. 7 · 28*a* are movable, and when the tape is suddenly driven past the heads by the capstan, the mechanism provides a buffering supply of tape. A servomechanism is used to drive the upper and lower reels, maintaining enough tape between the capstan and tape reels to keep the supply of tape around the tension arms constant.

Another arrangement for isolating the high-inertia tape reels from the basic tape drive is shown in Fig. 7 · 28*b*. This system isolates the tape from the capstan drive by means of two columns of tape which are held in place by a vacuum. A servosystem then maintains the correct length of tape between reel and capstan drive. Both this and the previous system use continuously rotating capstans to actually drive the tape, and "pressure rolls" to press the tape against the capstan when the transport is activated. Brakes are also provided for fast stopping.

Using systems of this sort, the start and stop times can be on the order of 1 msec. These are the times required to accelerate a tape to a speed suitable for reading or writing and the time required to fully stop a moving tape. The speeds at which the tapes are moved past the heads vary greatly, with most tape transports having speeds in the range from 50 to 200 in. per sec. A very fast (900 in. per sec) mechanism has been constructed at Lincoln Laboratory in which the tape is driven directly by the reels of the tape transport. A tape system of this sort is designed to transfer only large quantities of data to and from the machine's main fast-access storage in a single operation. The slower tape speeds, combined with fast starting and stopping, are probably more adaptable to systems in which smaller amounts of data must be transferred. Some systems have changeable cartridges with a reel of tape in each cartridge. The manufacturers of these systems feel that this protects the tape and facilitates changing the reels.

Tapes vary from ¼ to 3 in. in width; however most tape is from ½ to 1 in. wide. Generally about 7 channels or tracks are used for each ½ in. of width, so a 1-in. tape may have 14 channels. The surface of the tape is generally in contact with the READ or WRITE head. Output signals from the READ heads are generally in the 0.1 to 0.5 volt range. The recording density varies; however, 200, 556, or 800 bits per in. per channel are standard.

Although the reliability of tape and tape-recording techniques is continually being improved, the fundamental limitation lies in the access time for information. If a tape system must search for information, the times required are always several orders of magnitude larger than the operating speeds of the machine. For this reason, magnetic tape is used only as a bulk storage device, but in this area, it is a most economical and convenient means of storage.

7 · 18   Digital recording techniques

Although the characteristics and construction of such storage devices as magnetic drums, tape recorders, and magnetic-disk storage devices may vary greatly, the fundamental storage process in each consists of storing a binary 0 or 1 on a small area of magnetic material. Storage in each case is dynamic, for the medium on which the information is recorded is moved past the reading or writing device.

Although the process of recording a 0 or 1 on a surface may appear straightforward, considerable research has gone into both the development of the recorded patterns used to represent 0's and 1's and the means for determining the value recorded. There are two necessities here: one is that the packing density should be made as great as is possible; that is, that each cell or bit occupy as little space as is possible, thus economizing on the amount of tape used to store a given amount of information; and the second is that the reading and writing procedure be made as reliable as is possible. These two interests are conflicting, since when the recorded bits are packed more and more closely together, the distortion of the playback signal is greatly increased.

In writing information on a magnetic surface, the digital information is supplied to the recording circuitry, which then codes this information into a pattern which is recorded by the writing head. The techniques which are used to write information on a magnetic medium can be divided into two categories, the *return-to-zero* (RZ) techniques and the *non-return-to-zero* (NRZ) techniques. The methods for reading information written using either technique also vary. Both basic techniques will be described below, along with the recorded waveshapes and the waveshapes later read by the READ heads and translated by the reading system.

1   *Return-to-zero Recording Technique.* Figures 7 · 29a and 7 · 29b each illustrate a different version of the return-to-zero recording technique. In Fig. 7 · 29a there is no current through the winding of the WRITE head, except when a 1 or a 0 is to be recorded. If a 1 is to be recorded, a pulse of positive polarity is applied to the winding on the WRITE head, and if a 0 is to be written, a negative pulse is applied to the winding. In either case the current through the WRITE-head winding is returned to zero after the pulse, and remains there until the next bit is recorded. The second set of waveforms on this drawing illustrates the remanent flux pattern on the magnetic surface after the writing head has passed. There is some distortion in this pattern due to the fringing of flux around the head.

If this pattern of magnetization is passed under a READ head, some of the magnetic flux will be coupled into the core of the head.

The flux takes the lower reluctance path through the core material of the head instead of bridging the gap in the head (Fig. 7 · 22), and when the amount of flux through the core material changes, a voltage will be induced in the coil wound around the core. Thus, a change in the amplitude of the recorded magnetic field will result in a voltage being induced in the coil on the READ head. The waveforms in Fig. 7 · 29a and b illustrate typical output signals on the READ-head windings for each of the return-to-zero techniques. Notice that the waveform at the READ head is not a reproduction of the input current during the WRITE process, nor of the pattern actually magnetized on the magnetic material.

The problem is therefore to distinguish a 1 or a 0 output at the sense winding. Several techniques have been used for this. One consists of first amplifying the output waveform from the READ winding in a linear amplifier. The output of this amplifier is then strobed in the same manner that the output from the sense winding of a core plane is strobed. For drum systems the correct timing for the strobe, which must be very accurate, may be determined by the timing signals recorded on the timing track. If the output from the READ amplifier is connected to an AND gate and the strobe pulse is also connected as an input to the same AND gate, the output will be a positive pulse when the recorded signal represents a 1.

It is important that the timing pulse be very sharp and occur at the right time relative to the reading and writing of the bits.

A fundamental characteristic of Fig. 7 · 29a return-to-zero recording is that for a 1, the output signal during the first half of each bit time will be positive with regard to the second half; and that for a 0, the first half of the output signal during each bit time is negative with regard to the output during the second half. This is sometimes exploited in translating the signal read back.

In the return-to-zero system in Fig. 7 · 29a, the magnetic field returns to zero flux when a 1 or 0 pulse is not present. This makes it impossible to write over information which has previously been written, unless the position of each cell is very accurately located. If a 0 pulse is written directly over a previously recorded 1, the flux generated will reverse the polarity of the recorded field only if the writing head is in exactly the right position when the 0 is recorded. The timing of the writing of information is therefore very critical for this system, and it is rarely used except with magnetic drums, where the timing may be very accurately established by timing tracks. An alternate technique involves erasing all flux before writing new information, but this involves an additional erase head and is seldom used.

The second method for recording information in a return-to-zero

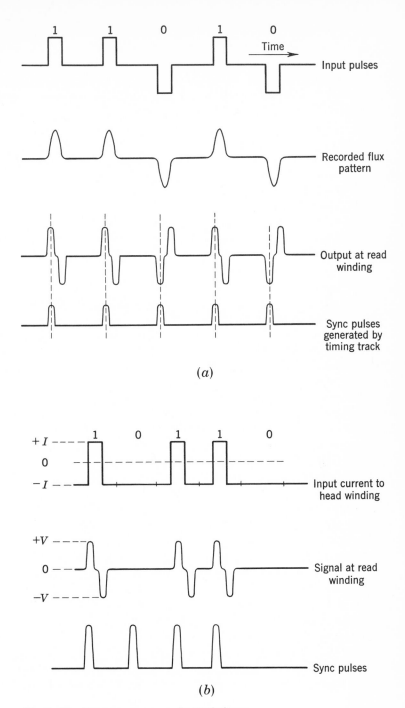

Fig. 7 · 29   Return-to-zero recording techniques.

system is illustrated in Fig. 7 · 29b. In this case the current through the winding maintains the head saturated in the negative direction unless a 1 is to be written. When a 1 is written, a pulse of current in the opposite direction is applied to the winding at the center of the bit time. The outputs at the sense winding are also illustrated in the figure. In this case there will be an output at the sense winding only when a 1 is written. This output may be amplified and strobed just as in the previous case. The timing here is not so critical when information is being "written over," as the negative flux from the head will magnetize the surface in the correct direction regardless of what was previously recorded. The current through the winding in this case, and in all those which follow, is assumed to be sufficient to saturate the material on which the signals are being recorded.

2   *Non-return-to-zero Recording Techniques.* Figure 7 · 30 illustrates three recording techniques, each of which is classified as a non-return-to-zero system. In the first, the current through the winding is negative through the entire bit time when a 0 is recorded, and is positive through the entire bit time when a 1 is recorded. The current through the winding will therefore remain constant when a sequence of 0's or 1's is being written, and will change only when a 0 is followed by a 1 or when a 1 followed by a 0 is written. In this case a signal will be induced in the sense winding only when the information recorded changes from a 1 to a 0 or vice versa.

The second technique illustrated is sometimes referred to as a "modified non-return-to-zero" technique. In this system the polarity of the current through the WRITE winding is reversed each time a 1 is recorded and remains constant when a 0 is recorded. If a series of 1's is recorded, the polarity of the recorded flux will therefore change for each 1. If a series of 0's is recorded, no changes will occur. Notice that the polarity has no meaning in this system, only changes in polarity. Therefore a signal will be read back only when a 1 has been recorded. This system is often used for tape recording, so a 1 must be recorded somewhere in each cell along the tape width. That is, if 10 tracks are recorded along the tape, one of these must be a timing track which records a sequence of 1's each of which defines a different set of cells to be read, or the information must be coded so that a 1 occurs in each set of 10 cells which are read. Alphanumeric coded information[7] is often recorded on tape, and the code may be arranged so that a 1 occurs in each code group.

The third non-return-to-zero technique in Fig. 7 · 30 is sometimes called a *phase-modulated* system. In this case a 0 is recorded as a ½-bit-time negative pulse followed by ½-bit-time positive pulse, and

[7]Alphanumeric codes will be described in Chap. 8.

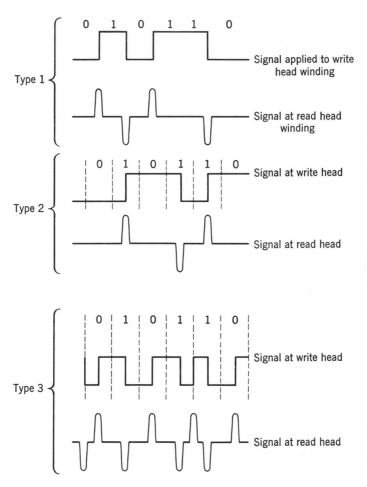

Fig. 7 · 30   Three types of non-return-to-zero recording.

a 1 is recorded as a ½-bit-time positive pulse followed by a ½-bit-time negative pulse. This technique is often used in high-speed systems.

The reading of information which has been recorded consists of two steps. First, the output from the READ head is amplified, and then the amplified signals are translated by logical circuitry. Figure 7 · 31 shows a translation technique for the first non-return-to-zero illustrated in Fig. 7 · 30. The output signals may be either from the output flip-flop or serial pulses. The sync pulses occur each time a cell passes under the READ heads in the system.

The flip-flop (Fig. 7 · 31) responds to positive pulses only. Positive signals at the recording head will therefore "set" the flip-flop to 1, and the inverter will cause the negative pulses to be made positive. These

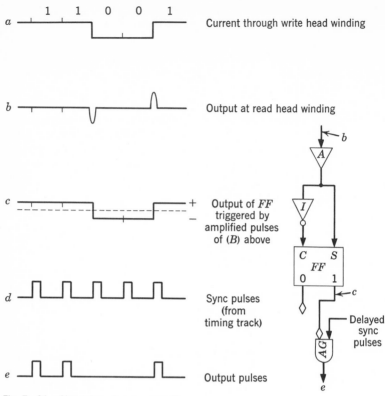

Fig. 7 · 31   Non-return-to-zero recording.

positive pulses will reset the flip-flop. The output of the flip-flop may be used by the computer by connecting an AND gate to the 1 output, delaying the sync pulses, and connecting them to the AND gate. Also, a serial representation of the number stored along the surface may be formed.

7 · 19   Magnetic-card random-access memories

In an attempt to manufacture memories with access times which are less than those obtainable by the use of magnetic tape and to still provide large quantities of storage, several types of ingenious devices for handling digital data recorded on a magnetic media have been devised.

One of these is called a *magnetic-card random-access memory*. For this type of memory the tracks for recording the digital data are placed on cards instead of along the surface of a plastic tape or on the surface of a magnetic disk or drum. The National Cash Register system uses 3.25 × 14 in., 0.005-in. thick oxide-coated mylar cards, and the RCA 3488 system, 16- × 4.5-in. mylar cards. In both systems, 256 of these cards are then packaged in a magazine which can be changed. By means of a system of binary-coded addresses which are notched into each card, a given card in the magazine may be accessed by the system for read-in and writing on the selected card. When a given card has been selected, it is dropped into a card-handling device which accelerates the card and moves it past a set of reading or writing heads. After the card has been read from or written onto, the card is returned to the stack of the remaining 255 cards until another demand for access to a card is given.

For the NCR system, the set of 256 cards contains 5,555,200 alphanumeric characters, and the average access time is said to be on the order of 200 msec. Data is recorded along 56 magnetic tracks on each card. These 56 tracks are broken down into 7 channels and a given alphanumeric character is recorded in parallel on 8 tracks simultaneously, 6 for the alphanumeric character, 1 for the clock, and 1 for parity. The recording is at a density of 250 per in. in the longitudinal direction, and the tracks are spaced 0.05 in. apart.

The cards are moved past the READ or WRITE heads by means of a revolving capstan, consisting of a rotating drum. The selection system for the cards is by means of a set of rods; since there are 256 cards in a given magazine, the cards are suspended by eight selection rods and two gating rods. If a given selection rod is rotated 72°, the tab is no longer in contact with the rod. When a given card is selected by a given position of the eight different rods, all the nonselected cards are supported by at least one of the rods. After the eight rods have been moved to the correct positions, the two gating rods running alongside the cards are rotated. This will cause the selected card to be released and dropped into the capstan area, where the card is then accelerated and moved by the READ and WRITE head.

Considerable use is made of vacuum and blower system, both in the handling of the selected card and in the spacing of the cards which are hanging suspended from the eight selection rods. The RCA 3488 cards have a maximum of 166,400 binary-coded, 7-bit characters on each card, 256 cards per magazine, and eight magazines per 3488 system. Two 3488 systems may be operated in parallel; RCA points out that the total amount of information which can be stored would provide about 25 characters for each person in the United States. The cards in this system are notched along their sides rather than at the end, and a card is selected and handled by electronically controlled bars and grippers. Reading and writing are again performed by moving the selected card by the READ-WRITE heads using a rotating drum.

Another example of a random-access storage device is the cartridge-loaded tape-loop machine, which uses continuous magnetic-tape loops as its storage medium. Here storage capacity on a given cartridge depends upon the type of cartridge and recording machine, and generally varies from 3 million to 40 million alphanumeric characters. A typical multiple-loop cartridge consists of a set of 38 in.-long continuous loops of standard computer magnetic tape. In a particular multiple-loop cartridge manufactured by the Potter Instrument Company, information is recorded on these types at a longitudinal density of 750 bits per in., with 48 tracks recorded across the 1-in. tape.

There are a number of other different variations on the two basic mechanisms which have been described, and other manufacturers and memories with advantages and disadvantages which are unique to the particular techniques used. Notice that all of the bulk or mass storage techniques which have been described are based upon writing on and reading from a moving magnetic surface, whether this moving magnetic surface be the surface of a drum, or a disk, or of a magnetic tape.

7 · 20   Read-only memories

Many digital systems use a type of storage device called a *read-only memory*. These memory devices have the unique characteristic that they can be read from, but that the computer cannot write information into them. The information stored in these memories is therefore introduced into the memory in some manner such that the information is semipermanent or permanent. Sometimes the information stored in a read-only memory is wired into the memory at the time of construction, and sometimes devices are used where the information can be manually changed.[8] In this section we shall study two types of read-only memories, bearing in mind that there are a number of different types now being constructed. The two types of memory we shall study, however, are characteristic of this particular class of memory devices, and most devices are variations on the principles which will be presented. The two types of read-only memories to be described are the *card-capacitor memory* and the *transformer read-only store*.

Card-capacitor memories can provide fast, economical storage for a microprogrammed control section of a digital computer (refer to Chap. 9) or for operational programs, test routines, tables of func-

---

[8]Some read-only memories can have their contents changed electrically, but slowly. It might be better to call these memories *nondestructive-read memories*.

tion values, and other information which is infrequently changed. The card-capacitor memory can be read from in fractions of a microsecond. One type of a capacitor memory is shown in Fig. 7·32. The memory basically consists of a set of word lines which are etched on one printed circuit board. Distributed along the word lines are the plates or small rectangles which contain one plate of a potential capacitor. The sense lines are orthogonal to the word lines, and small rectangles are also deposited connected to each sense line and located directly opposite the small rectangular conductor areas connected to the word line. Since each pair of the small rectangles which constitute the plates of the capacitors are separated only by the mylar dielectric, they will form a small capacitor.

Zeros are made by etching away part of a given plate connected to a word line. The result is that no capacitor will be formed at this particular junction. If a pulse is now applied to a selected word line, it will be coupled by the capacitor at the junction of that word line and a particular sense line, provided that the plate of the capacitor has not been etched away. If a pulse occurs on a given output line, the bit stored was a 1, if not, the bit stored was a 0. This corresponds to the presence or absence of the capacitor plate.

Another scheme has word lines and sense lines deposited on cards just as in Fig. 7·32, except that a metal card which is grounded is placed between the program cards. When a good conductor such as metal is placed between two would-be capacitor plates, there will be virtually no capacitive coupling between the plates, and in effect a capacitor will not exist. Therefore, if a metallicized card insulated on both sides by a layer of mylar (which insulates the metal from the printed circuit board) is sandwiched between the two boards on which word lines and sense lines have been deposited, a hole punched in the metal card at a given position where a word and sense line intersect will create a small capacitor (about 1 picofarad). If no hole is punched at a given position where a word and sense line intersect, no capacitor will be created at this point. Information is therefore introduced into this type of card-capacitor memory by punching holes in the metal card in a pattern according with the information to be stored.

This card-capacitor memory is operated in the following manner: When a pulse is introduced on a selected word line, the sense lines which intersect this word line will contain pulses wherever a hole has been punched in the card separating the word-line capacitor plates and the sense-line capacitor plates; however, those intersecting points where no hole has been punched in the metal card will not contain signals.

A schematic diagram showing four word lines and three sense

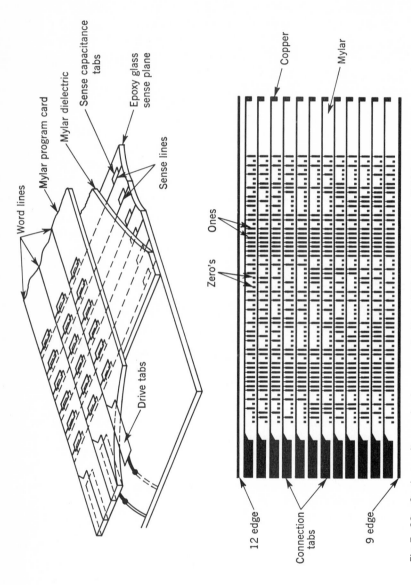

Fig. 7 · 32   Card-capacitor read-only memory for Model 30 in IBM 360 series. (IBM Corporation)

lines is shown in Fig. 7 · 33. For this particular memory, word 0 contains 110, word 1 contains 101, word 2 contains 101, and word 3 contains 001. Notice that if a pulse is applied to, for instance, word line 2, output signals will be capacitively coupled to the sense lines corresponding to the first and third bits of the output word. A selection matrix is used to select the correct word line just as is done in a thin-film memory, which is to say that the memory is a linear-selection memory and only one word line contains a pulse at a given time.

It should be noted that the signal at the output on a given sense line is divided by the ratio of the number 1's lying along the sense lines; that is, the combined capacitors lying along a given sense line form a capacitance to ground which is in series with the capacitor lying at the junction of the word line and sense line which is selected. For this reason, fast, large, voltage swings must be used on the word lines for memories of reasonable size. Nevertheless, this type of memory is in fairly wide use. The high speed at which a card-capacitor store may be operated and the ease with which the pattern of bits

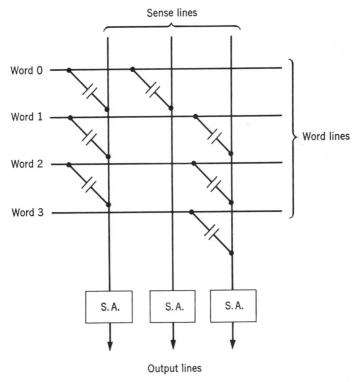

Fig. 7 · 33 Capacitor store schematic.

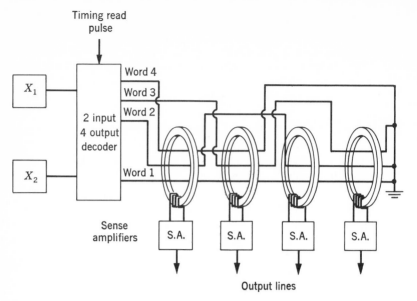

Fig. 7 · 34   Transformer read-only store.

stored in the memory may be changed makes the card capacitor store an attractive device for semipermanent or read-only memories.

A drawing of a simple transformer read-only store is shown in Fig. 7 · 34. In the drawing shown, only four words, each containing four binary digits, are presented. Each word corresponds to a word line just as in a previous memory, and one core is used for each output digit. A given word line either threads through or bypasses a core depending on whether the corresponding digit in that word is respectively a 1 or a 0. Therefore, for the drawing in Fig. 7 · 34, the information word number 1 is 1111, word number 2 contains 1011, word 3 contains 0101, and word 4 contains 1100.

In order to read a selected word from the memory, a pulse of current is passed through the corresponding word line which is selected, using a linear-selection technique as was explained previously. The current through the conductor which is selected causes an output current representing a 1 to appear at the sense winding of each core through which the word line is threaded. The cores through which the word line containing the current pulse does not pass will produce no output signal on their sense windings, thus signifying a 0. (There is a version of a type of memory called a "core rope," because the set of word lines and sense windings with cores attached give the appearance of a rope.) In effect, each core acts as a small transformer with a secondary for each bit containing a 1, and no secondary if a given bit is to store a 0. Enamel-insulated copper wires are used for the word and sense lines.

There are several versions of the transformer or rope read-only memory. The IBM 360 Model 40 uses flat tapelike conductors deposited upon printed circuit boards. A given conductor threads or does not thread a transformer which is inserted into the board, thus giving a configuration similar to that in Fig. 7 · 34. The principle of operation is fundamentally that explained, which is to say that currents are induced in given sense windings by whether or not a selected word line is threaded through a given core or transformer.

7 · 21 Tunnel-diode logic circuits

In the quest for higher speed, a semiconductor device known as a tunnel diode has been developed with the capability of switching from one to the other of its two states of operation in fractions of a nanosecond. While actual operating speeds of this magnitude are not presently attainable using these devices, the potential of the tunnel diode is very great, and tunnel diodes are presently used in several of the faster and larger digital machines, such as the IBM STRETCH computer and the Minneapolis-Honeywell 1800.

A tunnel diode is a two-terminal device similar in appearance to a conventional diode. A schematic diagram symbol for a tunnel diode is shown in Fig. 7 · 35, as is a graph of the operating characteristics of this device which plots current through the diode against voltage across the diode. If, for instance, we place a voltage of 0.4 volt across the input leads to the diode, a current of a little less than 0.25 ma will flow through the diode. Notice that as the voltage across the

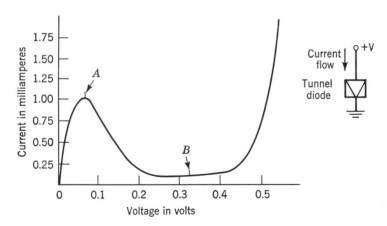

Fig. 7 · 35   Tunnel-diode symbol and voltage-current characteristic.

tunnel diode is increased starting at 0, the current through the tunnel diode first goes upward to a local maximum designated as point A, then drops downward into a valley with a minimum point marked B, and then starts upward again. In the region from point A to point B, the device demonstrates what is called "negative resistance," which is to say that when the voltage is increased, the current through the device is decreased. From the 0-volt point to point A, the tunnel diode shows the more conventional positive-resistance characteristic as it does from point B onward and to the right. It is this negative-resistance characteristic which makes the tunnel diode useful as a bistable device, and also enables the designer to obtain gain using a tunnel diode.

If we connect a voltage $+V$ and a resistor R to the tunnel diode, we then have the simple circuit shown in Fig. 7·36. Again, a graph of the operating characteristics of the tunnel diode is shown, and to this graph has been added what is called a "load line" for the resistance R and the positive potential V. When a device is operated in series with the resistance connected to a positive potential $+V$, its operating point must be somewhere on this load line. The load line intersects the abscissa at the point V, which in our case is 0.75 volt, and the ordinate at the point V/R, which is the current through the resistor if the resistor is grounded at its end, is 0.75 ma. The possible operating points for the tunnel-diode resistor combination are three, and these have been designated as A, B, and C on Fig. 7·36. It can be shown, however, that at point B, the circuit will be unstable because of the negative-resistance characteristic of the tunnel diode at that point, and that the circuit can only remain at point A or point C for any period of time. If we call the state of the circuit when the diode is operating at point A the 0 state, and operation at point C the 1 state,

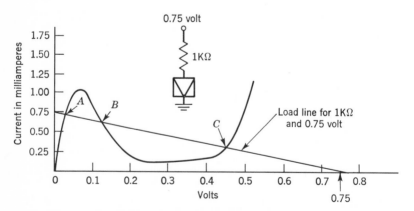

Fig. 7·36   Analysis of tunnel-diode resistor combination.

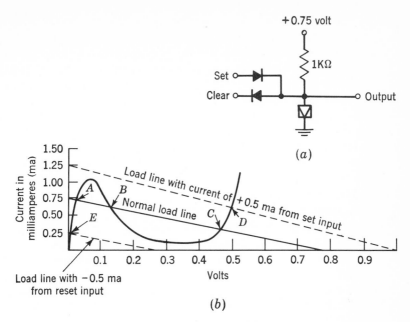

Fig. 7 · 37   Tunnel-diode circuit with SET and CLEAR inputs.

we have a bistable circuit consisting of only a single-tunnel diode and a resistor.

In Fig. 7 · 37*a*, two diodes have been added to the tunnel-diode resistor combination and the inputs to these diodes have been designated as CLEAR and SET. Let us consider the operation of the circuit when these inputs are used. Assume that the tunnel diode is at point *A*. If we inject an additional current of amplitude $+I = 0.5$ ma at the SET input, as shown in Fig. 7 · 37*b*, this has the effect of raising the load line to correspond to the dashed line which intersects point *D* on the graph. The circuit will then quickly switch to point *D* on the graph, and if the setting current of $+I = 0.5$ ma is then removed, the operating point of the circuit will move along the graph to point *C* and the circuit will be in the 1 state.

To reset the circuit to the 0 state, we apply a current of $I = -0.5$ ma at the CLEAR input. This will move the load line of the circuit down to the lower of the two dotted lines, and will move the operating point of the circuit back to point *E* on the graph. If this current is then removed, the operating point of the circuit will move upward to point *A* and the tunnel-diode resistor combination will be in its 0 state at point *A* on the graph.

If the tunnel diode is set to either the 0 or the 1 state as shown in this circuit, it will remain in this state until a CLEAR or SET pulse of current is injected, causing it to change states. For this reason a single tunnel diode can be used as a bistable storage device in the same manner as a flip-flop.

There are some disadvantages to the circuit in Fig. 7 · 37 however, and these should be pointed out. Notice that the input to the tunnel diode is connected to the output. Also notice that the difference in the 0-state voltage and 1-state voltage is quite small, less than ½ volt for the tunnel diode shown.

Because of their high speed, tunnel diodes are sometimes used to form logic gates as well as to store binary information. Sometimes tunnel diodes are used to accelerate the speed of more conventional transistor circuits, and the arithmetic units of several computers have used them in this manner as well as in storage registers. Because of the stand-by power required to keep each cell in operation and because of the noise generated in most of the readout schemes which have been invented for tunnel diodes, they have not been often used in large memories to date. However, tunnel diodes have been used as the storage elements in several smaller so-called scratch-pad memories for digital computers. A scheme used by IBM in their 7030 system is shown in Fig. 7 · 38, and we shall analyze this particular configuration keeping in mind that there are several other configurations using tunnel diodes.

Fig. 7 · 38 shows the basic configuration for a tunnel-diode memory consisting of four binary digits. This particular drawing has two word lines and therefore has two words, since this type of tunnel-diode memory is a linear-selection memory. The memory shown in Fig. 7 · 38 also has 2 bits per word. A word is selected by means of a word-line current on the correct word line. The waveform for the word-line current as well as for the output of the cell transformer connected to each cell, the current and bit line on the bit lines, and the bit-line readout voltages are also shown on Fig. 7 · 38. A bit line for this type of memory has a combined driver and sense amplifier so that current can be applied to the bit line. Also, voltages induced in the bit line may be sensed in an amplifier. The normal bias current through the bit line is such that each cell normally has two possible states, which are shown on the characteristic curves as corresponding to the voltages V_0 and V_1 (points A and B on the curve). When the word current is supplied on the selected word line, the cell-transformer output voltage is as shown in the waveforms in the figure. First, a negative-going voltage is applied across the diode. This drops the operating voltage across the diode as shown in the graph, forcing the cell down to the point C on the curve regardless of whether it was initially at point A or point B. However, it should be noted, if the cell was on point B, a large voltage change across the cell will be ob-

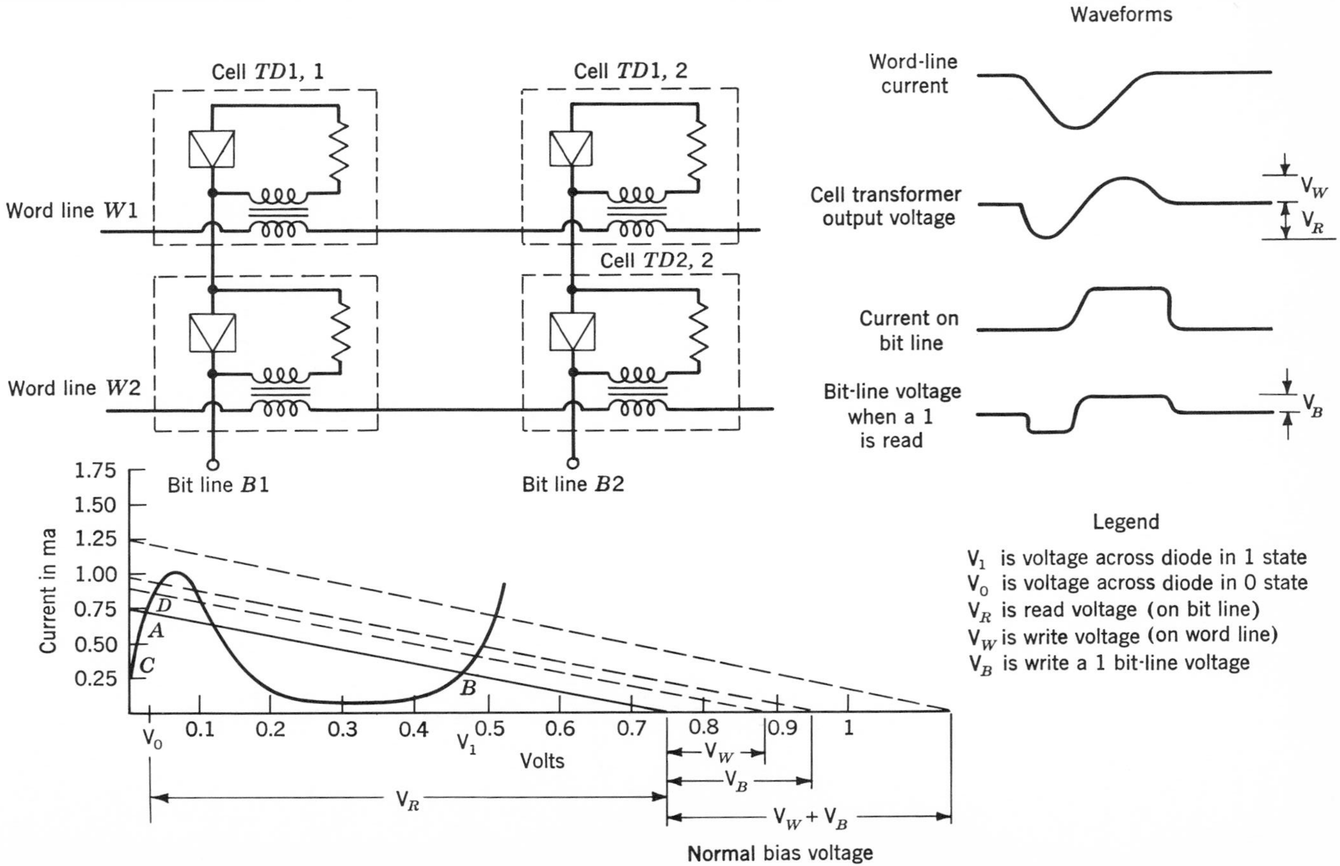

Fig. 7·38 Tunnel-diode memory.

served on the bit line and sensed in the sense amplifier indicating that the cell stored a 1, whereas the small voltage change when the operating point moves from point A to point C will be read as a 0-output voltage.

When the word-line current starts positive, a positive voltage will be induced on the transformer secondary connected to the selected word line, and this will be of amplitude V_W which will, since the cell is on the A state normally, move the operating point up to point D on the curve. If at this time the bit-line driver injects a current which induces a voltage V_B across the tunnel diode, this will increase the total bias on the cell to the point $V_W + V_B$ plus the normal-bias voltage, which will then switch the cell into a 1 state. If a given bit line does not contain the bias V_B or if a given word line contains $- V_B$, the cell will not be switched into the 1 state.

Notice that we read from the cell during the negative-going portion of the word-line current and write into the cell during the positive portion of the word-line current. A separate sense amplifier is connected to each bit line, so there would be two sense amplifiers and bit-line drivers connected to bit lines $B1$ and $B2$, respectively, for Fig. 7 · 38.

The transformers shown in Fig. 7 · 38 can be made on printed circuit boards using printed circuit techniques, and need not be actual core transformers although they often may be. Other than this, the memory required a tunnel diode and a resistor for each cell, plus a decoder matrix and word-line driver capable of driving the number of words in a memory. A separate sense amplifier and driver circuit are needed for each bit in the memory.

QUESTIONS

1 How many magnetic cores are required in a core-memory array for a computer with a word length of 35 binary bits and 4,096 different addresses in core memory? How many storage devices (flip-flops) will be required for the memory address register?

2 If we construct a 4,096 word–36 bit-per-word coincident-current magnetic-core memory, how many cores will be in the memory? How many sense amplifiers will be required? How many INHIBIT-line drivers? How many word-line drivers? How many X-selection drivers and how many Y-selection drivers? How many planes in the core memory and how many cores per plane?

3 The INHIBIT drivers are not used when a word is read from a core memory using a coincident-current selection system. True or false? Why?

4   If we use the coincident-current memory system described in Sec. 7·2 and if the current driver which drives the $-i_m/2$ current through the selection line X_2 in Fig. 7·4 is broken so that no current is ever driven through this line, we will never be able to read from or write satisfactorily into three cores, one of which is core X_2Y_1. What are the designations of the other two cores into which we will never be able to read or write correctly?

5   If the INHIBIT driver which is connected to the core plane storing the first binary digit of each computer word fails, what will be the value of the binary digit written into the selected core in this plane during each memory cycle?

6   Draw the waveforms for recording the binary sequence 101, showing the signal applied to the WRITE-head winding and the signal at the READ-head winding, for the type 1, type 2, and type 3 non-return-to-zero recording techniques.

7   Draw the schematic for a many-to-one decoder matrix with inputs from four flip-flops and 16 output lines. Use the same basic configuration as is illustrated in Fig. 7·8. How many diodes would be required for a decoder matrix of this type with 32 output lines and five input flip-flops?

8   For the RCA 3488 system of 256 magnetic cards which was described, how many binary digits are encoded on each card? How many binary digits may be stored in the entire system?

9   A magnetic drum has a circumference of 50 in. and a packing density of 90 bits per in. If the drum has 40 tracks, how many bits can be stored on the surface of the drum?

10   How many binary digits are recorded on each of the 38 in.-long continuous loops of computer magnetic tape described in Sec. 7·19, if no space is used between bits on the tape—that is, if binary digits are recorded continuously around the tape with no spacing beyond that of 750 bits per in. along the surface of the tape?

11   A magnetic drum has 128 tracks (exclusive of timing tracks) and 1,920 cells or binary bits recorded around each track. If the drum is used in a serial computer with a word length of 29 binary bits, and 1 "spacer bit" is left between words when recording, how many bits will be required to address a word on the drum? How many binary bits will be required to address a track? How many binary bits will be required to address a sector?

12   For the IBM 1311 disk memory described in Sec. 7·16, how many binary digits can be recorded on one surface of a given disk?

13   If a magnetic drum rotates at 25,000 rpm, what is the maximum access time required to read a word in a parallel system, assuming that there is no delay in decoding the address? What is the average random-access time?

14 Assuming that a disk in the IBM 1311 system rotates at a speed of 1,500 rpm as stated and that we read from eight tracks simultaneously, how many bits per second will be read from one of these disks?

15 A magnetic tape system has seven tracks for each ½ in. width of tape. The packing density per track is 250 bits per in., and the tape is moved at a speed of 75 in. per sec. If the tape width is 1 in., how many bits may be read per sec?

16 If we read from eight heads or write from eight heads simultaneously on the magnetic-disk memory described in Sec. 7·16 manufactured by the Data Products Corporation, how many bits per sec can we transfer in that system?

17 If we expand the transistor-diode matrix for selecting word lines shown in Fig. 7·19 so that we select one of a set of 256 film or core lines each time a binary number of eight binary digits is applied, how many transistors and how many diodes are required, not including the decoder matrices which select one of the 16 Y drivers and one of the 16 X drivers for the system?

18 Suppose that the all-transistor switch for a decoder shown in Fig. 7·20 is used. How many transistors are required to make a 4,096-output-line decoder matrix, not counting the decoder matrix which selects one from 64 lines in each of the y and x axes?

19 Duplicate the tunnel-diode curve in Fig. 7·37, then draw a load line for resistance of 1 kilohm and a +1 volt supply voltage. What are the stable operating points for this circuit?

20 If we have a +1 volt supply and a 1-kilohm resistor as in Question 19 and a 0.3-ma current is used to CLEAR and SET the tunnel diode, the circuit will SET but will not CLEAR. Show why, using the technique in Fig. 7·37.

21 Change the value of the resistor in Fig. 7·37 so that with a +1 volt supply and current of ±0.5 ma we can safely SET and CLEAR the tunnel diode.

22 If we make a 64-word memory of 8 bits, how many diodes are required for the decoder matrices for a coincident-current core memory and for a linear selection thin-film memory? Assume the diodes in the decoder are arranged as in Fig. 7·8. How many diodes and transistors are required for a 4,096-word thin-film linear selection memory, using a diode switch of the type in Fig. 7·19 and the decoder scheme in Fig. 7·8?

23 For the coincident-current memory, the word-line drivers are turned on twice, and for the thin-film memory the word-line drivers are only turned on once. Discuss the reason for this. Do thin-film word-line drivers need to drive current in two directions? Do the bit-line drivers? For coincident-current core memories, which drivers

need drive current in only one and which need to drive current in both directions?

24 Draw the waveforms for the signals at the WRITE head and at the READ head for the non-return-to-zero recording systems for the sequence of binary digits 001.

8

Input-output
devices

The input-output devices provide the means of communication between the computer and the outer world. In order to solve problems or process data, the data and instructions must be inserted into the machine, and the machine must deliver the results of its calculations. It has been difficult to produce input and output devices that can keep up with the machine speeds, and there is a constant demand for faster and faster printers, card readers, etc.

The general sequence of events in the processing of information for business or the solving of scientific problems is as follows: first a program is written which describes the sequence of calculations which the machine is to perform; the data, such as the cost of a ton of steel in China or the distance of Mars from Venus at some particular time, is then collected and also readied for insertion into the machine. The machine then reads the program plus the data and stores this information. Having stored the necessary program and data, the machine is started at the first instruction in the program. After completing the series of calculations which it must perform, the machine prints out the results. The program contains orders which direct the machine to print the final results for the user of the machine. Partial results are sometimes also printed, often for purposes of program checking.

It is first necessary to insert the program and the data into the machine via the input devices. The input devices to an ordinary calculator consist of the keys of the calculator. Numerical data is introduced into the machine via these push buttons; when some sort of operate button is pushed, the machine performs the necessary operation, and then the next piece of data must be introduced via the push buttons.

If all data were inserted by means of push buttons or switches, the digital machine would be subject to the same basic limitations as the desk calculator: one or even a group of human beings would be in the system and would be slowing things up. It is therefore desirable to have some fast means for recording both instructions and data in a manner which may be read by the machine and then performed at machine speeds. A medium proposed by Babbage and still used today is the punched card. A rectangular card is perforated by a number of holes, and the position of each hole determines its meaning. The input program and data are punched into the cards. The cards are then placed in a card reader connected to the machine, and the command to read is given to the machine. The card reader senses the holes in the cards and transmits this information to the computer, which then stores it. In this manner, the program is read into the machine.

When the program has been read into the machine and the necessary operations have been completed, it is necessary for the machine to print out the data so that it may be used. There is a great variety of output devices now available. Business applications generally require that the results be printed in tabular form, or perhaps on a series of checks as in a payroll accounting operation. Scientific results are more likely to consist of numerical data which must be clearly printed with little chance for error (and such accuracy is also of prime importance in computers used to calculate payroll checks). For each of these applications, one type of output device may be more desirable than another. However, the great majority of applications require that the outputs from the machine be printed on a piece of paper. The principal output devices are therefore printers, ranging from electromechanical typewriters which print one letter or digit at a time, to high speed printers capable of printing hundreds of characters at a time. Several of these, as well as some more unusual output devices, will be described.

8 · 1   Differences in business and scientific uses

There are distinct differences in the ratio of data to program length in business and scientific problems. The business problems generally have shorter programs which process large amounts of data. For instance, programs which calculate payrolls or programs which maintain an inventory control are liable to be relatively short in length by comparison to the volume of data they must process. On the other hand, scientific problems are more liable to have long, complicated programs containing many calculations but using relatively little input data.

Computers used for business problems must not only be able to handle large amounts of input data but they must also deliver much information, generally in the form of printouts, to the user. A machine which calculates the payroll for a large company must print thousands of checks. The same principle applies to machines doing calculations for banks or other large businesses where volumes of business statements must be printed. For this reason, there is a premium on speed in the input-output devices for business machines.

8 · 2 Perforated tape

Perforated (punched) tape is one of the most popular mediums for storing the programs and data to be read into a digital machine. When the first large computers were designed, telegraph systems had been using perforated paper tapes for some time, and as a result, devices for punching and reading paper tapes had already been fairly well developed. The tape used is of many types and sizes. A medium-thickness paper tape has been used a great deal, and oiled tapes and plastic tapes are also used. The widths of the tapes used have varied from ½ to 3 in. In general, information is punched into the tape a line at a time. Figure 8 · 1 illustrates a section of a perforated tape. Multiple channels are used (just as on magnetic tape, a channel runs lengthwise along the tape), and a fixed amount of information is punched as a pattern of bits in each lateral line.

The preparation of these paper input tapes is sometimes referred to as *keyboarding*. In this step the operator of a tape-punching machine is presented with a copy of a program or input data. The operator then punches, by means of the tape-punching machine (tape punch), a number of holes into the tape. The holes represent, in coded form, the input information to the machine. The tape-punching device used may be one of a number of types; however, the more popular devices resemble a typewriter, and the keyboards of these tape punches contain conventional symbols, similar to those on an ordinary typewriter. The keyboards of many tape-punch machines are identical to the keyboards of manual typewriters used in businesses, and sometimes electric typewriters are converted to tape-punching machines by attaching a punching device which is actuated by the typewriter mechanism.

When a key on the tape-punch keyboard is depressed, the binary-coded symbol for the character selected is punched into the tape and the tape then advances to the next line. In most cases, the tape-punch device also prints on a separate piece of paper, in the same manner as a typewriter, the character which was punched, as well as printing the characters along the rows of the tape. There is then a typewritten copy of the program which may be checked for errors in addition to

Channels

1 2 3 4 5 6 7

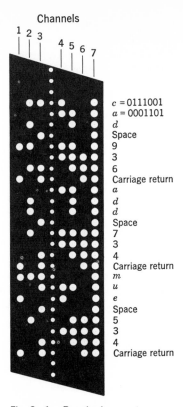

c = 0111001
a = 0001101
d
Space
9
3
6
Carriage return
a
d
d
Space
7
3
4
Carriage return
m
u
e
Space
5
3
4
Carriage return

Fig. 8 · 1   Punched paper tape.

the paper tape punched with the coded symbols. This printed copy of the program is referred to as the "hard copy." Many of the tape-punch machines are able to read a perforated tape and type printed copy from this tape. A punched section of tape may be placed in the tape reader attached to the tape-punch machine, and a typed copy of the information which was punched in the tape may be made.

8 · 3   Alphanumeric codes

The numbers and instructions which the programmer writes generally consist of decimal digits for the numbers and letter codes for the instructions. When the program is keyboarded, the operator of the tape punch types the program just as it might be typed on paper. If the programmer writes ADD 1245, the keyboard operator will type just these characters. Since computers operate using either binary or binary-coded-number systems, the input information must be in a binary code but must include not only numerical but also alphabetic characters. The number of binary bits in a code group will generally be larger than for binary-coded-decimal systems, since there are 26 letters plus 10 decimal digits. (The least number of bits with which it is possible to code 36 different symbols is 6[1].) A code which contains both letters and numbers is referred to as an *alphanumeric* code. Most alphanumeric codes contain additional symbols such as capital letters and punctuation marks. Code groups which designate such operations as spacing, carriage return, etc., are also useful.

Many alphanumeric codes have been used. For example, Table 8 · 1 lists the Flexowriter FL code which has been used by several digital machines. The typing mechanism resembles a typewriter, can type capital letters, periods, and commas, and has all of the other common facilities of a typewriter. If the upper-case or shift key is depressed, all characters following this will appear as in the upper-case column until the lower-case key is depressed.

There are seven hole positions in each line of the tape (refer to Fig. 8 · 1); however, only six of these are used in the actual code. The seventh hole is used to indicate whether or not the information in each line is to be used. If the seventh hole is punched, the tape reader will read that particular line of the tape and transmit the information in the line to the computer. This is useful, as it is convenient occasionally to leave gaps between parts of the information typed, and by simply leaving the seventh hole blank, the tape reader will continue to move the tape until it encounters a punched hole in the seventh position.

A punched hole in the tape is commonly used to represent a 1, and the absence of a hole, a 0. The small feed holes are used to keep the tape aligned as it passes through the reader, to tell the reader when to read a line, and also as a means of moving the tape in some tape readers.

Suppose the order code which causes the computer to clear and add is *cad;* in this case the card-punch operator will punch the letter *c*, and then *a*, and then *d*. The first line of the tape will then contain 011100, and the second, 000110 (refer to Fig. 8 · 1). This will be followed by the address in storage to be added into the accumulator. Generally, the address to be used will be written by the programmer in decimal, not binary, form. Notice that the numbers are not coded in a reasonable form for use by even a binary-coded-decimal ma-

---

[1]By using a code group which changes the meaning of the characters which follow it, the number of characters which may be used is increased. For instance, when the shift key on a typewriter is depressed, all the following characters will be capitalized, or a 9, for example, may be changed to a bracket. Notice that there are more than 2^6 characters in Table 8 · 1.

TABLE 8·1 THE FLEXOWRITER FL ALPHANUMERIC CODE

LOWER CASE	UPPER CASE	CHARACTER 123456	DECIMAL VALUE	LOWER CASE	UPPER CASE	CHARACTER 123456	DECIMAL VALUE
a	A	000110	6	0	0	111110	62
b	B	110010	50	1	1	010101	21
c	C	011100	28	2	2	001111	15
d	D	010010	18	3	3	000111	7
e	E	000010	2	4	4	001011	11
f	F	011010	26	5	5	010011	19
g	G	110100	52	6	6	011011	27
h	H	101000	40	7	7	010111	23
i	I	001100	12	8	8	000011	3
j	J	010110	22	9	9	110110	54
k	K	011110	30			000101	5
l	.L	100100	36	space bar		001000	8
m	M	111000	56	=	.	001001	9
n	N	011000	24	+	/	001101	13
o	O	110000	48	color change		010000	16
p	P	101100	44	.	)	010001	17
q	Q	101110	46	,	(	011001	25
r	R	010100	20	-	–	011101	29
s	S	001010	10	back space		100011	35
t	T	100000	32	tabulation		100101	37
u	U	001110	14	carr. return		101001	41
v	V	111100	60	stop		110001	49
w	W	100110	38	upper case		111001	57
x	X	111010	58	lower case		111101	61
y	Y	101010	42	nullify		111111	63
z	Z	100010	34				

chine. The code for 2 is 001111 and the code for 3 is 000111. Conversion from an alphanumeric code to the computer code will be discussed in Sec. 8·5.

Some computers, especially those which perform business operations, are constructed to handle nonnumeric characters. For instance, items may be assigned letter designations, and it is convenient if the computer can handle these letters as code groups. In describing the operation of the arithmetic element and the various binary-coded-decimal systems, no mention was made of how nonnumeric data was handled. Because computers operate using essentially binary representation, some sort of binary coding must be used, and there are now several different systems. Machines such as the IBM 1401 and the Minneapolis-Honeywell 200 series have six-binary-digit characters for each place in the computer word.[2] Four of the digits are used to represent a decimal digit in a normal binary-coded-decimal system such as the 8, 4, 2, 1 code. When the computer adds or multiplies or performs other arithmetic operations, only four of the binary digits are used and the other two digits are ignored. When alphabetic or other nonnumeric characters are to be manipulated, then all six binary digits are used.

There has been an attempt to standardize on an alphanumeric code which will be agreeable to both manufacturers and users, and the American Standards Association has published an American Standard Code for Information Interchange (abbreviated the ASCII code). This code is now widely used in the newer machines, and a number of the major manufacturers are now using the code in order that their equipment may be compatible with that of other manufacturers. This code is shown in Table 8 · 2. Notice that the decimal digits are represented by the normal 8, 4, 2, 1 code preceded by the three binary digits 011, so that decimal 1 becomes 0110001, decimal 2 is 0110010, decimal 7 is 0110111, etc. To expand on the code, the letter A is 1000001, B is 1000010, etc. There are various codes such as "end of message," "who are you," "skip," "carriage return," etc., which are very useful in communications systems and in editing data processed in computers.

A section of tape showing this code expanded to 8 bits per character and punched on eight-hole tape is shown in Fig. 8 · 2.

It should be noted that the interpretation of the characters is purely arbitrary, the "meaning" being only the meaning assigned by the programmer. The computer operates using signals which are essentially binary in character, and the programmer must arrange the computer operations so that the binary-coded characters are correctly handled.

8 · 4 Tape readers

The function of the paper-tape reader is to sense the coded information punched in the tape and deliver this information to the computer. Most of the tape readers used in teletype and office equipment are electromechanical devices. In many of these devices mechanical "sensing pins" are used to determine the symbol punched into each line of the tape. There will, in a system of this type, be a sensing pin

[2]These computers also have end-of-word (the 1401), or end-of-word and end-of-item (the 200) bits or as a further example, the IBM 1620 has 4 bits per address for binary-coded decimals plus an end-of-word bit. This machine requires two 4-bit characters for a single alphanumeric character. All of these machines carry parity bits, which will be explained later.

TABLE 8·2 THE AMERICAN STANDARD CODE FOR INFORMATION EXCHANGE

	000	001	010	011	100	101	110	111
0000	NULL	DC_0 ①	ƀ	0	@	P		
0001	SOM	DC_1	!	1	A	Q		
0010	EOA	DC_2	''	2	B	R		
0011	EOM	DC_3	#	3	C	S		
0100	EOT	DC_4 (Stop)	$	4	D	T		
0101	WRU	ERR	%	5	E	U		
0110	RU	SYNC	&	6	F	V		
0111	BELL	LEM	'	7	G	W	Unassigned	
1000	FE_0	S_0	(	8	H	X		
1001	HT / SK	S_1	)	9	I	Y		
1010	LF	S_2	✳	:	J	Z		
1011	V_{TAB}	S_3	+	;	K	[		
1100	FF	S_4	(Comma) ,	<	L	＼		ACK
1101	CR	S_5	—	=	M	]		②
1110	SO	S_6	★	>	N	↑		ESC
1111	SI	S_7	/	?	O	←		DEL

Example: | 100 | 0001 | = A

b_7----------------b_1

The abbreviations used in the figure mean:			
NULL	Null Idle	CR	Carrige return
SOM	Start of message	SO	Shift out
EOA	End of address	SI	Shift in
EOM	End of message	DC_0	Device control ① Reserved for data Link escape
EOT	End of transmission	DC_1-DC_3	Device control
WRU	"Who are you ?"	ERR	Error
RU	"Are you . . . ?"	SYNC	Synchronous idle
BELL	Audible signal	LEM	Logical end of media
FE	Format effector	SO_0-SO_7	Separator (information)
HT	Horizontal tabulation		Word separator (blank, normally non-printing)
SK	Skip (punched card)	ACK	Acknowledge
LF	Line feed	②	Unassigned control
V/TAB	Vertical tabulation	ESC	Escape
FF	Form feed	DEL	Delete Idle

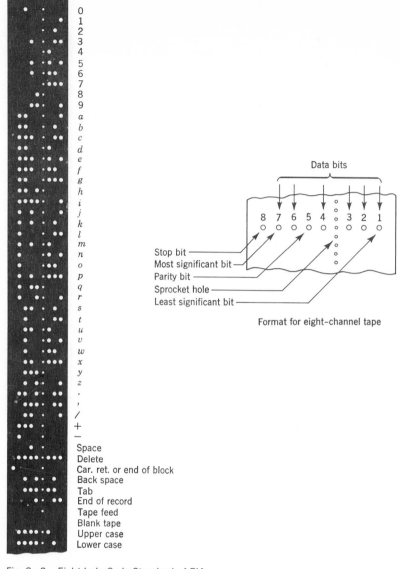

Data bits

```
        8  7  6  5  4  °  3  2  1
                         °
        O  O  O  O  O  °  O  O  O
                         °
                         °
                         °
Stop bit ──────────────┐ °
Most significant bit ──┐│ °
Parity bit ───────────┐││ °
Sprocket hole ──────┐ │││
Least significant bit ┘│││
```

Format for eight-channel tape

Fig. 8 · 2   Eight-hole Code Standard of EIA.

for each information channel, plus a means of moving the tape and positioning it for reading. The tape is not moved continuously but only a single line at a time, stopped while the coding is sensed, and then moved to the next line. The motion of the sensing pins operates a switch, the contacts of which are opened or closed depending on whether or not there is a hole in the tape. Another type of reader uses a "star wheel" to sense the absence or presence of holes in the tape as shown in Fig. 8 · 3. A complete reader mechanism is shown in Fig. 8 · 4, indicating the relative complexity of these devices.

When the input is to a digital machine, the motion of the tape through the reader will generally be controlled by the computer. Each time the tape is to be advanced and a new character read, the computer will supply the reader with a pulse which will cause it to advance the tape to the next character. In order to read characters as fast as possible, a line will generally be read at the same time as the advancing pulse is transmitted. Since there will be a delay due to inertia before the tape is actually moved, the reading of the state of the sensing relays will occur during this delay period. In this case, when a STOP character is sensed, the reader will proceed to the next character before actually stopping.

In order to speed up the reading process, a large number of digital computers use photoelectric cells or photodiodes to read the characters punched into the tape. In this case, a light-sensitive cell is placed under each channel of the tape, including the "tape feed hole" or "sprocket channel." A light source is placed above the tape, so that the light-sensitive element beneath the hole in the tape will be energized and will produce a signal indicating the presence of the hole. The signals from the light-sensitive elements are then amplified and supplied to the computer as input information.

The tape feed hole will be used in this case to determine when the outputs of the light-sensitive elements are to be sensed. The tape in a

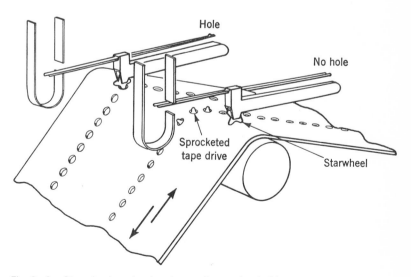

Fig. 8 · 3   Star-wheel mechanism for reading perforated tape.

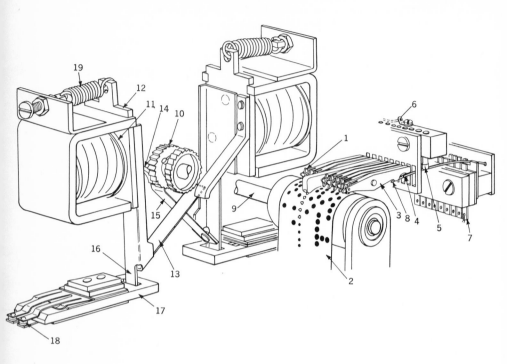

Tape reading and stepping mechanization of Ohr-Tronics Model 119 tape reader.
When star wheel (1) senses hole in paper tape (2), arm (3) is rocked counterclockwise
under the urging of contact wires (4) which limit on lower surface of contact screw (5).
Electrical circuit is thus completed from common lug (6) to lug (7). Longer wire (8)
urges arm (3) against mechanical limit (not shown) to reduce bounce. Drive shaft (9)
extends to rear through panel (not shown) and carries bidirectional ratchet (10).
Energization of coil (11) attracts armature (12) and engages pawl blade (13) under next
tooth. Pawl depressor (14) disengages opposing pawl blade (15). Tip (16) of armature
moves card (17) to open interrupter switch contacts (18). Upon deenergization of coil
(11), pawl blade (13) steps shaft (9) under urging of spring (19). Interrupter switch
recloses near end of armature return. Pulsing of other coil (20) steps tape in reverse
direction.

Fig. 8 · 4   Mechanism of an electromechanical tape reader.

reader of this type is generally friction-driven and moved continuously until a STOP character is sensed. Extremely fast starting and braking of the tape are very desirable features, and most readers are capable of stopping the tape on any given character.

The operation speeds attainable with various tape readers are generally expressed as the number of characters per sec which can be read. Mechanical sensing readers have been designed to operate at speeds as high as 200 characters per sec although speeds of from 10 to 60 characters per sec are more common. Present-day photoelectric readers operate at speeds of up to 1,000 characters per sec.

8 · 5　Alphanumeric and binary-coded tapes

We have seen that the tape reader is capable of sensing information punched into the paper tape and supplying this information to the computer. The data will be in alphanumeric coded form, however, and may not be readily usable by the machine. The machine must therefore interpret the information from the reader, and this may be done in a number of ways. Generally one of the first steps in putting a new machine into operation consists of writing a set of programs, one of which is used to convert the binary-coded characters from the paper tape reader into computer binary-coded or binary-coded-decimal words. The manner in which these programs are prepared falls outside the context of this book; however, as noted in Chap. 2, the machine itself, by means of previously prepared programs, is able to perform the conversion. This permits the programmer to use decimal numbers while preparing the program and alphabetic characters for the instructions. The programmer can write ADD, the operator of the tape-punching machine can punch ADD as three characters on the tape, and the machine will then translate this into the correct set of binary digits. Likewise, the number 0.4059 may be written in decimal form, and the machine itself will convert this to the correct binary number. The converted program may be stored and then run, or a binary-coded tape may be punched by the conversion programs.

A converted tape will be coded in machine language and may be read directly in and operated. In this case, there will be two punched tapes for each program, one the alphanumeric coded tape, and the other the binary tape with the same program converted to machine language. If the program is stored on magnetic tape, it may be called for by means of its address, read into the machine, and then operated.

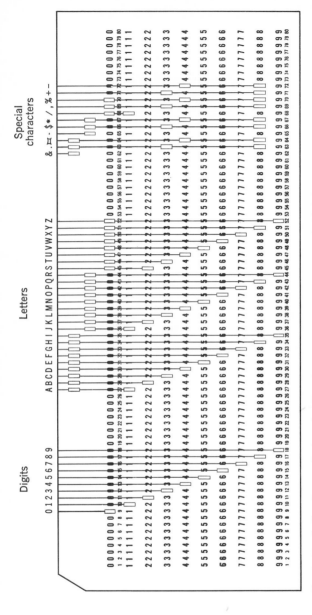

Fig. 8·5 Coding for punched cards. (This figure was used on page 41 of "Digital Computing Systems" by Samuel B. Williams, McGraw-Hill Book Company, and on page 25 of "High-speed Data Processing," McGraw-Hill Book Company.)

8 · 6   Punched cards

Probably the most widely used input medium is the punched card. While there are a number of sizes of punched cards, the most used card at present is a 12-row, 80-column card which is 3¼ in. wide and 7¾ in. long (Fig. 8 · 5). The thickness of the cards used varies, although at one time most of the cards were 0.0067 in. thick. There is now a tendency to make the card somewhat thinner.

Just as with tape, there are numerous ways in which punched cards may be coded. A popular code is the "Hollerith" code, which is an alphanumeric code in which a single character is punched in a column of the card. The basic code is illustrated in Fig. 8 · 5. As an example, the symbol A is coded by means of a punch in the top and "one" rows of the card and the symbol 8 by a punch in the "eight" row of the card. There are other types of cards with different hole positions on the cards, just as there are many ways of preparing the cards to be read into the computer. The most common technique is very similar to that for preparing punched tape, in that a card-punch machine with a keyboard similar to that of a typewriter is used. The card punch generally also makes a hard copy of the program as it is punched into the cards. Quite often the card punch also prints the characters punched into a card on the face of the card itself. In this way, a card may be identified without examining the punches. Each character is generally printed at the top of the card directly above the column in which the character is punched.

The card-punch machine contains a hopper in which the blank cards are stacked. The operator of the card punch then causes a card to enter the punching area and the program's list of instructions or numerical data is then punched into the card. The card punch punches the card laterally, a column at a time, starting at the left. If a key of the card punch is depressed, the code for the character is punched into a column of the card, and the card is then moved so that the next column on the right is under the punch.

Generally, when a program is punched into cards, only one instruction and its associated address or addresses are punched into each card. Then, if an error is made in programming, the erroneous instruction may be changed by throwing the incorrect card away and replacing it with a correct card.

8 · 7   Card readers

Most card readers are electromechanical devices which read the information punched into a card, converting the presence or absence of a hole into an electric signal representing a binary 0 or 1. The punched cards are placed into a hopper, and when the command to read is given, a lever pushes a card from the bottom of the stack. Generally the card is then moved lengthwise over a row of 80 "READ brushes." These brushes read the information punched along the bottom row of the card. If a hole is punched in a particular row, a brush makes electrical contact through the hole in the card, providing a signal which may be used by the computer. The next row up is then read, and this process continues until all rows have been read, after which the next card is moved into position on the brushes.

Just as is the case with punched tape, there are two types of cards which may be used to read in data: alphanumeric cards which contain the instructions and numbers punched in coded form, possibly the Hollerith code which was shown, and binary cards which contain the program instructions and numbers after they have been converted by the machine to binary form and punched into the cards in the format of the machine. Since the Hollerith and other codes are very uneconomical in their use of cards, a binary deck of cards in machine language will be much smaller than a deck of cards containing the same information in the original form.

8 · 8   Buffering

The most obvious difference between the input equipment which has been discussed and the internal operation of the computer memory and arithmetic elements is that the input equipment is inherently much slower. It is often impractical to synchronize the input devices completely with the high-speed electronic circuitry. For this reason, the input equipment may not read directly into the machine, but rather may communicate with some sort of buffering device. The buffering devices must be capable of operating at the speed of the input devices and also at the speed of the electronic circuitry.

The first and most obvious characteristic which the buffering device must possess is the ability to store the information received from the input device. The second property the buffer must have is the ability to transfer the information stored into the machine at a rate considerably faster than that of the input device reading the punched card or perforated tape.

Buffering devices vary considerably in complexity. The simplest buffer consists of several registers, generally denoted as *in-out registers*, each of which can accept information from one of the input devices (or transfer information to an output device), and from which information can be transferred to the machine's high-speed storage. These registers may be flip-flop registers, or perhaps circulating registers which store information in serial form. The information from the tape or card readers is then stored in buffer registers until it is transferred into high-speed memory, following which the register is cleared and the next set of characters on the tape or cards is read.

In some cases the buffering device may be larger and consist of a small core memory which can be filled by the tape or card reader and then read into the machine. This will speed up the input process considerably as the machine may be running another program while the next program is being read into the buffer's high-speed memory. Since the information stored in the large buffering device may be read at the machine rate, the transfer of information from the buffer may be made faster than with direct-reading techniques.

8 · 9   On-line and off-line operation

One form of such buffering consists of first recording the program to be read in on magnetic tape and then reading from the tape into the machine. A number of devices are available which will read punched tape or cards and transfer the information punched into them onto magnetic tape. This process takes place outside the central computer. Since the magnetic tape may be read much faster then punched cards or paper tape, the time required to read in information will be reduced.

In general, there are two distinct ways in which input-output equipment may be operated, "on line" and "off line." "On-line operation" refers to the reading of paper tape or cards directly into the machine, through, for instance, in-out registers which are a part of the machine's internal circuitry, or into some sort of buffering device directly connected to the machine's internal memory. "Off-line operation" consists of transferring onto magnetic tape (or into some other high-speed reading medium) the coded data which has been punched into punched paper cards or tape. The data may then be read by the computer at a higher speed than would be possible with either the paper cards or tape. Some machines have been designed in such a way that during the operation of "keyboarding" the coded alphanumeric characters may be recorded directly on magnetic tape, eliminating the intermediate punched-card or punched-tape step. The difficulty here lies in checking the magnetic tape, which cannot be inspected visually, and in making changes in the program.

8 · 10   Character recognition

A great deal of research is still going into the development of devices which will read printed characters directly from paper into a machine. There are two general techniques; in the first, the characters are specially formed and some material having magnetic characteristics is generally used instead of ordinary ink. In this case, the letters used are of a standard size, and they are so designed that the reading device is able to differentiate between characters according to certain distinct differences in the shapes. In this way, printed material may be read directly by the computer.

Banks were among the first businesses to use character-recognition systems of this sort. The checks used by these banks are printed with the amount of the transactions and with certain code numbers designating the type of transaction. The computer can then read the checks directly, eliminating the intermediate step of punching the amounts and types of transactions into cards or tape.

The second type of direct reading involves reading directly from a printed page. In this case, any size or shape of type may be used, and the computer is required to read the printed characters. Many schemes have been invented to transfer the shape of written characters from a printed page into a computer memory, and many additional schemes have been tried to interpret the information stored. The essential difficulty is in determining the characteristics of printed symbols which enable us to tell one from the other. Certain differences in these symbols are obvious—an *o* is not likely to be confused with a *t*—but it is less simple to tell the difference between an *a* and an *o*. If these characters are set in different sizes and styles of type, the listing of specific rules which will enable a machine to differentiate between characters becomes very difficult. Because it would be so convenient to have machines with the ability to read printed matter in this way, a great deal of research is now being done in this area, and devices which can read printed material are now being marketed.

8 · 11　Output equipment

Although many types of output equipment are now in use in the computer industry, the most popular form of output from a computer is undoubtedly the printed word. Other types of display devices in common use include neon lights and oscilloscopes, and some computers are even equipped with loudspeakers. (Programs which will play music through the loudspeakers have been written, and attempts have been made to compose using a computer.)

Neon lights are generally used to indicate the states of the storage devices of the principle registers of the machine (the accumulator, perhaps the in-out registers, etc.). These lights are sometimes used as output devices for simple programs where the answers may then be read visually; however, such lights are generally used as trouble-shooting aids, often to trouble-shoot the operation of the machine. The lights are also used to trouble-shoot programs. If, for instance, a program calls for the addition of two numbers which cause the accumulator to overflow, the machine will be stopped and the location[3] of the faulty instruction sequence in the program may be read from the lights on the console of the machine.

· 12 Printers

The fact remains that the most convenient and useful method by which the computer can deliver information is by means of printed characters. For the sake of convenience, the printer should have the ability to print alphabetical characters, decimal digits, and also common punctuation marks. It would be possible to print all the information processed by the computer in pure binary form or some form of coded binary, but not many banks would appreciate receiving a check for $1010.011, and most scientists and engineers, despite their admitted abilities in this direction, would prefer to have a printout which reads 130 rather than 10000010.

It is obvious that the printer must therefore operate from binary-coded characters rather than directly from binary. The process here is the inverse of the encoding procedure in which a key corresponding to an alphanumeric character is depressed, causing a coded binary character to be punched into a tape or card. In this case, coded groups of binary bits are delivered to the printer, which decodes them and then prints the correct characters. The basic binary code groups may contain 5 through 8 bits, generally depending on the coding for alphanumeric characters which the printer provides.

The information delivered to the printer operated on line will be in the form of electronic signals directly from the machine. If the printer is operated off line, the reading and decoding of data stored on punched tape, punched cards, or magnetic tape may be a part of the printing operation. Since the electronic circuitry of the computer is able to operate at speeds much higher than those of mechanical printing devices, it is desirable that a printer operated on line be capable of printing at a very high speed. Even if the printer is operated off line, speed is highly desirable, since the volume of material to be printed may be quite large.

Most of the original printers were converted electric typewriters, and this type of printer is still popular. If the code used contains 8 bits per character and the printer is operated on line, the computer will deliver 8 bits to the printer, which will decode them and energize a solenoid which will actuate the correct key of the typewriter. The

[3]The program counter contains the address of the instruction being performed. Details of this section of the control element will be presented in the next chapter.

codes used generally include coded characters such as those in Sec. 8 · 3, including codes for spacing between words, carriage return, and other operations necessary to typing. The speed of such typewriter type printers is relatively low, perhaps from 10 to 30 characters per sec.

Other types of character-at-a-time printers utilize slightly different principles. One type has a number of "pallets," each of which has a raised character on the surface nearest the roller or contact drum, mounted in a movable type basket. The type basket is positioned electromechanically by a decoder, and the back of the pallet is then struck by a hammer which forces the pallet against the page. An inked ribbon is positioned between the pallet and the page (like a typewriter ribbon); the character on the pallet is thereby printed on the page, the roller is then moved to the left, and another character is printed. Sometimes the pallets are contained in a rectangular "type box" which is also positioned by the action of the decoding mechanism, and the correct pallet is then struck by a hammer. Both the typewriter mechanisms and type-bar and type-box mechanisms are capable of printing up to perhaps 40 characters per sec.

If a number of type bars are located in a row along the drum, and positioning mechanisms and hammers are provided for each bar, a *line-at-a-time printer* may be constructed. In this case, it is generally desirable for the printer to be provided with some sort of accumulator which can store all the bits which will determine the characters in a complete line. If each character contains 6 bits, and 50 characters are printed across the page, storage for 300 binary bits will be necessary. Each 6-bit coded character must be decoded and the respective type bar positioned before the hammers can cause a line to be printed. This type of printer can print up to four lines per sec, a speed much higher than that of the character-at-a-time printer.

Even faster printers are constructed in which the raised characters are distributed around a "print wheel" which revolves constantly. In this case, the print wheel does not contain moving parts like the pallets just described, but consists of a motor-driven drum with a number of bands equal to the number of characters printed per line. A set of all the characters which are used is distributed around each band. The print wheel is revolved continuously. When the selected character is in position, the print hammer strikes the ribbon against the paper and thus against the raised character on the print wheel which is located behind the paper. A printer of this type requires a decoder and a memory for each character position along the line, and also a character-timing encoder for each position, which determines when the selected character is in position. Printers of this type can print up to 1250 lines per min. with 160 characters per line.

Two types of these printers are shown in Figs. 8·6 and 8·7. Figure 8·6 shows the IBM 1403 printer in which the paper is moved vertically in front of a *chain* of raised characters of type. This chain is continually moving in the horizontal direction so that each of the 48 different characters continually pass by each of the 100 printers' positions in each line. (Other numbers of characters per line are available.) When a character to be printed passes the position where it is to be printed, the armature hammer magnet is energized striking a hammer and forcing the paper against the type at that position. An inked ribbon is placed between the paper and type so that the character is impressed on the paper in ink.

Figure 8·7 shows the major mechanical components of the DIAN Series-N printer which has a type roll or wheel with 17 circular tracks of printed characters, and is therefore a 17-character-per-line printer. This type roll is continually revolving, and when a selected character passes by the position it is to be printed in, the print actuator pushes the chosen ballistic hammer against the paper, forcing the paper against the selected character on the type roll. The type roll is continually inked by an ink roll and no ribbon is used. In this system, a code disk and shaft encoder are used to tell which character is currently in a position to be printed. Shaft encoders will be discussed in a section which follows. Figure 8·7 shows that the paper is moved horizontally after each line is printed.

·13 Cathode-ray tube output devices

Cathode-ray tubes are often used as auxiliary output devices. The tubes were first used to display curves, the coordinates of which were calculated by programs. More recently, the cathode-ray tube has been used a great deal to display characters as well, especially in real-time systems. The cathode-ray tube is a very fast output device and such tubes are sometimes used in conjunction with a camera, so that the display on the tube face may be photographed and thereby recorded permanently.

Two distinct types of cathode-ray tubes are used with computers. The first is identical to the cathode-ray tube which is used in oscilloscopes. The computer generally supplies this sort of tube with two numbers, one representing the vertical position of the spot to be displayed and the other the horizontal position of the spot. These two numbers are converted to two voltages proportional to the numbers by means of a digital-to-analog converter (these will be described later in this chapter). The voltages from the two digital-to-analog converters are then used to position the beam of the tube. The electron beam is then gated on for only a short period of time and there-

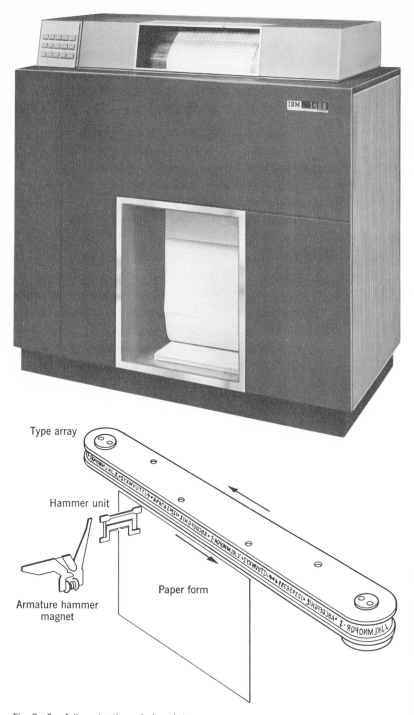

Type array

Hammer unit

Armature hammer
magnet

Paper form

Fig. 8 · 6   A line-at-a-time chain printer.

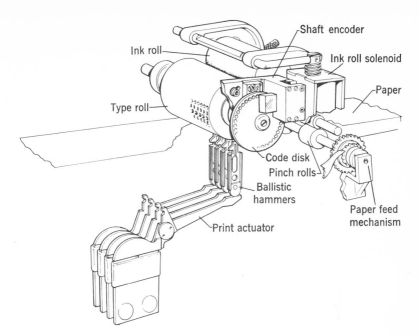

Fig. 8 · 7   A line-at-a-time drum printer.

fore only one spot is displayed at a time. Because of the high speed of this process, however, a large number of spots is generated per second, and what is essentially a continuous curve is thereby formed.

Characters such as letters and numbers may also be generated in this manner. Techniques have been devised whereby characters are selected by the computer and then traced on the face of the tube.

The demand for displays of this sort has led to the development of a tube called the "Charactron." A cutaway view of a Charactron tube is shown in Fig. 8 · 8. This tube is capable of displaying data at the rate of over 100,000 words per min. The character-forming part of the Charactron tube illustrated contains a small matrix through which 64 characters have been cut. The electron beam passes through the selection plates which direct it through the selected character in the matrix. The beam is thus formed in the shape of the selected character. The focus coil controls the size of the character formed and the deflection yoke then positions the shaped beam on the tube face.

8 · 14   Other output devices

Two other output devices are high-speed card- or tape-punching machines. The information from the computer is punched into either paper cards or tapes, so that the output medium resembles the input

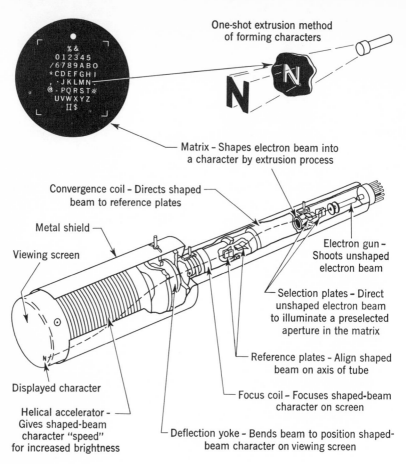

One-shot extrusion method of forming characters

Matrix – Shapes electron beam into a character by extrusion process

Convergence coil – Directs shaped beam to reference plates

Metal shield

Viewing screen

Electron gun – Shoots unshaped electron beam

Selection plates – Direct unshaped electron beam to illuminate a preselected aperture in the matrix

Reference plates – Align shaped beam on axis of tube

Displayed character

Focus coil – Focuses shaped-beam character on screen

Helical accelerator – Gives shaped-beam character "speed" for increased brightness

Deflection yoke – Bends beam to position shaped-beam character on viewing screen

Fig. 8·8 Charactron-shaped beam-display tube. (Stromberg-Carlson Division, General Dynamics Corporation)

medium. If the output is to be used, the punched cards or tapes must then be interpreted and printed; the perforated tapes and cards may therefore be thought of as an intermediate step.

Magnetic tape is also used as an intermediate storage medium for off-line output equipment operation. Since magnetic tape may be recorded much faster than either cards or tape may be punched, the computer's output operation is speeded up. In this case, a magnetic tape reader and translator is required to sense and interpret the binary-coded information recorded, and finally a printer is needed to print the information.

One advantage of these devices lies in the speed-to-cost ratio attainable. A high-speed magnetic tape recorder will be much faster than a high-speed printer, and the final printing may then take place on a slower printer, which interprets the recorded tape and prints the final result. This is another case of off-line operation, in which the final operation is performed at the speed of a faster output device and the computer is therefore not slowed down as much as it would be if a low-speed printer were used. Even the magnetic tape recorder devices, however, are inherently much slower than the computer.

8 · 15   Error-detecting and -correcting codes

The process of transferring information into the machine and from the machine is especially liable to error. Although card and tape readers are constructed with the highest possible regard for correct operation and the occurrence of errors is relatively infrequent, errors still do occur and it is desirable to detect them whenever possible. To facilitate the detection or correction of errors, two classes of codes have been invented, (1) error-detecting codes and (2) error-correcting codes. The first type of code enables the equipment to detect the errors which occur in the coded groups of bits, and the second type of code corrects the errors automatically.

Both error-detecting and error-correcting codes require that redundant information be sent along with the actual information being processed. Sometimes the additional information is cleverly concealed, as in the case of the 2-out-of-5 code which will be described, or sometimes the redundant information is obvious, as with a parity-checking code. Two types of error-detecting codes will be described. These codes are commonly used for card and tape readers and for the storage of information on magnetic tape. When an error is detected using one of these codes, the machine is generally stopped and an alarm light indicates the source of the error.

1   *The 2-out-of-5 Code.* A code which has been very popular in communications and switching circuits is the *2-out-of-5 code* shown in Table 8 · 3.

Although this code requires 5 bits to represent each decimal digit (instead of the 4 bits normally required), its important feature is that each group of bits contains exactly two 1's. A code of this type provides the machine with the ability to detect certain errors which may occur. If an error is made in reading or transferring a number, and if the resulting group of bits contains more or less than two 1's, the error may be detected. For instance, if $00110(2_{10})$ is read as (00111), the error may be detected, since there are three 1's in the incorrect code group. Notice that if, in the 8, 4, 2, 1 binary-coded-decimal system, 0010 was erroneously changed to 0011, the error

TABLE 8 · 3   TABLE 8 · 4

0 = 00011		
1 = 00101		
2 = 00110		
3 = 01001		
4 = 01010		
5 = 01100		
6 = 10001		
7 = 10010		
8 = 10100		
9 = 11000		

DECIMAL	BCD	PARITY BIT
0	0000	0
1	0001	1
2	0010	1
3	0011	0
4	0100	1
5	0101	0
6	0110	0
7	0111	1
8	1000	1
9	1001	0

could not be detected by examining the result. The 2-out-of-5 code will correct any single error which may occur, and most double, triple, quadruple, etc., errors, where a single error is an error in 1 bit (00110 to 00100), a double error is a change in 2 bits (00110 to 01111), etc. It may be seen that certain combinations of errors cannot be detected. For instance, if 00110 is changed to 01010, the error will not be detected.

2 *Parity Checking.* Another means for detecting errors which may occur is the "parity check." This type of checking is the most widely used. It is of considerable use in checking to see if numbers have been correctly transmitted through various sections of the machine, and to see if numbers which have been stored are read out correctly. The check is based on the use of an additional bit, known as a "parity bit," in each code group. The parity bit associated with each code group in an "even parity-bit" checking system has such a value that the total number of 1's in each code group plus the parity bit is always even. (An "odd parity-bit" checking code has a parity bit such that the sum of the 1's in the code group plus the parity bit is always an odd number.) The example shown in Table 8 · 4, which uses an 8, 4, 2, 1 code, has an even parity bit which makes the sum of the 1's in each code group an even number.

If a single error occurs in transmitting a code group—for instance if 0010, 1 is erroneously changed to 0011, 1—the fact that there is an odd number of 1's in the code group plus the parity bit will indicate that an error has occurred. If the values of the parity bits had been selected so that the total sum of the 1's in each code group plus the parity bit was odd instead of even, each parity bit would be the complement of the parity bit shown above and the code would be an odd parity-bit checking code.

The technique of parity checking is doubtless the most popular method of detecting errors in stored code groups, especially for storage devices such as magnetic tape, paper tape, and even for core and drum systems.

If the parity-bit system is used, an additional bit must be sent with each code group. For instance, if the 6-bit Flexowriter FL code group is used, each line of a printed tape will have an additional hole position which will contain a 1 or 0. When the tape is read by the tape reader, each code group will be examined together with the parity bit; and in an even parity-bit system, an alarm will be generated if the number of 1's in a group is odd.

This type of checking will detect all even numbers of errors. Suppose that an even parity check is used and the code group to be sent is 0010; the parity bit in this case will be a 1. If the code group is erroneously read as 0110, the number of 1's in the code group plus the parity bit will be odd and the error will be detected. If, however, a double error is made and 0010 is changed to 0111, the error will not be detected since the number of 1's will again be even. A parity-bit check will only detect odd numbers of errors.

(The rule above will also apply when the parity bit is in error. For instance, consider an even parity-bit checking system where 0010 is to be sent and the parity bit is 1. If the parity bit is changed to 0, the number of 1's in the code group plus the parity bit will be odd, and the error will be detected.)

The parity check may also be used to check entire words. In this case, the procedure is the same as it is with the shorter code groups; the parity bit is arranged to make the total number of 1's in each word plus the parity bit even or odd, depending on the system used.

There are many types of error-correcting codes, and some very clever and sophisticated coding schemes are used in both communications and computer systems. For instance, magnetic tape is a memory device which is especially prone to errors. Most of these errors are due to either imperfections in the tape or foreign matter which gets between reading heads and the tape and causes the tape to be physically pushed away from the reading head causing the recorded signal to be incorrectly interpreted. Such errors are said to be caused by "dropout." These errors tend to lie in a single track, and there are several clever codes which have been used to detect and correct such errors.

One such coding scheme consists of a two-dimensional code where a parity check bit is added along each row of the tape, and finally a complete row of check bits is added after a given number of rows.

Suppose we are recording data in rows of seven information bits (using the ASCII code) plus a parity check bit and we choose to add

TABLE 8 · 5

BINARY-CODED CHARACTERS	MEANING	ROW NUMBER
1 0 0 0 0 0 1	A	1
1 0 0 0 1 1 0	F	2
1 0 1 0 1 0 0	T	3
1 0 0 0 1 0 1	E	4
1 0 1 0 0 1 0	R	5
0 1 0 0 0 0 0	blank or (space)	6
1 0 1 0 1 0 0	T	7
1 0 0 1 0 0 0	H	8
1 0 0 0 1 0 1	E	9

column 1, column 2, column 3, column 4, column 5, column 6, column 7

a parity check row each nine rows of data. Table 8 · 5 shows a given set of rows to be recorded.

Now we add a parity check to each row of the list of binary-coded characters and, finally, a row containing a parity check digit on each column. We will use odd parity checks.

The set of binary digits shown in Table 8 · 6 would comprise the information recorded. Now let us assume that all errors occur only in a single column (two errors never occur in a row). (This is the

TABLE 8 · 6

							parity checks	
1	0	0	0	0	0	1	1	
1	0	0	0	1	1	0	0	
1	0	1	0	1	0	0	0	
1	0	0	0	1	0	1	0	
1	0	1	0	0	1	0	0	
0	1	0	0	0	0	0	0	
1	0	1	0	1	0	0	0	
1	0	0	1	0	0	0	1	
1	0	0	0	1	0	1	0	
1	0	0	0	0	1	0	1	parity checks

TABLE 8 · 7

1	0	0	0	0	0	1	1
1	0	0	0	1	1	0	0
1	0	1	0	0	0	0	0
1	0	1	0	0	0	1	0
1	0	1	0	0	1	0	0
0	1	0	0	0	0	0	0
1	0	1	0	0	0	0	0
1	0	0	1	1	0	0	1
1	0	0	0	0	0	1	0
1	0	0	0	0	1	0	1

assumption if the above is recorded on magnetic tape.) Then suppose we receive the digits shown in Table 8 · 7.

A check will indicate that the parity bits in the third, fourth, seventh, eighth, and ninth rows indicate an error and that the fifth parity check from the left in the last row indicates that the column contains an error. This means we should change the fifth bit from the right in rows three, four, seven, eight, and nine. This will correct the errors.

Study will indicate that this code can be used to correct errors providing that an odd number of errors occur and all errors occur in a single column. If an even number of errors occur in a single column, the code cannot make a correction but does not permit the errors to pass through the system undetected. Only errors occurring in two or more columns will allow undetected errors to pass.

This code may be made much stronger by recording the number of 1's in each column at the end of the data, rather than simply using single parity check bits. This is particularly useful on magnetic tape where data may be recording in very long blocks (so the columns may contain thousands of digits), and the checking information may be added only at the ends of blocks.

8 · 16 Input-output devices for systems with analog components

Not all of the inputs to digital machines consist of alphanumeric data which may be directly punched into cards or tape. Computers used in data-reduction systems or in real-time control systems often have inputs which are expressed as the physical position of some device, or as electric signals which are analog in nature. An example of a physical position which might be used as an input to a digital computer is a real-time control system in which a computer is used automatically to point a telescope. If, by some system of gears, the position of the telescope along an axis is related to the position of a shaft, the position of this shaft must be read into the computer. This will involve the translation of the shaft position into a binary-coded number which may be read by the machine.

Changing a physical displacement to a digital representation is called *analog-to-digital conversion,* and a device which performs analog-to-digital conversion is called a *coder.* There are two major types of coders: (1) those which convert mechanical displacements into a digital representation and (2) those which convert an electric analog signal into digital-coded signals.

Suppose an analog device has as its output a voltage which is to be used by a digital machine. Let us assume that the voltage varies within the limit 0 to 63 volts d-c. We can then represent the voltage values with a set of 6-bit numbers ranging from 000000 to 111111, and for each value the input voltage may assume, assign a corresponding value of the 6-bit number. If the input voltage is 20 volts, the corresponding digital value will be 010100. If, however, the input signal is at 20.249 volts d-c, the 6-bit binary number will not completely describe the input voltage, but will only approximate the input value. The process of approximating the input value is called *quantizing*. The number of bits in the binary number which represents the analog signal is the *precision* of the coder, and the amount of error which exists between the digital output values and the input analog values is a measure of the *accuracy* of the coder. For instance, if the output of the coder is a binary number containing 15 binary bits, but the error existing between the correct output signals and the output binary numbers from the coder averages 4 bits, the coder will have more precision than accuracy.

Not only are the inputs to the computer sometimes in analog form, but it is often desirable for the outputs of the computer to be expressed in analog form. An example of this lies in the use of a cathode-ray tube as an output device. If the output from the computer is to be displayed as a position on an oscilloscope tube, then the binary-coded output signals from the computer must be converted to voltages or currents, which may be used to position the electron beam, and which are proportional to the magnitude of the output binary number represented by the computer's output signals. This involves digital-to-analog conversion, and a device which performs this conversion is called a *decoder*. When digital computers are used in control systems, it is generally necessary to convert the digital outputs from the machine to analog-type signals which are then used to control the physical system.

8 · 17 Analog-to-digital coders

The type of coder which will be briefly described below converts a shaft position to a binary-coded digital number. There are a number of different types of devices which will perform this conversion; the type described is representative of the devices now in use, and it should be realized that more complicated coders may yield additional accuracy. Also, it is generally possible to convert a physical position into an electric analog-type signal and then convert this signal to a digital system. For instance, a shaft may be mechanically coupled to a potentiometer with a d-c voltage across the ends of the resistance. If the output signal is then taken from the potentiometer tap, the d-c output signal will be related to the shaft position. In general, though, more direct and accurate coders can be constructed by eliminating the intermediate step of converting a physical position to an analog electric signal.

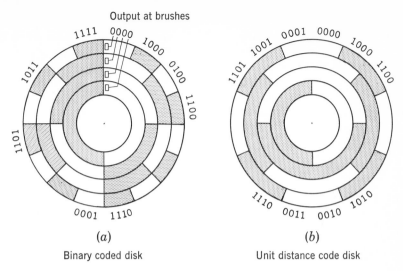

Output at brushes

(a)

Binary coded disk

(b)

Unit distance code disk

Fig. 8 · 9   Shaft-position coder disks.

Figure 8 · 9a illustrates a coded-segment disk which is coupled to the shaft. A set of brushes are then attached so that a single brush is positioned in the center of each concentric band of the disk. Each band is constructed of several segments made of either conducting material (the darkened areas), or some insulating material (the unshaded areas). A signal is connected to the conductor and if a given brush makes contact with a segment of conducting material, a 1 signal will result, but if the brush is over the insulating material, the output from the brush will be a 0. The four output lines of the coder shown will represent a 4-bit binary number. There are 16 distinct intervals around the coder disk, each corresponding to a different shaft-position interval and each causing the coder to have a different binary-number output.

A photoelectric coder may be constructed using a coder disk with bands divided into transparent segments (the unshaded areas) and opaque segments (the shaded areas). A light source is placed on one side of the disk and a set of four photoelectric cells on the other side, arranged so that one cell is behind each band of the coder disk. If a transparent segment is between the light source and a light-sensitive cell, a 1 output will result; and if an opaque area is in front of the photoelectric cell, there will be a 0 output. By increasing the number of bands around the disk, more precision may be added to the coder. The photoelectric type of coder has greater resolution than the brush type and even greater resolution may be obtained by using gears and several disks.

There is one basic difficulty with the coder illustrated; if the disk is in a position where the output number is changing from 011 to 100, or in any position where several bits are changing value, the output signal may become ambiguous. Since the brushes are of finite width, they will overlap the change in segments; and no matter how carefully it is made, the coder will have erroneous outputs in several positions. If this occurs when 011 is changing to 100, several errors are possible; the value may be read as 111 or 000, either of which are values with considerable errors. In order to circumvent this difficulty, a number of schemes have been used, generally involving two sets of brushes with one set displaced slightly from the other. By logically choosing from the outputs available, the "ambiguity" may be eliminated at a slight cost in accuracy.

Another scheme for avoiding ambiguity involves the use of a "Gray" or "unit-distance" code to form the coder disk (Fig. $8 \cdot 9b$). In this code 2 bits never change value in successive coded binary numbers. Using a Gray-coded disk, a 6 may be read for a 7 or a 4 for a 5, but larger errors will not be made. Table $8 \cdot 8$ shows a listing of a 4-bit Gray code.

If the inputs to the machine are from a coder using a Gray code, the code groups must be converted to conventional binary or binary-coded decimal before use. This conversion may be simply performed, either sequentially or combinatorially.

TABLE 8·8

DECIMAL	GRAY CODE $a_3a_2a_1a_0$
0	0000
1	0001
2	0011
3	0010
4	0110
5	0111
6	0101
7	0100
8	1100
9	1101
10	1111
11	1110
12	1010
13	1011
14	1001
15	1000

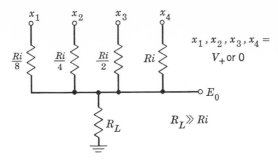

Fig. 8 · 10 Digital-to-analog resistor network.

8 · 18 Decoders

The problem of converting a digital output to an analog voltage can be resolved by several techniques, the most straightforward of which involves the use of a resistor network. Sometimes diodes and other elements are used in more complicated decoders, but a basic type of resistor-network decoder is illustrated in Fig. 8 · 10, which shows a resistor net with four inputs. Each input is assumed to carry a binary signal which is at either ground potential, representing a 0, or at a positive potential V_+, representing a 1. The output at E_0 will then be a d-c potential in the range 0 to V_+ and will be proportional to the value of the binary number represented by the inputs.

For instance, if the input number is 0111, the output voltage at E_0 will be $\frac{7}{15}$ V_+; if the input is 1111, the output E_0 will be V_+; and if the input is 0001, the output E_0 will be at $\frac{1}{15}$ V_+ volts d-c. In order to achieve accuracy, the resistors should all be of the precision type. Also, the input voltages representing the binary values must be accurately established and, since the load on the inputs will vary with the value of the input numbers, the inputs should be capable of delivering the necessary current without a shift in the voltage level. More precision can be added by increasing the number of inputs and adding a resistor for each input.

There are many other types of decoders, and the design and construction of coders and decoders represents a growing area in the computing field. Many decoders are very specialized, especially those used in control systems. For instance, automatic milling machines are often controlled by a digital computer which must have its digital outputs converted into the mechanical motion of the milling machinery. The use of digital computers in large industries such as the petroleum industry also involves the utilization of many different types of coder and decoder devices.

8 · 19   Electronic high-speed analog-to-digital converters

There are several types of coders for converting an electric analog signal to a digital form. What is basically needed is a device which converts a d-c signal to a binary number proportional to the d-c level of the signal. Suppose we have a d-c voltage with an amplitude which is in the interval 0 to +15 volts. If we wish to convert this to a four-digit binary number, we will want the number 0000 for 0 to 0.5 volt, 0001 for 0.5 to 1.5 volts, 0010 for 1.5 to 2.5 volts, 1111 for 14.5 volts or greater, etc. (Notice that the binary number corresponds to the center of the interval.)

A simple analog-to-digital converter can be made using a resistor network such as that in Fig. 8 · 10, a START-STOP flip-flop, a four flip-flop binary counter, four level converters, and a high-gain d-c amplifier.

The basic configuration is shown in Fig. 8 · 11. The flip-flops X_1, X_2, X_3, and X_4 are arranged in a binary counter which counts 0000, 0001, 0010, ... , 1111. Each flip-flop drives a level converter such that when the flip-flop's output is a 1, the output of the level converter is -15 volts d-c; and, when the flip-flop's output is a 0, the level-converter output is 0 volts d-c.

The high-gain d-c amplifier is designed so that when the input to the amplifier is positive, the output of the amplifier represents a 0; but, when the input is negative, the output goes to a 1, thus setting the START-STOP flip-flop (and stopping the counter).

Now let us assume that a start signal is given, clearing the flip-flop counter to 0000. All the outputs from the level converters will be at 0 volts and (unless the input analog signal is less than +0.5 volt d-c, the 180-kilohm resistor to -15 volts will cause the input to the amplifier to be negative[4]) the amplifier's output will be a 0 and the clock pulse will pass the first AND gate.

If the input signal is 0 to 0.5 volt, the amplifier will have a level output of a 1 and will set the START-STOP flip-flop to a 1 so that no clock pulses will pass.

If the input signal is greater than +0.5 volt, the counter will count, thereby causing the negative current into the junction of the 10-, 20-, 40-, and 80-kilohm resistors to increase until the input to the amplifier goes negative, thus stopping the counter.

If, for instance, the analog signal input is at +9 volts d-c, the input to the amplifier will be negative until the counter goes from 1000 to 1001; and, when the counter is a 1001, the clock pulses will be stopped, giving the right value for the signal.

[4]The 180-kilohm and -15 volt combination contribute as much current to the junction of resistors at the amplifiers input as a -0.5 volt signal at the input for the analog signal.

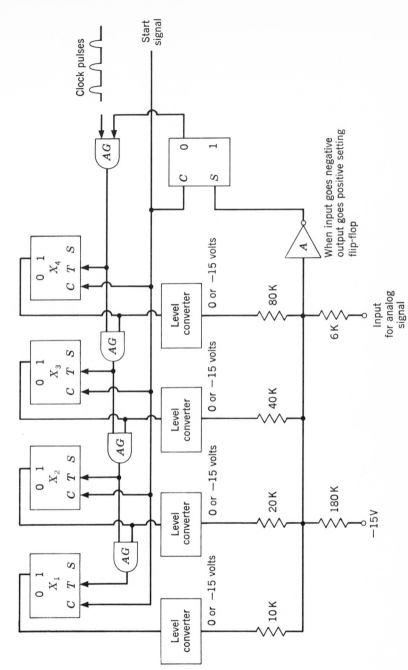

Fig. 8 · 11   Analog-to-digital converter.

There are several other types of analog-to-digital coders. For instance, several commercial digital voltmeters use a "voltage-controlled oscillator" with a frequency proportional to the input voltage. That is, the oscillator has a higher output frequency when the input voltage is greater. This oscillator operates into a counter which is enabled during a fixed-time period. The counter is started at zero. The higher the frequency of the oscillator, the higher the counter counts; therefore, the higher the voltage, the higher the count during the period. The count will thus be representative of the d-c level of the input signal.

Analog-to-digital converters are commonly made to give either seven to fifteen binary digits or three to five decimal digits for outputs. The fastest converter now on the market makes 10 million conversions per second; more (modestly-priced) converters operate at much lower frequencies. Slow analog-to-digital converters primarily intended for manual use or slow-speed recording are called *digital voltmeters*. These almost invariably operate using binary-coded decimal. Display devices then convert the binary-coded decimal to a decimal number which is displayed and can be read by an operator.

QUESTIONS

1 Using the Flexowriter code in Table 8 · 1, an operator keyboards the following:

> add 641
>
> cad 932
>
> sub 841

How many lines will be punched in the paper tape? How many holes will be punched in the tape?

2 Write out in binary form the first line of the program in Question 1 using the ASA code in Table 8 · 2.

3 If the short program in Question 1 is punched into cards according to the code in Table 8 · 2 using normal procedures, how many holes will be punched into the cards used? If a mistake is made during keyboarding, will it be easier to correct if cards or tape are used? Explain why.

4 Generally, programs are punched into cards with an instruction word per card. The first line of the program in Question 1 would go on one card. How many holes will be punched in the first card for the code in Fig. 8 · 5?

5 List the binary code groups for each decimal digit in the excess 3 binary-coded-decimal code in Chap. 3, and assign a parity bit for an even parity-bit checking system to each code group. List the values of the parity bits for the same excess 3 code for an odd parity-bit checking system.

6 Each of the following groups of digits consists of a code group of eight digits in the ASA code in Table 8 · 2. A single column of parity checks has been added as indicated in the figure, and a single row of parity checks has been added at the end of the set of message digits. In addition, errors have been added so that the data are not correct at present. Correct these groups of data and then convert each seven-digit character to the alphanumeric character it represents. The parity checks are odd parity checks:

a. 0 0 1 0 0 0 1 1   b. 0 1 1 0 0 1 0 0
   0 1 1 0 1 0 0 0   0 1 0 0 0 1 1 0
   0 1 1 0 0 0 0 1   0 1 0 1 0 1 0 1
   0 0 1 0 0 0 1 1   0 0 1 0 0 0 1 1
   0 0 1 1 0 0 1 0   0 0 0 1 0 0 0 0
   0 0 0 1 0 0 0 0   0 0 1 0 0 0 1 0
   0 1 0 0 1 1 0 1   0 0 1 0 0 0 1 1
   0 1 1 1 1 1 0 1   0 1 0 0 0 1 1 0
   0 1 1 0 0 0 1 1   0 1 0 1 0 1 1 1
   0 1 1 0 1 0 0 0   1 0 1 0 0 0 1 1 parity check row
   0 0 1 0 0 0 1 1
   1 1 0 0 1 0 0 0 parity check row

7 How many bands must a coder disk similar to that in Fig. 8 · 9 have for an analog-to-digital converter which has a precision of 10 binary digits? List the successive code groups for a 5-bit unit-distance code which counts from 0 to 31_{10}.

8 It was mentioned in the chapter that more powerful parity check systems can be formed by adding columns with the number of 1's in each column written at the end as a binary number. For instance,

$$
\begin{array}{c}
0 \\
0 \\
1 \\
\end{array}
$$

if we wish to encode 1011 we add   0 then forming the following
                    1101   01001
                    1100   01110
                    1110   10000

```
                    10110
                    11010
                    11001
encoded block of data: 11100 Now if one or more errors occur in the
                    01001
                    01110
                    10000
```

same column, they can be corrected by simply noting that the column does not agree with the number of 1's recorded at the end, and that there are parity checks in the rows of the block of data containing errors. By simply changing these errors, we will convert the message back to its original form. Here are two other blocks of data which include errors. Correct the errors in these blocks of data and write the alphanumeric code for each set of seven digits in a row to the right of the rows. The code is that in Table 8 · 2, so the parity checks are as indicated in the figure and not in the rightmost column.

```
a. 0 0 1 0 0 0 1 1            b. 0 1 1 0 0 0 1 0
   0 1 1 0 1 0 1 0               0 1 0 0 0 0 0 1
   0 1 1 0 0 0 1 1               0 1 0 0 0 1 0 0
   0 0 1 0 0 0 0 1               0 0 0 1 0 0 0 0
   0 0 1 1 0 0 1 0               0 0 1 0 0 0 1 1
   0 0 0 1 0 0 0 0               0 1 1 0 0 0 0 1
   0 1 1 1 0 1 1 0               0 1 0 1 0 1 1 1
   0 1 1 1 1 0 0 1               0 1 1 1 0 1 0 1
   0 1 0 0 0 1 0 1               0 0 1 1 0 0 1 0
   0 1 1 1 0 1 0 1               0 0 0 1 0 0 0 0
   0 0 0 1 0 1 0 0⎤              0 0 1 1 0 1 0 1⎤
   0 1 0 0 1 1 0 1⎥ check        0 1 1 0 0 1 0 0⎥ check
   0 1 0 1 0 0 1 1⎥ digits       0 1 1 1 0 0 1 1⎥ digits
   0 0 1 0 0 0 0 0⎦              0 0 0 0 0 0 0 0⎦
```

9   If the signals to each of the four inputs to the digital-to-analog converter resistor network in Fig. 8 · 10 are from the 1 outputs of flip-flops which have +8- and 0-volt logic levels (+8 volts represents a 1), what will be the potential at E_0 if the flip-flops represent the binary number 0101? If the flip-flops represent 1010? 1111?

10 Show an error pattern the code in Question 8 will not correct but will detect and one which it will neither correct nor detect.

11 Characters are generally read from punched paper tape a line at a time. When the Flexowriter FL code in Table 8 · 1 is used, the computer will be supplied with 6 information bits each time a line with a hole in the seventh is read. If the computer used is a serial computer, the 6 bits will arrive in parallel and must be changed to serial

form. By loading a six-place shift register in parallel and then shifting the register at the machine's pulse repetition frequency, the bits representing the character can be converted to serial form. Draw a block diagram of a six-flip-flop shift register along with the input lines necessary to load the register (assume that there are six input lines— one to each flip-flop—from the tape reader and that a given input line will contain a pulse if a hole is in the respective position of the tape).

12 Which of the sets of errors in Question 6 would have been detected if the error-correcting system in Question 8 had been used? Which of these sets of errors in Question 8 could have been corrected by the error-detecting and -correcting scheme in the Question 6, and which would only have been detected?

13 For the A to D converter in Fig. 8 · 11, if the 40-kilohm resistor is made 50-kilohm by error, which of the following voltages would be incorrectly converted?

a. +10 volts   *b.* +3 volts
c. +2 volts   *d.* +8 volts
e. +8 volts   *f.* +13 volts

Design a 6-bit analog-to-digital converter using the same scheme which is shown in Fig. 8 · 11.

14 The code in Question 8 is not generally able to correct double errors in a row or errors in the checking numbers at the end, but will almost always detect each of these. Explain this statement.

9

Computer
organization
and control

The preceding chapters have described techniques whereby arithmetic and logical operations may be performed and information may be read into and from various machine-storage devices. In order to utilize the speeds and information-handling capabilities of the techniques and devices which have been illustrated, it is necessary to sequence automatically the various operations which occur at speeds compatible with those of the rest of the machine. The control element must therefore be constructed of high-speed electronic circuitry. The basic circuits used in the control element of a digital computer are those described in Chap. 4, and most of the concepts underlying the functioning of the control element are those presented in Chaps. 5 and 6.

Present-day digital computers are generally divided into two classes: the special-purpose computer and the general-purpose computer. A special-purpose computer is one in which the sequence of operations is predetermined, not by a set of instructions (program) read into the machine, but by the actual construction of the control circuitry. A special-purpose machine therefore has a fixed sequence of operations which is wired into the machine when it is constructed, and which cannot be changed except by a change in the wiring. A general-purpose machine, on the other hand, is one in which the sequence of instructions (program) which the machine performs is read into the machine via the input devices, and may be changed by simply reading in a new program. This type of machine is also referred to as a "stored-program" computer.

This division of digital machines into two categories is not as clear-cut as it may at first appear. Many machines, such as those used in aircraft- and missile-control systems or as a part of industrial process-control systems, are special-purpose machines because the sequence of the operations which are performed is wired directly into the control circuitry. Other machines, such as the large machines which are used at computing centers for business and science, are clearly general purpose, as the programs for these machines are always read in and are changed quite frequently. On the other hand, a large class of machines exists in which the program sequence is determined by a read-only memory, the contents of which may be changed, thus changing the sequence of operations. The earlier machines of this type had plugboards which were not easily changeable, and in order to change the program, the plugboard for the machine had to be rewired—a time-consuming process. As this type of machine was further developed, the process of wiring and changing the plugboards which determined the program became easier and faster, thus making such machines appear more and more similar to the general-purpose computers. As a final step in the transition, some of these machines were constructed using read-only memories to store the program. The contents of these memories could be changed, although slowly (see Chap. 6), which caused them to operate much as a general-purpose computer does. The techniques employed here are relatively inefficient, but viewed externally, the machines appear to operate in the area defined as "general purpose." The classification at this point is purely arbitrary, and the differences between the two types of machines are relative since the machines are performing similar functions.

It should be noted that most of the machines classed as special purpose are capable of altering their sequence of operations, depending on the data. That is, the machines have "conditional branches" (refer to Chap. 2) which depend on the numerical results, but the sequence of operations is altered only in that the computer skips to another position of the program. The basic sequence of operations in each section of the program does not change; only the path through the program is altered.

This chapter will deal primarily with the general-purpose, stored-program computers. The special-purpose computer is designed for a particular purpose, and although the simplicity of its design and economy of its construction cannot be denied, the details of these machines vary greatly from one to another, and do not fall in the context of this book.

The "control element" may be defined as "those parts of a digital computer which effect the carrying out of instructions in proper sequence, the interpretation of each instruction, and the application of the proper commands to the arithmetic element and other circuits in accordance with this interpretation."[1]

[1] "IRE Standards on Electronic Computers: Definition of Terms, 1956," published by the Institute of Radio Engineers.

The function of the control circuitry is to interpret the instruction words and then sequence the necessary signals to those sections of the machine which will cause the machine to perform the instruction. Previous chapters have shown how the application of the correct sequence of control signals to the logical circuitry in the arithmetic element enables the computer to perform arithmetic operations, and how binary words may be stored and later read from several types of memory devices. In order for the machine to function, the operation of the sections of the machine must be directed, and the control circuitry performs that function.

9·1 Construction of instruction word

We have defined a computer word as an ordered set of characters handled as a group. Also, the computer word is considered to be a basic unit of information in a machine.[2] Basically all words consist of a set of binary digits, and the meaning of the digits depends upon several different factors. For instance, the bits 0100 0100 could represent the decimal number 68 in a pure binary machine, and the decimal number 44 in a binary-coded-decimal machine which uses an 8, 4, 2, 1 code. Thus the meaning of a set of digits is sometimes determined by the machine. In addition, other interpretations are possible, for instruction words are stored just as are data words, and the digits could represent an instruction to the computer. Since each memory location can store either an instruction word or a data word, the programmer must see that the instruction words are used to determine the sequence of operations which the machine performs, and that reasonable meanings are assigned to the data words.

In general, the single-address machine will start with the word stored in some specified location, interpret the contents of this location as an instruction, and then continue taking instruction words from the memory locations in order unless a halt or branch instruction is encountered. The data to be used in the calculations will be stored in another part of the memory. Since the machine can store either instructions or data in the same storage registers, considerable flexibility of operation results. For instance, if the computer memory element could store only 8,000 words, one program might contain 5,000 instructions, leaving 3,000 locations for the storage of data, and another program might use only 1,000 instruction words, leaving 7,000 locations for data. The machine user is therefore free to allocate

[2]Some of the new computers will handle words of different lengths, in which case the "basic word" is generally considered to be the data word normally handled as a unit. Other machines have completely variable word lengths. There is now a tendency to speak of a data *field*, where a field is any group of characters handled as a unit.

the memory as necessary, and problems with many steps and few numbers, or with much data and few instructions, can be handled by the same machine. It should be noted that machines which have both a high-speed inner memory and a lower-speed auxiliary memory will use the high-speed inner memory for the instruction words and for intermediate results, and the lower-speed storage devices for any data which cannot be accommodated in the high-speed memory. For instance, if a computer has a high-speed magnetic-core memory plus a number of magnetic-tape devices, the program instructions may be stored in the magnetic-core storage and the data to be used in the tape storage. Then, as portions of the data are read into the core memory and calculations are performed, more data is read from tape to cores and more calculations are performed, until all the data has been processed. The machine takes its instruction words only from the inner memory; if instructions are stored on tape, they must be transferred into the inner memory before they are performed by the computer.

An instruction word in a digital machine generally consists of several sections. The number of divisions in the word depends on the type of computer; for instance, a three-address computer would be more likely to have a complicated word structure than a single-address computer. Let us deal with the single-address word first. Each instruction word must contain at least two sections, first the operation code which defines the operation to be performed, such as addition, subtraction, etc., and second, the address part which contains the location of the number to be added or subtracted (the operand).

If 5 binary digits of the word are used to specify which order is to be performed, there must be some coding system to indicate each of the various orders. Since 5 bits have been allocated to describe an order, 2^5 or 32 different orders could be used, and a different binary number would be associated with each order. Each instruction will have an *operation* or *OP code,* consisting of the set of binary digits which the machine is to interpret.

If the machine's internal number system is binary-coded-decimal or an alphanumeric code, the operation code may then consist of one or more decimal numbers or letters. For instance, A is the operation code for adding, and S the operation code for subtracting in the IBM 1401 computer, which operates in a binary-coded-decimal system. Since the machine uses an eight-binary-digit code group to express an alphanumeric character, the operation code as expressed in the machine is eight binary digits long. If a machine uses an alphanumeric code internally, with six binary digits per alphanumeric character, the operation code might consist of two letters and be expressed in the machine as 12 binary digits.

The Raytheon 7180 is an example of a single-address binary machine, having 32 basic instructions and an operation code of 5 binary digits packaged in a 20-binary-digit word. Fourteen binary digits are then used for the address of the operand in the memory, and a single digit is used to indicate whether or not an index register is to be used. (This subject will be discussed later.) The basic format of the instruction word for this computer is such that the operation code for the Raytheon 7180 machine occupies digits 0 through 4; digit 5 is used to indicate whether or not the particular instruction is indexed; and digits 6 through 19 are used to designate the address in memory of the word to be used.

Six typical instructions in this machine are shown in Table 9 · 1, and the effect of each instruction in the machine is shown in the same table. If, for instance, the machine reads a binary instruction word from the memory for which the five operation-code digits are 00100 the machine will multiply the number which is in the accumulator of the machine when the instruction word is read by the number located at the address given by binary digits 6 through 20 in the instruction word. In the case of a TRANSFER instruction, the instruction word contains the operation code 01001 and if the contents of the accumulator when the instruction word is read are negative, the machine will transfer to the address given by digits 6 through 20 in the instruction word, taking the next instruction word from this address. If the number in the accumulator at this time is 0 or is positive, the machine will not transfer to this address but will instead take its next instruction word in sequence from the memory.

The complete set of instructions for the DDP-24 is shown in Table 9 · 2. The DDP-24 is manufactured by the Computer Control Corporation and is a medium-sized single-address computer. In this table, A refers to the accumulator, B to the register used to store the least significant digits of products, etc., and EA is the address portion of a computer-instruction word. Octal OP codes, as well as the mnemonic codes, are given. To explain a typical instruction, the addition instruction has an octal OP code of 10, so the binary code is 001000. The mnemonic code is ADD and the notation $(A) +$ $(EA) \rightarrow A$ says that the sum of the accumulator plus the word in memory at the address given by EA (which is the location given by the address part of the instruction word) is placed in the accumulator.

As further examples, JMP with a binary OP code of 111100 causes the machine to take the next instruction word from the address given by the address portion of the JMP instruction word. Notice the multiplication instruction multiplies a word in memory by the B register, not the accumulator, also a characteristic of many IBM machines.

OP CODE (MNEMONIC CODE)	OP CODE IN BINARY	MEANING OF INSTRUCTION
ADD	00010	Adds the number at the address in memory given by the address part of the instruction word to the number in the accumulator and stores that number in the accumulator.
MUL	00100	Multiplies number at the address in memory given by address part of the instruction word by the number in the accumulator, and stores the most significant digits and sign in the accumulator and the least significant digits in an MQ register.
DVD	00101	The combined number formed by the accumulator and MQ register is divided by the number at the address given in the address part of the instruction word. The quotient replaces the number originally in the MQ, and the remainder replaces the number originally in the accumulator.
STO	11000	The contents of the accumulator are stored in the location given by the address part of the instruction word.
AND	01111	Each bit in the accumulator is AND-ed with the corresponding bit of the word located at the address in memory given by the address part of the instruction word. The resulting bits replace the original contents of the accumulator.
CLA	00001	Loads the number at the address in memory given by the address part of the instruction word into the accumulator.

Subscripts such as in $A_{2\text{-}24}$ are very useful notational devices. They indicate the bits of the register involved, so that, for instance, STD causes only the bits in the tenth to the twenty-fourth positions in the accumulator to be stored at the location given by the address (EA) in the instruction word, and these go into the tenth through the twenty-fourth positions in that word of the memory.

TABLE 9·2 OPERATION CODES FOR DDP-24 COMPUTER

	OP CODE					
	MNEMONIC	OCTAL	FUNCTION	X	I	O'F
LOAD & STORE	CRA	60	$O \rightarrow (A)$			
	IAB	57	$(A) \quad (B)$			
	LDA	24	$(EA) \rightarrow (A)$	X	X	
	LDB	23	$(EA) \rightarrow (B)$	X	X	
	STA	05	$(A) \rightarrow (EA)$	X	X	
	STB	03	$(B) \rightarrow (EA)$	X	X	
	STC	04	$(A)_{1-9} \rightarrow (EA)_{1-9}$	X	X	
	STD	06	$(A)_{10-24} \rightarrow (EA)_{10-24}$	X	X	
	TAB	55	$(A) \rightarrow (B)$			
ARITHMETIC	ADD	10	$(A) + (EA) \rightarrow (A)$	X	X	X
	ADM	20	$(A) + |(EA)| \rightarrow (A)$	X	X	X
	BCD*	36	(EA) BCD $\rightarrow (A)$ Binary	X	X	
	BIN*	37	(EA) Binary $\rightarrow (A)$ BCD	X	X	(X)
	DIV	35	$(A, B)/(EA) \rightarrow$ (quotient to B, remainder to A)	X	X	(X)
	MPY	34	$(B) \times (EA) \rightarrow (A, B)$			X
	RND	62	$(A) + 1 \rightarrow (A)$, if $(B)_2 = 1$			
	SBM	21	$(A) - |(EA)| \rightarrow (A)$	X	X	X
	SUB	11	$(A) - (EA) \rightarrow (A)$	X	X	X
LOGICAL	ANA	15	$(A) \cap (EA) \rightarrow (A)$	X	X	
	ERA	17	$(A) \oplus (EA) \rightarrow (A)$	X	X	
	ORA	16	$(A) \cup (EA) \rightarrow (A)$	X	X	
SHIFT	ALS**	41	Shift $(A)_{2-24}$ left, positions specified by $(EA)_{19-24}$	X	X	
	ARS**	40	Shift $(A)_{2-24}$ right, positions specified by $(EA)_{19-24}$	X	X	
	LGL**	47	Shift $(A)_{1-24}$ left, positions specified by $(EA)_{19-24}$	X	X	
	LLR**	43	Rotate $(A, B)_{1-24}$ left, positions specified by $(EA)_{19-24}$	X	X	
	LLS**	45	Shift $(A, B)_{2-24}$ left, positions specified by $(EA)_{19-24}$	X	X	
	LRR**	42	Rotate $(A, B)_{1-24}$ right, positions specified by $(EA)_{19-24}$	X	X	
	LRS**	44	Shift $(A, B)_{2-24}$ right, positions specified by $(EA)_{19-24}$	X	X	
	NRM	46	Shift $(A, B)_{2-24}$ left until $(A)_2 = 1$, See Manual			
	SCL**	65	Shift $(A, B)_{2-24}$ left and decrement index register, positions specified by $(EA)_{19-24}$	X	X	
	SCR**	64	Shift $(A, B)_{2-24}$ right and increment index register, positions specified by $(EA)_{19-24}$	X	X	

X = Indexable
I = Indirectly Addressable
O'F = Overflow possible
  * Optional
 ** If indirect address not specified (I = O),
    address portion of instruction is effective operand
(X) = Improper divide possible

	OP CODE		FUNCTION	X	I	O'F
	MNEMONIC	OCTAL				
JUMP	JMP	74	Jump to EA	X	X	
	JOF	73	Jump to EA, if overflow indicator set	X	X	
	JPL	70	Jump to EA, if sign $(A) = 0$	X	X	
	JRT	25	Jump to location specified by $(EA)_{11-24}$, restore interrupt	X	X	
	JST	27	Jump to EA $+$ 1 and store location in (EA)	X	X	
	JZE	71	Jump to EA, if $(A) = 0$	X	X	
	SKG	12	Skip next instruction, if $(A) > (EA)$	X	X	
	SKQ	13	Skip next instruction, if $(A) \geq (EA)$	X	X	
INDEX	ADX**	54	$(X) + (EA)_{11-24} \to (X)$	X	X	
	IRX	67	$(EA)_{11-24} + 1 \to (EA)_{11-24}$ and (X)	X	X	
	JIX	72	Jump to EA, if $(X) \neq 0$	X	X	
	JXI	75	$(X) + 1 \to (X)$, Jump to EA, if resultant $(X) = 0$	X	X	
	LDX**	56	$(EA)_{11-24} \to (X)$	X	X	
	STX	66	$(X) \to (EA)_{11-24}$	X	X	
	TAX	63	$(A)_{11-24} \to (X)_{11-24}$			
INPUT/OUTPUT	DMB	32	Dump memory starting at EA	X	X	
	FMB	31	Load memory starting at EA	X	X	
	INA**	52	Input $\to (A)$, according to mask in (EA)	X	X	
	INM	07	Input $\to (EA)$	X	X	
	ITC**	51	Inhibit or enable interrupt, according to mask in (EA)	X	X	
	OCP**	53	Select I/O, according to mask in (EA)	X	X	
	OTA**	50	$(A) \to$ Output, according to mask in (EA)	X	X	
	OTM	22	$(EA) \to$ Output	X	X	
	SKS**	61	Skip next instruction, if sense line not set sense line specified by $(EA)_{11-24}$	X	X	
CONTROL	HLT	00	Stop computer operation until start button pressed			
	NOP	77	Perform no operation			
	XEC	02	Execute instruction at EA	X	X	

Word formats

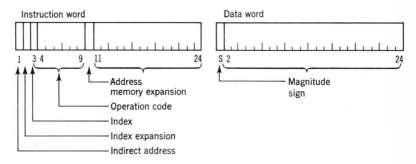

Instruction word

Data word

1 3 4   9 11   24   S 2   24

Address
memory expansion
Operation code
Index
Index expansion
Indirect address

Magnitude
sign

9 · 2   Multiple-address computers

1   *The Two-address Machine.* The number of divisions in the basic computer instruction word is determined primarily by the number of addresses which are referred to. Many computers have two-address instruction words. A two-address computer will generally have a basic instruction word with three sections (Fig. 9 · 1), the first consisting of the operation-code section and the second and third sections each containing the address of a location in memory.

Different machines use these addresses differently. For instance, both addresses in a two-address machine may specify operands, and the result will be stored at the first of the addresses. Another alternative is to have the first address specify the location of the word to be used, and the second address the location in memory of the next instruction to be used. The Minneapolis-Honeywell 200 and IBM 1401 are examples of two-address machines in which each address refers to an operand, and the Bendix G15 and IBM 650 have modified two-address instruction words.

2   *The Three-address Machine.* The three-address machine generally uses two addresses to indicate the operands to be used and the third address to indicate the location in which the result is to be stored (Fig. 9 · 1). For instance, consider the three-address instruction word in Fig. 9 · 1. The first section of the word indicates the operation to be performed—for instance, add, subtract, multiply, etc. The first two of the three addresses are used to indicate the locations of the operands to be used. For instance, if the instruction is an ADD instruction, the contents of location *A* will be added to the contents of location *B*. The last address indicates the location in which the result is to be stored; as in the instruction "add *A* to *B* and store the contents in *C*." The machine will take its instructions from the memory in order, unless instructed to branch. The instruction word, and therefore the basic computer word for a three-address system, must be of moderate length. As a result, most three-address computers have been business computers in which the word lengths are liable to be longer than those of purely scientific machines. The three-address machines are not terribly popular at this time, although at one time they were more popular than two-address machines. Typical three-address machines were the National Bureau of Standards' DY-SEAC, the Datamatic Corporation's DATAMATIC 1000 and DATAMATIC 800, and the Radio Corporation of America's BIZMAC.

3   *The Four-address Machine.* If the basic instruction word contains four addresses (Fig. 9 ·1), three are generally used as in the three-address machine, and the fourth is used to indicate the location of

the next instruction. If we designate the four addresses as A, B, C, and D, a MULTIPLY instruction will cause the contents of address A to be multiplied by the contents of B and stored in C. The next instruction will then be taken from memory address D. Typical four-address machines were the National Bureau of Standards' SWAC, and the Raytheon Manufacturing Company's RAYDAC.

There are many variations in the formats used for instruction words and in the complexity of the operations performed. Some machines, for instance SEAC, had both three- and four-address instruction words. Other machines, LINK, for example, require two computer words to form a complete instruction word. The formats for computer words vary from machine to machine, as do the lists of instructions which the machines can perform. Certain basic operations, such as adding, subtracting, multiplying, branching, etc., are fundamental, however; and these operations will be described in the following sections.

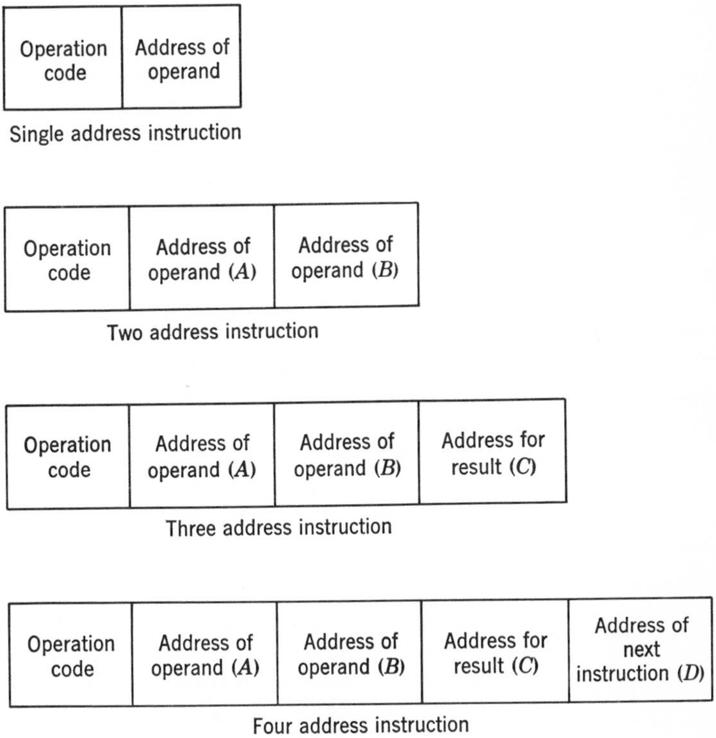

Operation code	Address of operand

Single address instruction

Operation code	Address of operand (A)	Address of operand (B)

Two address instruction

Operation code	Address of operand (A)	Address of operand (B)	Address for result (C)

Three address instruction

Operation code	Address of operand (A)	Address of operand (B)	Address for result (C)	Address of next instruction (D)

Four address instruction

Fig. 9 · 1   Formats for instruction words.

9 · 3 Instruction time and execution time— organization of control registers

A digital computer proceeds through the execution of a program with a basic rhythm or pattern in its sequence of operation which is produced by the necessity of drawing both instructions and operands from the same memory. Let us examine the single-address type of computer, bearing in mind that the two-address, as well as three- and four-address machines, operate in essentially the same manner and require essentially the same control registers, although the pattern of the execution of instruction differs according to the number of operands in the particular machine and the format of the instruction word.

The basic pattern or sequence of operations for most instructions in a digital machine of the single-address type consists of an alternation of a time period called the *instruction cycle*, followed by a period of time called the *execution cycle*. During the instruction cycle, an instruction word is obtained from the memory, interpreted, and the memory is given the address of the operand to be used. During the execution cycle, the memory obtains the operand to be used (for instance, the multiplier if the instruction is in multiplication or the augend if the instruction is an addition), and the operation called out by the instruction word is then performed upon this operand.

Almost all machines now being made use either a core memory, a thin-film memory, or a rod memory for the storing of both instruction words and operands or data. There will be no harm in assuming that we have a core memory since all three types of memory operate with essentially the same characteristic when viewed externally.

The cycle time for a core memory is fixed, and once we tell the memory that we wish to read from it or write into it, a certain period of time will elapse before we can instruct the memory that we are again ready to read or write. If we are reading from the memory, the selected word will be delivered a short time after the memory has been given the address of the word to be read and instructed to read. During the remaining portion of the memory cycle, the memory will rewrite this word into the location from which it was read.

If the memory is to be written into, the word to be written as well as the address at which we wish to write it must be given the memory. A write signal must also be given, telling it to write this word at the location or address which we have given. As discussed in Chap. 7, the address at which we write into or read from in the memory is given by means of a memory address register, and the word to be written into the memory is delivered to a register called the memory buffer register; when we read from the memory, the word is also delivered to a memory buffer register.

During the instruction cycle, the instruction word is transferred by the memory into the memory buffer register. In order to obtain this word, we must tell the memory to read and give the memory the address to read from. During the instruction cycle the instruction word which was read into the memory buffer register is interpreted and the address of the operand to be used is delivered to the memory address register. For many instructions this will be a part of the instruction word, the address part of which was read from the memory during the instruction cycle. During the execution time or execution cycle, an operand is obtained from the memory or written into the memory, depending upon the instruction word which was interpreted during the previous instruction time period.

If the instruction being interpreted is an ADD instruction, the location of the augend is given in the address part of the instruction word, and this address must be given to the memory address register. The memory then obtains the desired word from the memory and puts it into the memory buffer register. The computer must add this word to the word already in the accumulator. Afterward, the computer must give the memory the address of the next instruction word to be used and command the memory to read this word.

Notice that the machine alternates between instruction times and execution times. Also notice that during the execution time, we must store somewhere in our control circuitry the operation code of the instruction word which was read from the memory, the address of the operand to be used (which was a part of the instruction word read from the memory), and also the address of the next instruction word to be read from the memory and used.

As a result, there are several registers which are basic to almost every digital computer. These are shown in Fig. 9·2 and are described in the following:

1 *The Instruction Counter.* This is a counter of the same length as the address section of the instruction word. The counter can be cleared or a 1 can be added to the contents of the counter. A typical logic diagram for the instruction counter could consist of the counter shown in Fig. 4·20 having two input signals, a CLEAR line, and an ADD 1 line. This counter keeps track of the instruction to be used in the program, so that normally during each instruction time the counter will be incremented by 1, which will give the location of the next instruction word to be used in the program. If, however, the instruction is a TRANSFER instruction, we may wish to place another number into this counter. It is necessary to clear the counter to 0 when a program is started.[3]

[3]Most machines make it possible to load a selected address into the operation counter and thereby start the machine at that selected address.

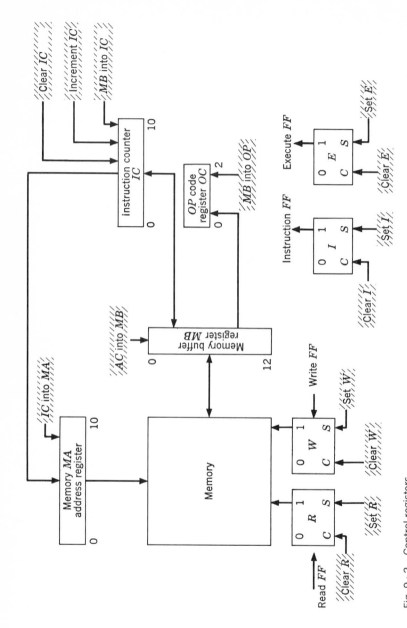

Fig. 9 · 2 Control registers.

It must also be possible to transfer the contents of this counter into the memory address register, which is used to locate a word in memory. Normally, the instruction counter will be increased by 1 during the performance of each instruction, and the contents of the counter will be transferred into the memory address register at the beginning of each instruction time.

2   *The Operation-code Register.* When an instruction word is read from the memory, the operation-code section of this word must be stored in order to determine what instruction is to be performed. If the computer has an operation code with a length of five binary digits, the operation register will be five binary digits in length and will contain the operation code part of the instruction word which is read from the memory. We must therefore be able to transfer a section of the memory buffer register into the operation-code register during the instruction time period.

3   *The Memory Address Register.* This register contains the location of the word in memory to be read or the location to be written into.

4   *R Flip-flop.* When this flip-flop is turned on, it tells the memory to read a word. (The flip-flop is turned off shortly thereafter, for it need not be on during the entire memory cycle.)

5   *W Flip-flop.* Turning this flip-flop on tells the memory to write the word located in the memory buffer register at the location given by the memory address register.

6   *I Flip-flop.* When this flip-flop is on, the computer is in an instruction cycle.

7   *E Flip-flop.* When this flip-flop is on, the machine is in an execution cycle.

9 · 4   Sequence of operation of control registers

Let us further consider the construction of the control circuitry of a digital machine. A block diagram of the control register's memory, memory address register, and memory buffer register is shown in Fig. 9 · 2. This figure shows the instruction counter and the operation register which were discussed in the previous section, as well as WRITE and READ (W and R) flip-flops which tell the memory whether it should write a word into the memory or read a word from the memory. It also shows an *I* flip-flop which tells the computer whether or not it is an instruction cycle, and an *E* flip-flop which tells the computer when it is in an execution cycle.

The control signals necessary to the operation of this small single-address machine are also shown on the diagram and are as follows: There is a CLEAR IC line which will clear the instruction counter to 0. (This is often connected to a pushbutton which clears the counter when the program is to be started.) There is an **MB INTO IC** control signal which causes the contents of the memory buffer register to be transferred into the instruction counter, and there is an **INCREMENT IC** control signal which causes the instruction counter to be incremented by 1. This counter could be constructed as shown in Fig. 4·20, except that we would need also the control logic in Fig. 6·4 which is used to transfer the contents of one register into another. In this case, we would have the memory buffer register as the lower register in Fig. 6·4 and the instruction counter as the upper register. Another control signal is the **MB INTO OP** which transfers the first five digits of the memory buffer register which contains the operation code of an instruction word into the five flip-flops in the operation register. The memory address register has two control signals. The **IC INTO MA** control signal causes the contents of the instruction counter to be transferred into the memory address register, and the **MB INTO MA** control signal causes the last 16 digits of the memory buffer register (which comprise the address part of an instruction word) to be transferred into the memory address register.

During each instruction cycle of the machine we must first turn the READ flip-flop on, and at the same time (or earlier) transfer the contents of the instruction counter into the memory address register. The memory will now read an instruction word into the memory buffer register, after which time we can enable the **MBR INTO OP** line, transferring the operation-code section of the instruction word into the operation-code register. The next actions which the machine will take will now be dependent upon the contents of the operation-code register.

9·5 Controlling arithmetic operations

Consider the problem of directing the arithmetic element as it performs an instruction word. Let us add an accumulator and a B register to the registers in Fig. 9·2, thus forming the block diagram shown in Fig. 9·3. There are five more control signals which are required to perform such instructions as add, subtract, clear and add, and store. These are:

1 *CLEAR ACCUMULATOR.* This signal sets all the flip-flops in the accumulator to 0. Figure 6·1 showed a block diagram of a possible configuration for clearing a register.

2 *ADD.* This signal causes the B register to be added to the accumulator and the sum transferred into the accumulator.

3 *SUBTRACT.* This signal causes the B register to be subtracted from the accumulator and the difference placed in the accumulator.

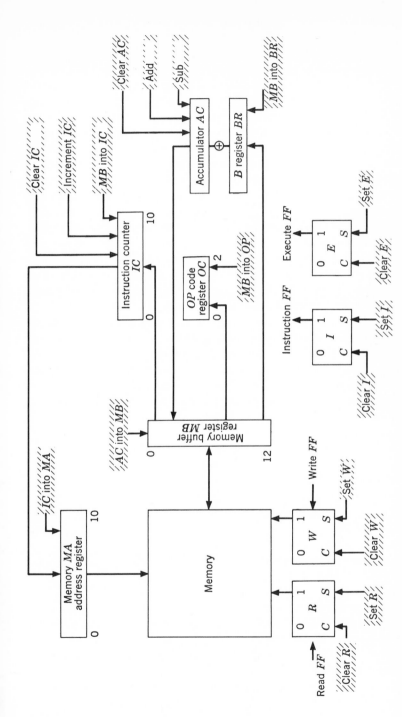

Fig. 9·3   Control registers and arithmetic registers.

4   *MB INTO BR*. This signal transfers the memory buffer register into the *B* register.
5   *AC INTO MB*. This causes the contents of the accumulator to be transferred into the memory buffer register.

Figure 9·4 shows a single accumulator flip-flop and a single *B* register flip-flop, along with the control signals and gates required for these operations. The accumulator and *B* register are basically composed of as many of these blocks as there are bits in the basic computer word. (The carry into the least significant bit is connected to the SUBTRACT signal when 2's complement addition is used, or to the carry-out of the sign digit when the 1's complement system is used.)

One further thing is needed. We must distribute our control signals in an orderly manner; some sort of a time base which will indicate where we are in the sequence of operations to be performed is required. In order to do this, each memory cycle is broken into four equal time periods, the first of which we call T_0, the second T_1, the third T_2, and the fourth T_3. If we are in the first of these time periods, we need a signal which will tell us it is now time T_0; then during the second period we need a signal which will tell us it is time T_1, etc.

Figure 9·5 shows two ways of generating such timing signals. Both have a clock signal input, and the clock is assumed to be running so that during a memory cycle we obtain four clock pulses. If it requires 2 μsec to read into or write from the memory, a clock pulse will be generated every ½ μsec. Therefore, the clock will run at a rate of 2 megacycles.

Both of the circuits shown have four output lines which are designated T_0, T_1, T_2, and T_3. When the machine is in time period T_0, the output line T_0 will carry a 1 signal and T_1, T_2, and T_3 will be 0's; at time T_1 only, line T_1 will have a 1 signal on it, etc. (The ring counter is started in state 1000; a check will indicate the 1 is continually circulated.)

Let us now write, in a short table, the sequence of operations which must occur during each of the ADD, SUBTRACT, CLEAR AND ADD, and STORE instructions. Notice that when the instruction-cycle flip-flop I is on, the operations during times T_0 and T_1 are always the same. In Table 9·3 the control signal to be turned on or made a 1 is listed to the left and what the signal does is listed to the right.

From the above table of operations, it is possible to design the control section of this small machine. The inputs are the operation code stored in the OP-code register, the timing-signal distributor, and the I and E flip-flops.

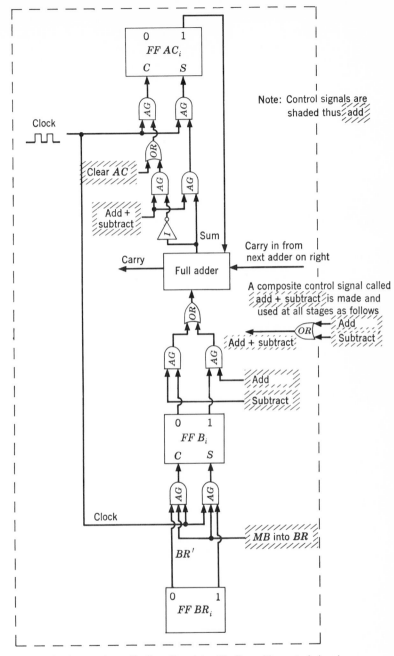

Fig. 9 · 4 Accumulator flip-flop–*B*-register flip-flop with control signals.

TABLE 9·3   SEQUENCING OF CONTROL SIGNALS

ADD	LIST OF CONTROL SIGNALS TO BE TURNED ON	COMMENTS
I and T_0	SET R	Tells memory to read instruction word.
I and T_1	MB INTO OP, CLEAR R	Transfers OP-code part of instruction word into OP-code register; turns READ flip-flop off.
I and T_2	INCREMENT IC	Add one to the instruction counter preparing for the next instruction.
I and T_3	MB INTO MA, CLEAR I, SET E	Transfers the address part of the instruction word (which is in the memory buffer register) into the memory address register. Puts the machine in an execute mode.
E and T_0	SET R	Turns the READ flip-flop on, telling the memory to read a word.
E and T_1	MB INTO BR, CLEAR R	Transfers the contents of the memory buffer register into the B register. Since the memory buffer register now contains what was read from the memory, it is the augend which is transferred into the B register; also turns READ flip-flop off.
E and T_2	ADD	The contents of the accumulator are added to the B register and the sum placed in the
E and T_3	IC INTO MA, SET I, CLEAR E	accumulator. The contents of the instruction counter are transferred into the memory address register, giving the location of the next instruction word to the memory. The instruction-cycle flip-flop is turned on and the execution-cycle flip-flop turned off.

CLEAR AND ADD	LIST OF CONTROL SIGNALS TO BE TURNED ON	COMMENTS
I and T_0	SET R	Tells memory to read instruction word.
I and T_1	MB INTO OP, CLEAR	Transfers OP-code part of instruction word into OP-code register; turns READ flip-flop off.
I and T_2	INCREMENT IC	Add one to the instruction counter, preparing for the next instruction.
I and T_3	MB INTO MA, CLEAR I, SET E	Transfers the address part of the instruction word (which is in the memory buffer register) into the memory address register.
E and T_0	SET R	Turns the READ flip-flop on telling the memory to read a word.
E and T_1	MB INTO BR, CLEAR AC	Transfers the memory buffer register into the B register and also clears the accumulator so if the B register is now added to the accumulator, the accumulator will contain the word read from memory.
E and T_2	ADD	The contents of the accumulator are added to the B register and the sum placed in the accumulator.
E and T_3	IC INTO MA, SET I, CLEAR E	The contents of the instruction counter are transferred into the memory address register, giving the location of the next instruction word to the memory. The instruction-cycle flip-flop is turned on and the execution-cycle flip-flop turned off.

SUBTRACT	LIST OF CONTROL SIGNALS TO BE TURNED ON	COMMENTS
I and T_0	SET R	Tells memory to read instruction word.
I and T_1	MB INTO OP, CLEAR R	Transfer OP-code part of instruction word into OP-code register; turns READ flip-flop off.
I and T_2	INCREMENT IC	Add one to the instruction counter preparing for the next instruction.
I and T_3	MB INTO MA, CLEAR I, SET E	Transfer the address part of the instruction word (which is in the memory buffer register) into the memory address register. Puts the machine in an execute mode.
E and T_0	SET R	Turns the READ flip-flop on, telling the memory to read a word.
E and T_1	MB INTO BR, CLEAR R	Transfers the contents of the memory buffer register into the B register. Since the memory buffer register now contains what was read from the memory, it is the augend which is transferred into the B register; also turns READ flip-flop off.
E and T_2	SUB	The contents of the accumulator are added to the B register and the sum placed in the accumulator.
E and T_3	IC INTO MA, SET I, CLEAR E	The contents of the instruction counter are transferred into the memory address register, giving the location of the next instruction word to the memory. The instruction-cycle flip-flop is turned on and the execution-cycle flip-flop turned off.

STORE	LIST OF CONTROL SIGNALS TO BE TURNED ON	COMMENTS
I and T_0	SET R	Tells memory to read instruction word.
I and T_1	MB INTO OP, CLEAR R	Transfers OP-code part of instruction word into OP-code register; turns READ flip-flop off.
I and T_2	INCREMENT IC	Add one to the instruction counter, preparing for the next instruction.
I and T_3	MB INTO MA, CLEAR I, SET E	Transfers the address part of the instruction word (which is in the memory buffer register) into the memory address register.
E and T_0	SET W, AC INTO MBR	Transfers word to be read into memory from accumulator into the memory buffer register.
E and T_1	CLEAR W	Turns WRITE flip-flop off.
E and T_2		
E and T_3	IC INTO MA, SET I, CLEAR E	The contents of the instruction counter are transferred into the memory address register, giving the location of the next instruction word to the memory. The instruction-cycle flip-flop is turned on and the execution-cycle flip-flop turned off.

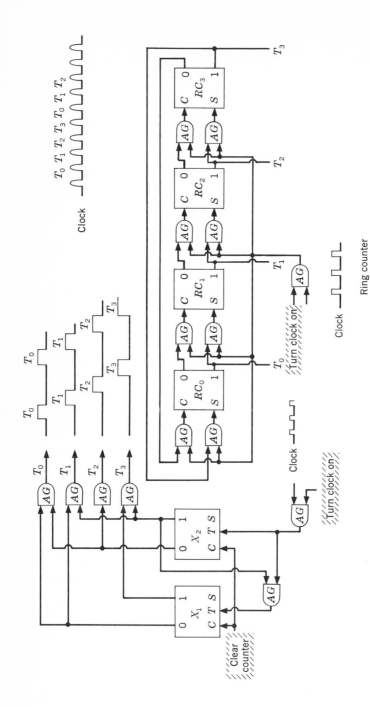

Fig. 9 · 5   Two types of timing-signal distributors.

Notice, for instance, that when it is time T_0 and we are in an instruction cycle, we always turn the READ flip-flop on, telling the memory to read the instruction word located at the address in the memory address register. Then we assume that the memory places this word in the memory buffer register before time T_1, so at time T_1 we transfer the operation-code part of the instruction word into the OP-code register. These two facts tell us that we should logically AND the output line T_0 from the timing-signal distributor with the 1 output of the I flip-flop, and connect the $T_0 \cdot I$ signal to the SET input of the READ flip-flop; and then we should connect a $T_1 \cdot I$ signal to the control line which transfers the first 5 bits of the MB into the OP register. This is shown in Fig. 9 · 6.

What happens next is always dependent on the OP-code register, so we now connect a decoder matrix with $2^5 = 32$ outputs to that register (assuming we will use all the combinations by adding more instructions). We then have a set of signal lines, so that line $00000 = $ ADD will carry a 1 signal when we are adding (since the operation code for ADD is 00000); $00001 = $ SUB will carry a 1 if, and only if, we are subtracting, since the OP code for subtract is 00001; $00010 = $ CLA will be a 1 only when we clear and add, etc. We combine these lines and the timing-signal distributor lines and the I and E flip-flop lines to give us all the control signal needed to run the machine. Figure 9 · 6 shows the complete control circuitry required. A comparison of this figure with the timing and control-signal chart will show how the control circuitry words and signals are manufactured when they are needed.

More instructions can be added by adding to the timing and control-signal chart and also by adding the required gates to the control circuitry. Analyzing the machine in this way, we can already see how the control circuitry directs the operations performed in the machine, alternating the acquiring of instructions from the memory and the performance of the instructions.

9 · 6   Typical sequence of operations

It will be instructive to analyze the control circuitry in Fig. 9 · 6 during an addition instruction and a STORE instruction. Each instruction will be started with the I (instruction cycle) flip-flop on, and with the timing-signal distributor having an output on line T_0 so that the AND gate at the upper right of the figure will be turned on by I and T_0, thus setting the READ flip-flop to the 1 state and initiating a read from the memory. At this time, the memory address register is assumed to have the address of the instruction which will read into the memory buffer register.

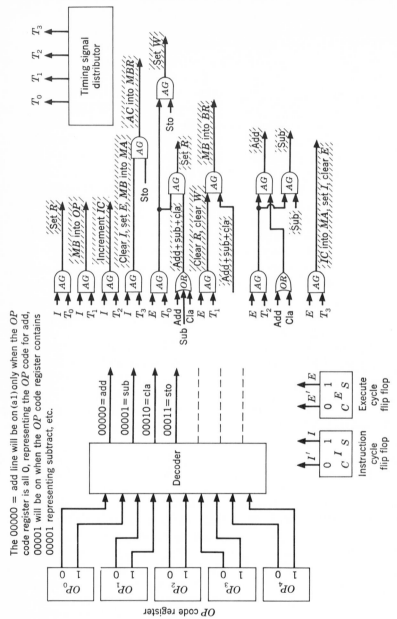

Fig. 9·6 Control circuitry for four-instruction computer.

By time T_1, the word read from the memory will have been read into the memory buffer register so that when we have the control state I and T_1, the contents of the memory buffer register which comprise the OP-code section of the instruction will be transferred into the operation code register, and the computer will be in a position to decode the operation code and determine what instruction is to be performed.

At time I and T_2 the instruction counter is incremented by 1 so that the instruction counter now contains the address of the next instruction to be read from the memory. The AND gate connected to the I and T_2 input signals is used to turn on the INCREMENT IC control signal, and its output is designated with the name of that control signal.

Similarly, at time I and T_3 the memory buffer register is transferred into the memory address register by the MB INTO MA signal, thus transferring the address part of the instruction word into the memory address register. The next word read from the memory or written into the memory will then be at the address designated by the address part of the instruction word which was just read from the memory.

At the same time, the instruction cycle flip-flop is cleared by the CLEAR I signal and the execution flip-flop is set on by the SET E signal, thus changing the state of the machine from an instruction cycle to an execution cycle.

At time E and T_0 then, during an ADD instruction, we set the R flip-flop on, thus telling the memory to read the word at the address currently in the memory address register. In this case, this address will be the address part of the instruction word which is being executed. Then, at time E and T_1 we transfer the contents of the memory buffer register into the BR. The memory buffer register at that time contains the word which has been read from the memory, so that we now have the word which has been addressed by the instruction word in the B register for the addition. At the same time, we clear the READ flip-flop.

Notice that the CLEAR R and CLEAR W lines are used to clear both the READ and the WRITE flip-flop simultaneously. There is no harm in clearing both flip-flops, since only one will be on at any given time.

If the instruction is an ADD instruction at time E and T_2, we shall add the contents of the B register to the contents of the accumulator. Since the B register contains the word which has been read from the memory and since the accumulator has not been changed, the sum will then be transferred into the accumulator so that the sum of the word read from the memory and the previous contents of the accumulator will now lie in the accumulator. Then, at time E and T_3 we transfer the instruction counter into the memory address register (thus giving the address of the next instruction to be performed to the memory), at the same time clearing the EXECUTE flip-flop, setting the instruction cycle flip-flop on, and changing the machine from an execution cycle flip-flop to an instruction cycle.

Since the I flip-flop is on and it is time T_0, the SET R control line will now go high thus telling the memory to read a word. The next instruction word will be read from the memory and can then be interpreted.

Let us also examine the operation of the STORE instruction which was just described. When the instruction flip-flop is on and we are in an instruction cycle when time T_0 arrives, the R flip-flop will be set on telling the memory to read just as for an addition, subtraction, or clear and add; and the same thing will happen during time I and T_1. Since the memory-buffer-register flip-flops now contain the operation code of the instruction at time I and T_1 it will be transferred into the OP-code register.

At time I and T_2, we will increment the instruction counter so that the address of the next instruction in memory now lies in the instruction counter; and at time I and T_3, we will clear the instruction flip-flops and turn on the execution-cycle flip-flop, thus putting the machine in an execution cycle.

At time E and T_0, however, if the instruction is a STORE instruction, we will set the WRITE flip-flop on instead of the READ flip-flop, thus initiating a write into the memory. We will also transfer the contents of the accumulator into the memory buffer register, so that the word written into the memory will be the current contents of the accumulator register, and so that after the WRITE cycle has been terminated, the accumulator will have been written into the memory at the address which was given by the instruction word.

At time E and T_1, we simply clear the WRITE flip-flop for we have already told the memory to write; nothing need be done for we are now writing the word into the memory. At time E and T_3 the instruction counter is transferred into the memory address register by the IC INTO MA control signal, thus giving the address of the next instruction to the memory. The instruction-cycle flip-flop is turned on and the execution-cycle flip-flop turned off, thus turning the machine to the instruction-cycle state. The machine will now execute an instruction cycle by reading the next instruction word from the memory, interpreting it, and continuing onward in the program.

The preceding example demonstrates how it is possible to logically design a machine which will execute a given sequence of operations and thereby cause the machine to perform each instruction word which is read from the memory. Although only four instructions were demonstrated in this particular example, more instructions can be added in exactly the same manner by simply writing down what must be done when an instruction word is read from the memory, listing the operations which must be performed, and providing gates which will generate the control signals necessary to the performance of each instruction. Subsequent sections will discuss shifting, branching instructions, floating-point instructions, and indexing instructions. All of these may be incorporated into the machine shown by simply adding gates to the control circuitry and providing for the additional gates necessary for the transfers and operations between the registers of the machine.

It is possible to implement control circuitry in other ways. A particular technique called microprogramming was invented by A. D. Booth, and the references contain a description of this particular technique. Essentially, this technique consists of using a read-only memory and letting the operation-code part of the instruction word address the read-only memory. The control signals are read from the read-only memory instead of being formed by a gating network as shown in the previous example. Also, the next address of a control word may be read from the memory. There are some advantages of this system and it has been used in a few machines. In actual practice, microprogramming is not too different from the technique shown, however, simply being an implementation of the design technique which has just been demonstrated and which provides some additional flexibility in that the operation codes and interpretation of the instructions may be changed by changing the contents of the read-only memory which stores the sequence of control signals to be executed.

The general form of the control-signal generating scheme is shown in Fig. 9 · 7. It shows a timing-pulse distributor with eight different time divisions; each time would be one-eighth of the memory-cycle time.

9 · 7   Branch-type instructions

The BRANCH or TRANSFER instruction varies from the normal instruction in several ways.[4] For single-address machines, only one word, the instruction word, must be located in memory. Also the contents of the instruction counter may be modified instead of being simply increased by one. There are two types of BRANCH instructions, conditional and unconditional. For the unconditional

---

[4]A survey indicates that about half the manufacturers call these instructions BRANCH instructions and the other half call them TRANSFER instructions.

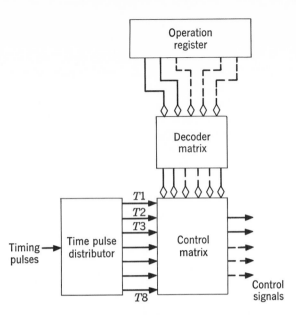

Fig. 9 · 7   General configuration of control circuitry.

BRANCH instruction, the contents of the address register are always transferred into the instruction counter. The next instruction performed will then be the instruction at the location indicated by the address section of the instruction word. In most single-address machines, however, the conditional BRANCH instruction will cause the machine to branch only if the number stored in the accumulator register of the arithmetic element is negative. If the number in the accumulator is positive, the contents of the instruction counter will simply be increased by one, and the next instruction will be taken in the normal order.

During a conditional BRANCH instruction, the sign bit of the accumulator of the arithmetic element must be examined by control circuitry. If the sign bit is a 1, the number stored is negative, and so the number in the address register is transferred into the instruction counter. If the sign bit is a 0, a 1 is added to the instruction counter and the computer proceeds.

In order to demonstrate how a typical BRANCH-ON-MINUS instruction (BRM) operates in a single-address computer, we will modify the control circuitry shown in Fig. 9 · 6 so that the small machine will also include a BRM instruction. Let us give the operation code 00100 to BRM, so that the line beneath the 00011 = STO line will be high from the decoder attached to the OP-code register in Fig. 9 · 6 when a BRM instruction is in the register.

The first two cycles of the instruction are the same as all cycles. First, the memory is told to read and then the instruction word is read from the memory into the memory buffer register. This word is then transferred into the OP-code register so that after time T_1 and the beginning of time T_2, the line $00100 = $ BRM will be high and all the other output lines from the decoder will be low. Now, let us make a small table for a BRANCH-ON-MINUS instruction showing what must be done in order to carry out this instruction. Table $9 \cdot 4$ shows the steps which must be taken.

If at time T_2 during the instruction cycle, a BRM instruction OP code is in the OP-code register, one of two things must happen. We wish to either increment the instruction counter and give this number as the address of the next instruction to be taken from the memory, or we wish to transfer the contents of the address portion of the instruction word into the instruction counter. Which of the two choices we take depends upon the sign bit of the accumulator which is called AC_0. If the accumulator contains a negative number, it will have a 1 in AC_0 and if it contains a positive number, it will have a 0 in flip-flop 0. Therefore, if I and T_2 AND AC_0', we want to increment the instruction counter; and if I AND T_2 AND AC_0 happens to be the

TABLE $9 \cdot 4$

BRANCH ON MINUS	LIST OF CONTROL SIGNALS TO BE TURNED ON	COMMENTS
I and T_0	SET R	Tells memory to read instruction word.
I and T_1	MB INTO OP, CLEAR R	Transfers OP-code part of Instruction word into OP-code register; turns READ flip-flop off.
I and T_2 and AC_0'	INCREMENT IC	If the sign digit of the accumulator AC_0 is a 0, we want to increment the instruction counter and use its contents as the address of the next instruction.
I and T_2 and AC_0	MB INTO IC	If the sign digit of the accumulator is a 1, the accumulator is negative, and we want to use the address in the instruction word as the address of the next instruction word.
I and T_3	IC INTO MA	This transfers the instruction counter into the memory address register. Notice the E flip-flop is not turned on as we are ready to read another instruction word; and EXECUTE cycle is not needed.

case, we wish to transfer the memory buffer register into the instruction counter. This is shown in the table above. During time T_3 of this instruction cycle, we want to transfer the instruction counter into the memory address register. We do not need to put the machine in an execution cycle, but can simply continue on to another instruction cycle, taking the word which has been the contents the address of which has been transferred into the memory address register as the next instruction. Therefore, we do not clear the instruction-cycle flip-flop or put a 1 in the execute-cycle flip-flop, but simply transfer the instruction counter into the memory address register.

The control circuitry which will implement these operations is shown in Fig. 9·8. The meaning of this is that the two particular AND gates in Fig. 9·6 which are connected to the I,T_2 and I,T_3 inputs will be replaced with the two circuits shown in Fig. 9·8. Notice that this logical circuitry, plus the circuitry in 9·6, is all that is needed

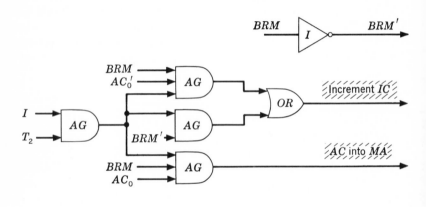

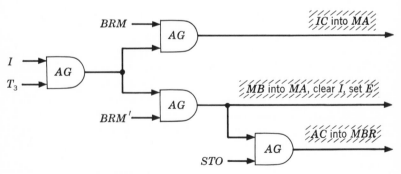

Fig. 9·8 Modification of control circuitry for BRANCH instruction.

to generate the control signals required for the BRANCH-ON-MINUS instruction.

Notice also that a BRM′ signal (the complement of BRM) is used rather than ORing together the instructions which are NOT BRANCH-ON-MINUS instructions. This saves control circuitry in that BRM′ can be made as shown in the figure by simply connecting the BRM signal to an inverter and designating this as BRM′.

Notice that the BRANCH-ON-MINUS instruction requires only one access to memory, and therefore only one instruction cycle for its execution.

For multiple-address computers, more trips to memory are sometimes required, as the unconditional BRANCH instruction may require the comparison of two numbers stored in memory. For instance, consider a three-address computer with the addresses a, b, and c. If the computer is to branch when the contents of $a < b$ and not branch when $a \geq b$, the number in locations a and b must be located in memory and the number from location b subtracted from the number at location a, and if the result is negative, the contents of register c are transferred into the instruction counter. If the result of the subtraction is positive, a 1 is added to the instruction counter (0 is here treated as a positive number).

9 · 8   SHIFT instructions

The instructions we have examined to date have been instructions which were always performed within a basic fixed number of memory cycles; that is, the ADD, SUBTRACT, CLEAR AND ADD, and STORE instructions were performed within exactly two memory cycles and the TRANSFER or BRANCH instructions required only one memory cycle. There are several classes or types of instructions which may require several memory cycles, because the instruction cannot be performed within, say, two memory cycles. Typical of these instructions are multiplication and division, which generally require more time than the two memory cycles normally require. Similarly, an instruction such as shift right or shift left could conceivably be performed in a single-memory cycle, since the operand is in the accumulator when the instruction word is obtained. However, if the instruction calls for a large number of shifts, it may require more than a memory cycle to complete the number of operations which are required. In this case, we could not initiate another memory cycle until we had finished shifting the requisite number of times. Similarly, for multiplication and division we could not initiate another memory cycle until we had finished our multiplication and division process.

In order to implement these types of instructions, we will therefore hand our control of the machine over to a simple control element which is dominated by a counter. This counter will sequence and count the number of steps which must be performed until the instruction has been completed, and will then put the machine in an instruction cycle and tell the memory to read the next instruction word.

The SHIFT-RIGHT instruction consists of two parts: an operation code and an address part. The operation code of 00101 tells the machine to shift the word in the accumulator right the number of times given in the address part, so that if we write 00101 for the OP code in an instruction word and then write 8 in binary form in the address part, the machine has been instructed to shift the binary number in the accumulator right eight binary digits.

Assuming that we have an accumulator with gates so that we can shift the accumulator digits right as was explained in Chap. 6, all we need is to apply eight consecutive SHIFT-RIGHT control signals to the accumulator and we will have shifted the number right eight places. Since there are only four pulses per memory cycle, we will not want to use the memory until we have completed our shifting. If, for instance, the instruction said shift right one, we could finish in one pulse time and start the next instruction cycle immediately after; but if the instruction word said shift right four, five or fifteen or more times, we would have to wait until we had completed shifting before we could initiate another instruction cycle and fetch the next instruction word from the memory.

In order to do this, we first prepare the machine for the shifting operation by incrementing the instruction counter so that the next word obtained from the instruction counter will contain the address of the next instruction word; and in order to count the number of shifts that we perform, we add another register called the step-counter register, which is a counter that counts downward from a given number to 0. We then transfer the memory-buffer-register address part into the step counter, so that the step counter contains the number of shifts to be performed. Then each time we shift, we decrement the counter by 1, so that when the counter reaches 0, we will have performed the requisite number of shifts.

Figure 9 · 9 shows two stages of a decrementing counter and also shows the gates necessary to transfer the memory-buffer-register contents into the step counter, which is designated as SC. The two rightmost or least significant digits of the counter are shown (SC_{n-1} and SC_n), as are also the two rightmost digits of the memory buffer register (MB_{n-1} and MB_n).

The actual number of stages in the step counter will be determined by the maximum number of shifts which the machine must ever make; and, since we will also use the same counter for multiplication

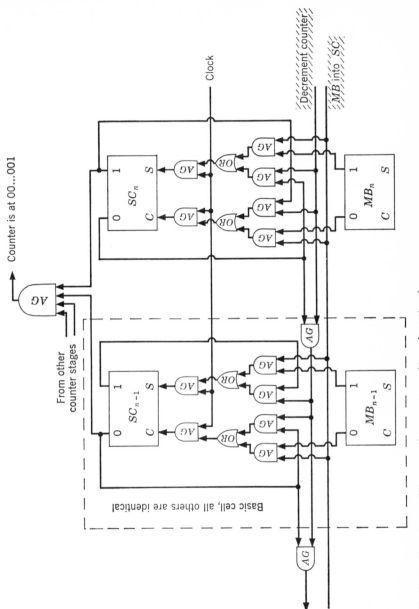

Counter is at 00…001

Clock

Decrement counter

MB into SC

From other counter stages

Basic cell, all others are identical

Fig. 9 · 9   Two stages of decrementing-counter and transfer network.

and division, by the maximum number of steps which will ever be required to multiply or divide. For a machine containing 21 binary digits in the basic computer word, the counter might well contain five flip-flops. For a machine with a basic computer word of perhaps 35 or 36 binary digits, the step counter might well contain six or even seven flip-flops.

Let us examine a possible sequence of operations for a SHIFT instruction. Times I AND T_0 and I AND T_1 are as usual. At I AND T_2 we increment the instruction counter. At time I AND T_3, we set a flip-flop called SR ON which tells the machine to start shifting. At the same time we clear the I flip-flop, so that the machine is in neither an instruction nor execution cycle, although it is actually executing an instruction. In this way, we do not initiate subsequent memory cycles and the machine effectively freezes in the shifting state until the SC has counted to 0, indicating that the requisite number of shifts have been performed. (Actually, notice that the step counter counts only to binary 1 rather than to 0 before the order to stop counting is given, for counting when the counter is at 0 would introduce an extra shift.) If we turn the counter SR flip-flop off when the output of the counter is at 00 . . . 001 signal and if we at the same time, turn the I or instruction cycle on, the machine will proceed to the next instruction cycle fetching the next instruction word from the memory and performing it. Table 9 · 5 shows this.

When the SR flip-flop is on, it will be necessary to stop the timing-signal distributor, so we arrange to disable this circuit using the SR flip-flop's output for this purpose.

Implementation of the above is straightforward. A three-input

TABLE 9 · 5

TIME	CONTROL SIGNAL TURNED ON	COMMENTS
I and T_0	SET R	Tells memory to read.
I and T_1	MB INTO OP, CLEAR R	OP code of instruction word is transferred into OP-code register. READ flip-flop is turned off.
I and T_2	INCREMENT IC, MB INTO SC	The instruction counter is prepared to obtain the next instruction word. The address part of the instruction word is transferred into the memory buffer register.
I and T_3	CLEAR I, SET SR	The instruction cycle flip-flop is turned off. The shift-right flip-flop is turned on.

AND gate with inputs I, T_3 and $00101 = SHR$ (the output from the decoder in Fig. 9·6) can be used to turn an SR flip-flop on and stop output from the step counter to turn it off, also turning I on. The input to the clock can be turned off when SR is on.

9·9 Multiplication—the use of algorithms in computer design

The preceding explanation of how the control circuits of a general-purpose computer are organized has shown how control signals which initiate operations within the registers of the machine can be generated in a given sequence, which is at the discretion of the designer of the machine. In each case, we analyzed the operation of the machine by writing the steps which the computer performs in order to add, subtract, branch, or perform other instructions. Then by examining the timing charts and the block diagrams of the circuitry, we saw how the machine followed out the instructions which were given to it in the instruction words.

When more complicated instructions such as multiplication and division are performed, the process is nevertheless essentially the same. The machine must perform a sequence of operations on the operational registers of the machine and on the word stored in the memory in order to execute a given instruction word. When we write down precisely the steps that must be carried out in order to affect a given instruction, we are writing what is called an algorithm. If an instruction word says "shift the accumulator right ten times" and we write down exactly what must be done to affect this instruction, we are writing an algorithm for a SHIFT-RIGHT operation. The table given for the SHIFT-RIGHT instruction is an example of such an algorithm. The logic circuits shown in the two stages of the decrementing counter and the block diagrams show the implementation of this algorithm.

The techniques which are used to multiply and divide and to perform other operations, such as converting binary-coded-decimal numbers to binary or binary numbers to decimal, are all examples of algorithms. We will examine an algorithm invented by A. D. Booth which is very widely used for multiplication. Mathematical details and justification of this algorithm may be found in the paper given in the reference. This algorithm shows a remarkably simple and direct way to multiply two binary numbers which are represented in 2's complement form. When this algorithm is used, two binary numbers in 2's complement form can be multiplied directly, complete with sign digits, and the product will be stored as a signed binary 2's complement number correctly represented in the machine.

In order to implement this algorithm and explain it, we will require an accumulator, B register, and memory buffer register as in Fig. 9 · 4, and a step counter as was explained previously. One other register is still required. It is called an MQ register (for Multiplier-Quotient register), and it must have the logical circuitry necessary so that we can transfer the accumulator contents into the MQ and shift the MQ register right at the same time we shift the accumulator right. That is, the combined accumulator and MQ are shifted right with the least significant digit of the accumulator being shifted into the sign digit of the MQ.

An instruction word for multiply in a binary single-address machine consists of two parts—an operation code (consisting of five binary digits for the simple machine we have been explaining) which tells the machine to multiply, and an address which tells where in the memory to find the multiplicand. The multiplicand is then multiplied by the number already in the accumulator. (It does not matter whether we call the number in the accumulator the multiplier or multiplicand or call the number in memory the multiplier or multiplicand, since $a \times b = b \times a$.)

When the OP code for multiplication is interpreted, the multiplier is in the accumulator and the multiplicand is in the memory (refer to Fig. 9 · 10). First, the contents of the accumulator, which will be the multiplier, are transferred into the MQ; then the multiplicand is read from the memory, so that the multiplicand will be in the memory buffer register. Then the multiplicand is transferred into the B register, and at the same time the step counter is set to a binary number equal to the number of operations which must be performed. This will be equal to the number of digits in the basic binary word.

To the right of the MQ in Fig. 9 · 10 is a flip-flop designated M into which the rightmost digit of the MQ is shifted when the accumulator-MQ is shifted right.

To begin with, a 0 is put in M. The rightmost digit of the MQ is examined as is also the digit in the M flip-flop, which will of course be at a 0 during the first operation. The rules for the Booth algorithm are then followed. (The rules for the Booth algorithm are also shown in Fig. 9 · 10.) Quite simply, at each step of the algorithm the control circuitry examines the rightmost or least significant digit of the MQ and the contents of the M register. These two binary digits can be in one of four possible states: (1) If both of these digits are 1's or both are 0's, the combined accumulator-MQ register is shifted right, thus shifting the rightmost digit of the MQ into M and initiating another step; again examining the least significant digit of the MQ and M. (2) If the $MQ = 1$ and $M = 0$, the B register, which contains the multiplicand, is subtracted from the accumulator and then the combined AC and MQ register is shifted to the right one place, with the

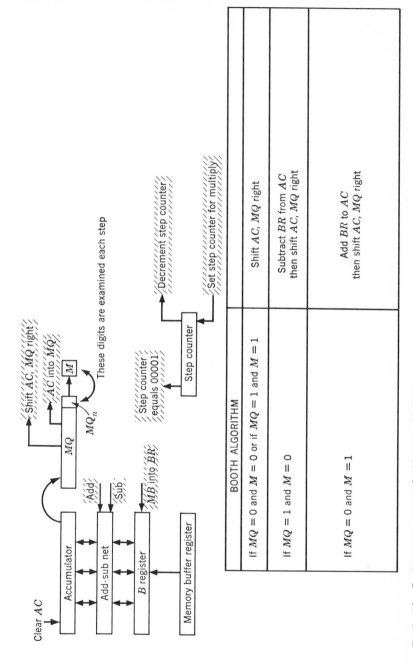

Fig. 9·10 Register arrangement for binary multiplication.

rightmost digit of the MQ again going into the M flip-flop. Then, another step is initiated. (3) If the MQ digit is a 0 and M is a 1, the B register is added to the accumulator and then the accumulator and MQ registers are shifted right, with the least significant digit of the MQ again going into M. Then, another step is initiated.

Each of the above operations is considered to be a single step in the algorithm, and as many steps are performed as there are digits in the basic computer word. After the performance of these steps, the product of the initial contents of the B register times the contents of the MQ will be stored in the combined accumulator-MQ register, except that the rightmost digit of the MQ will simply contain the sign of the multiplier (since when we multiply two N-digit numbers together, the product can have as many as $2N$ digits plus sign). Our original numbers each contained N digits of magnitude plus a sign; so the product will be equal to $2N$ plus 1 digit for the sign digit. This sign will be in the sign digit of the accumulator.

Let us now study the implementation of the Booth algorithm for multiplication. We see that four control signals must be generated— one to decrement the step counter, one which shifts the accumulator-MQ right, another which causes a subtraction of the B register from the accumulator, and still another which causes the addition of the B register to the accumulator. Since we must subtract before we shift right, or add before we shift right on some occasions, we will need at least one flip-flop to keep track of where we are. (Unless we provide for an addition and shift right and an addition or a subtraction and a shift right simultaneously.)

Figure 9 · 11 shows the logical circuitry necessary to generate all four of these control signals. We assume that we have a logical gating network necessary to (1) add the accumulator to the B register or subtract the B register from the accumulator; (2) shift the accumulator-MQ right, also shifting the least significant bit digit of the MQ into the M digit; and (3) the step counter as shown in Fig. 9 · 9. Now notice that the circuit in Fig. 9 · 11 operates as follows: If MQ_n is equal to M, we immediately tell the machine to shift, also decrementing the step counter, since the step counter is decremented when the AC-MQ shifted right. If, however, the MQ_n equals a 0 and M equals a 1, a SUBTRACT signal is generated at once. Also, the ADD OR SHIFT flip-flop will be in the 0 state and the circuitry will set the ADD OR SHIFT flip-flop to a 1. When the ADD OR SHIFT flip-flop is equal to 1 and the next clock pulse arrives, the AC-MQ is shifted right and the set counter is then decremented. The shifting of the AC-MQ right will cause a new pair of digits to be in MQ_n and M. If MQ_n equals a 1 and M equals a 0, we immediately tell the machine to subtract and set the ADD OR SHIFT flip-flop on. The next clock

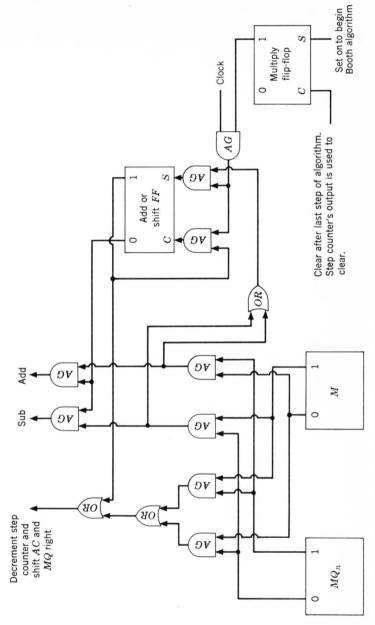

Fig. 9·11 Implementation of the Booth algorithm for multiplication.

pulse will then cause the machine to decrement the step counter and shift $AC\text{-}MQ$ right, and at the same time clear the ADD OR SHIFT flip-flop to 0. We will then examine the next MQ_n and M.

When the step counter indicates that we have performed the requisite number of operations, it will transfer control back to the main machine by turning on the I flip-flop. The multiplication will have been performed, and the product will be stored in the accumulator-MQ registers.

Because of the direct and simple implementation of the Booth algorithm for multiplication, it is safe to say that this is the most used algorithm for binary multiplication of numbers.

9 · 10   Distributed and centralized control

The control circuits for most of the earlier machines were distributed throughout the machine. The circuits which would cause the machine to add were located in one part of the machine and the circuits which would cause the machine to multiply in another. The function of the central control was therefore very limited. For instance, the operation decoder would simply energize the circuitry which would cause an addition; the necessary set of operations was directed by a small control circuit specifically designed to sequence the addition process, and then control was transferred back to the central control. Later machines tended to centralize the control element so that all the control circuits were interrelated and located in the same place and all the control signals throughout the machine originated in central control. This has proven to be an excellent technique for smaller machines.

Some of the newer very large machines are multiple-sequence machines, and there is again a tendency to decentralize control and construct smaller control elements which are distributed throughout the machine. In this way, a large machine can perform several sets of operations at the same time. For instance, the machine can be carrying out a series of calculations on numbers already stored while reading new information into the memory or printing the results of previous computations. However, the various parts of the machine must be capable of temporarily interrupting the flow of operations performed by other parts, so that the total amount of control circuitry becomes very large and complex. The problem is the usual one of speed versus simplicity.

Businesses often require extremely large files of data which are stored on relatively slow-access devices such as magnetic tape. In order to find the data, it is necessary for the computer to search through the tape, and this is time-consuming because the machine remains idle until the data are located. To circumvent this problem, the control element is constructed so that several programs may be operated at the same time. One of the programs is started and when a foreseeable delay is reached (for instance, when a search of tape is begun), the machine skips to a second program, remembering the last instruction performed in the first program. The calculations for the second program are performed while a section of the computer searches for the desired data for the first program. When the data are found, the computer delegates control back to the first program until another search is required. In this way, sections of the machine are operated in parallel.

An example of the economy of this sort of operation may be found in the running of two programs requiring many searches for data, the second program being a scientific-type program requiring little data but many calculations. If the first program requires 2 hours normally, but spends 1½ hours locating data, and the second program requires 2 hours full running time, both programs may be run in parallel with the computer branching control back and forth, and the total time required would be a little over 2½ hours. The GAMMA 60, a French machine, and the MIT TX-2 were early examples of machines of this type, as was the Minneapolis-Honeywell 800; but many of the newest machines provide this facility.

9 · 11   Index registers

An important addition to the list of instructions which can be performed was made in a computer developed at the University of Manchester. A register named the *B-box* was constructed, the contents of which could be added to the contents of the address register. When the B-box was used, the address of the operand located in memory would be at the address written by the programmer plus the contents of the B-box. The Manchester computer had only one B-box, but the idea proved so valuable that most of the modern computers have several. The American term for B-box is *index register*, and this term will be used.

The use of index registers facilitates the writing of iterative programs such as those described in Chap. 2, greatly reducing the number of instructions required in an iterative program. The index registers permit the automatic modification of the addresses referred to without altering the instructions stored in memory.

When index registers are included in a machine, an additional division is generally made in the computer instruction word. This section of the instruction word tells the computer if an index register is to be used, and if so, which index register to use. The basic instruc-

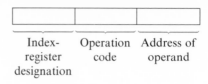

Index-   Operation   Address of
register   code   operand
designation

Fig. 9 · 12   Index register instruction word.

tion word is therefore broken, for a single-address computer, into three parts instead of two. A typical division is shown in Fig. 9 · 12.

Two additional instructions are also added; one is used to "load" the index register, and the other modifies the number stored in the specified index register or causes the computer to branch.

If an index register is not to be used, the programmer places 0's in the index-register-designation section of the word. If there are three index registers, there will be two binary digits in the index-register section of the word, and the index register desired can be selected by placing the correct digits in the index-register-designation section.

In order to describe the operation of the index registers, two new instructions will be introduced. We will designate one of these by the mnemonic code SIR (set index registers), and this instruction will cause the address section of the instruction word to be transferred into the index register designated by the index-register-designation bits in the word. For instance, 01 SIR 300 will load the number 300 into index register 01. Since the address register normally contains the address section of the computer word, all that is required is that the contents of the address register be transferred into the index register designated.

We will designate the second instruction with the mnemonic code BRI (branch or index). This instruction will cause the contents of the index register designated to be decreased by 1 if the number stored in the index register is positive. At the same time, the computer will branch to the address in the address section of the instruction word, taking its next instruction from that address. If the index register designated contains a 0, the computer will not branch but will instead perform the next instruction in normal order.

The index registers may be used during any normal instruction by simply placing the digits indicating the index register to be used in the index-register-designation section of the computer word. For instance, if index register 01 contains 300, and we write a clear and add instruction (CAD) as follows:

01 CAD 200

The computer will add the contents of index register 01 to the contents of the address register, and the address used will be the total of

TABLE 9 · 6

ADDRESS IN MEMORY	INSTRUCTION WORD			COMMENTS
	INDEX-REG. DESIGNATION	OPERATION CODE	ADDRESS SECTION	
0	01	SIR	99	The number 99 into index register 01.
1	01	CAD	201	Picks up number to be added.
2	00	ADD	301	Adds to total thus far.
3	00	STO	301	Stores the current sum.
4	01	BRI	1	Subtracts 1 from index register 01 and then branches to first instruction until index register 01 contains 0, then proceeds to next instruction.
5	00	HLT	0	

201 to 300	Contain numbers to be added.
301	Location at which sum is stored.

these two. Since index register 01 contains 300 and the address register will contain 200, the address from which the operand will be taken will be address 500 in memory.

An example of the use of an index register may be found in the short program shown in Table 9 · 6, which will add together all the numbers stored in memory addresses 201 to 300 and store the sum in address 301.

The program repeats the instructions at addresses 1 through 4 until index register 01 is finally at 0; then the computer does not branch and is halted by the next instruction.

Other techniques may be used to select index registers, especially in multiple-address machines. The NORC used an address-modification system where either 4000, 6000, or 8000 is added to the address to be modified. The NORC had three index registers designated $M4$, $M6$, and $M8$. The computer was a three-address machine, and any of the three addresses in an instruction word could be modified by a selected index register. The decimal number 20 was the operation code for addition. The instruction word

20	4030	4031	6029
Operation code	1st address	2d address	3d address

means "add the number at address 30 plus the contents of index register $M4$ to the number at address 31 plus the contents of index register $M4$, and store the sum at address 29 plus the contents of index register $M6$."

9 · 12 Floating-point operation

For fixed-point operations it is necessary for the programmer to *scale* the numbers used in the computations. In the fixed-point fractional-number representation machines which have been described, a number may be represented as a positive or negative fraction with a magnitude of less than 1. Since the actual values will range from large integers to small fractions, the programmer must scale the numbers used so that they lie within the range expressible by the machine [in the case of fractional fixed-point machines from $+(1 - 2^{-n})$ to $-(1 - 2^{-n})$ where n is the number of bits representing the magnitude of the number]. A *scale factor* is a multiplier, remembered by the programmer, by which a number is multiplied so that it falls within the range representable by the machine. For convenience, scale factors are commonly chosen to be powers of 10 for decimal machines and both 10 and 2 for binary machines, and an exponential notation system is used to keep track of the magnitudes.

When dealing with very large or very small numbers, a *mantissa* plus an *exponent* are often used to represent a number. For instance, 4,900,000 may be written as 0.49×10^7, where 0.49 is the mantissa and 7 is the value of the exponent, or .00023 may be written as 0.23×10^{-3}. The actual representation system may be expressed as $x = a \times r^p$, where x is the number to be represented, a is the mantissa, r is the base of the number system ($r = 10$ for decimal, and $r = 2$ for binary), and p is the power to which the base is raised.

By using this technique, numbers may be scaled, the exponent representing the value of the scale factor and the mantissa the number used by the machine. Since only the mantissa section is then used by the machine, the programmer must keep track of the exponents. The programmer must be careful not to let the intermediate results exceed the capacity of the registers and cause overflow, and also not to let the numbers be positioned so far to the right in the registers that precision is lost. The numbers must be correctly aligned when addition and subtraction is performed. (0.234×10^6 cannot be added, in the machine, to 0.123×10^8; the exponents must first be made to agree.)

The "bookkeeping" involved in scaling the numbers used and also the difficulty involved in maintaining precision during computations when the numbers used vary over a very wide range of magnitudes

| S | 1 | 2 | 3 | 4 | 5 | 6 | 7 | 8 | 9 | 10 |

Sign Exponent   Mantissa
bit

Fig. 9 · 13   Word structure for Datatron computer.

have led to two techniques whereby the machine keeps track of the radix (decimal) point. In the first of these, programmed *floating-point* routines automatically scale the numbers used during the computations while maintaining the precision of the results and keeping track of the scale factors. These routines are used with fixed-point computers. A second technique lies in building the floating-point operations into the machine. The logical circuitry of the machine is then used to perform the scaling automatically and to keep track of the scale factors. A floating-point number in a machine is expressed using the exponential notation system described above, and the machine keeps track of the exponent as well as the mantissa. The computer number word in a floating-point system may be divided into three sections: the first is the sign bit, indicating whether the number is negative or positive, the second part contains the exponent for the number to be represented, and the third part, the mantissa.

The Datatron Computer, manufactured by the Burroughs Corporation, has a floating-point system with the word structure shown in Fig. 9 · 13.

The Datatron computer system expresses numbers in a binary-coded-decimal 8, 4, 2, 1 system, and the basic word has 10 decimal digits plus sign. The sign bit is used the same as for fixed-point numbers, indicating whether the number stored is positive or negative. The first two decimal digits indicate the exponent of the number stored. This number ranges from 00 to 99, but the actual value for the exponent is obtained by subtracting 50 from the number stored. For instance, a stored value of 75 would indicate an exponent of 25, and a stored value of 40 would indicate an exponent of -10. Table 9 · 7 shows three examples of stored numbers:

TABLE 9 · 7

NUMBER IN NORMAL FORM		NUMBER REPRESENTED IN MACHINE
$+2468107100$	$=$	0.6024681071
-0.7484261	$=$	1.5074842610
$+964.2$	$=$	0.5396420000

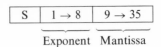

Exponent Mantissa

Fig. 9 · 14   Floating-point word for IBM 7090-7094.

Another example of a floating-point system may be found in the IBM 7090-7094 computers, which are internal binary computers with word lengths of 35 bits plus sign. A numerical word is divided as shown in Fig. 9 · 14.

IBM calls the exponent section of the word the *characteristic* and the mantissa section the *fraction*. The exponent section can express binary numbers from 0 to 11111111 or 255_{10}. The value expressed in the exponent is equal to the number in the exponent section minus 128, so that negative exponents are expressed as binary numbers from 0 to 01111111 or 127_{10} and positive exponents as binary numbers from 10000000(128) to 11111111(255). The exponent of a number can be formed, in this system, by adding 128 to the "normal" exponent. If the binary number to be expressed is 11.01, then the "normal" form would be 0.1101×2^2, and the machine would represent this number as 0.100000010 110100 . . . 0.

9 · 13   Performing arithmetic operations with floating-point numbers

A machine obviously requires additional circuitry to handle floating-point numbers automatically. It is actually possible to handle floating-point numbers by adding only control circuitry, but it is generally more reasonable to add to the arithmetic element circuitry also. Some machines come equipped with floating-point operations and there is additional equipment available which can be purchased and added to some machines, enabling them to perform floating-point operations. The total number of instructions for the machine is increased by the number of floating-point operations, since for each floating-point instruction there will be a distinct operation code (and a corresponding mnemonic code). The floating-point mnemonic operation codes are generally chosen to indicate the floating-point nature of the instruction, so that ADD becomes FAD (floating add), SUB becomes FSU (floating subtract), etc.

In order to handle the floating-point numbers, the machine must be capable of extensive shifting and comparing operations. The rules for multiplying and dividing are:

$$(a \times r^p) \times (b \times r^q) = ab \times r^{p+q}$$

$$(a \times r^p) \div (b \times r^q) = a/b \times r^{p-q}$$

The computer must be able to add or subtract the exponent sections of the floating-point numbers, and also perform the multiplication or division operations on the mantissa sections of the numbers. In addition, precision is generally maintained by shifting the numbers stored until significant digits are in the leftmost sections of the word. With each shift, the exponent must be changed. If the machine is shifting the mantissa section left, for each left shift the exponent must be decreased by 1. For instance, in a decimal computer, consider the word

$$0 . \quad 10 \quad \quad 0064$$

$$\text{Exp.} \quad \text{Mantissa}$$

To attain precision, the computer shifts the mantissa section left until the 6 is in the most significant position. Since two shifts are required, the exponent must be decreased by 2 and the resulting word is 0.08 6400. If all numbers to be used are scaled in this manner, the maximum precision may be maintained throughout the calculations.

For addition and subtraction, the exponent values must agree. For instance, to add 0.24×10^5 to 0.25×10^6, we must scale the numbers so that the exponents agree. Thus

$$(0.024 \times 10^6) + (0.25 \times 10^6) = 0.274 \times 10^6$$

The machine must also follow this procedure. The numbers are scaled as was described, so that the most significant digit of the computer mantissa section of each word contains the most significant digit of the number stored. Then the larger of the two exponents for the operands is selected, and the other number's mantissa is shifted and its exponent adjusted until the exponents for both numbers agree. The numbers may then be added or subtracted according to these rules:

$$(a \times r^p) + (b \times r^p) = (a + b) \times r^p$$
$$(a \times r^p) - (b \times r^p) = (a - b) \times r^p$$

If the result should overflow, the numbers must be shifted right and the exponent decreased by 1.

The mechanization of these processes is straightforward, but requires a number of additional steps over fixed-point operation for each instruction. The same sets of operations may also be programmed, but the machine operations will be faster because less trips to memory are required. The saving here is in operating time, but the offsetting factor is the additional complexity of equipment required. As a result, only the larger machines which put a premium on operating time have floating-point facilities.

9 · 14 Instruction-word formats

In order to study the organization of several types of machines, let us look at their instruction-word formats. Figure 9 · 15 shows several formats for single-address instruction words. At the top of the figure we find the fixed-point data words and the general instruction-word formats for the GE-635, which is a single-address computer with a 36-bit basic word. This is a large, very fast computer. There are 18 digits of address in each instruction word, 9 digits of OP code in the word so that $2^9 = 512$ different instructions could be used, a reserved and interim feature which occupies 3 bits in the basic instruction word. (This has to do with the fact that the GE-635 is a parallel processer where a number of arithmetic elements are shared between several memories.) There is also a tag section which designates index registers and the type of addressing used in a given instruction.

The GE-635 can perform arithmetic and logical operations on both full and half-words, and so two half-words are shown in the fixed-point data-words format listing. It is possible for instance, to add one half-word in one location in memory to a half-word stored in the accumulator.

The DDP-24 which is shown next on the list is manufactured by the Computer Control Corporation, and the instruction list was presented in Table 9 · 2. The basic computer word contains 25 binary digits. There is a bit which tells whether or not addressing shall be direct or indirect,[5] a reserve bit for optional index registers which may be added at the discretion of the owner of the machine, and an index bit which tells whether or not a given instruction is to be indexed. The OP code occupies 7 digits, so that up to 128 different instructions could be used. The address part of the instruction word contains 15 digits.

Beneath this is shown the PDP-8, a small machine manufactured by the Digital Electronic Corporation, which also manufactures a list of large machines. This machine has 12 digits in the basic machine word, in which 3 are used for the OP code. One digit then determines whether or not the addressing would be indirect or whether the address given in the address portion of the instruction word is to be used for direct or indirect addressing. Another digit, digit 4, is used to indicate which memory page is being addressed. (Since only 7

[5]An indirect address is an address telling where to find the address to be used.

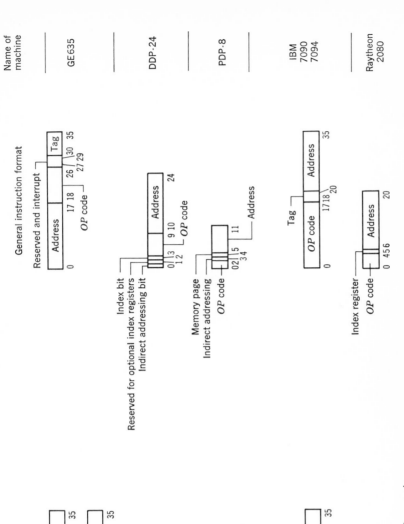

Fig. 9 · 15 Single-address instruction words.

digits are used for the address portion of the word, only 128 different locations in the memory could be addressed directly, and this is considered to be a page in the memory. The 4 digit then tells whether or not we are addressing the page in which the instruction lies or another page in the memory.) This machine is expandable. Instructions in addition to those which come in the basic and least expensive machine may be added, and a number of ingenious design features have been included in this machine to make it expandable beyond the basic machine and to increase its flexibility and usability.

Beneath this is shown the format for the IBM 7090 and IBM 7094, which are continuations of the IBM 704 and 709s series. All of the machines in this series contain a basic 36-binary-digit computer word. The operation codes consist of 18 binary digits. There is a tag section which tells whether or not an index register is to be used, and if so, which index register, and an address portion of 15 binary digits. This machine has a very large repertoire of instructions. Another type of instruction word is also shown in the figure, where the first 3 digits indicate that the instruction word is to be used to set up or modify an index register and which index register. The digits 3 through 17 are used to tell how much to change the value in the index register; if it is to be decremented or incremented. The address portion may or may not be used; most of these instructions are also TRANSFER instructions, and the address of the next instruction word is then in the address portion.

The last single-instruction word shown on the page is that of the Raytheon 7180, a general-purpose computer which is used in real-time control systems. This machine has a basic 21-binary-digit word and is a fixed-point binary-arithmetic machine with a 2's complement number system. The operation-code portion of the instruction word contains 5 digits, and the machine has 32 basic instructions. There is a single index register, and whether or not a given instruction is to be indexed is indicated by the fifth digit in the word. Fifteen digits are used to address the memory or, of course, to indicate how many of these binary numbers are to be shifted or cycled right or left.

Typical instruction-word formats for several double-address machines are shown in Fig. 9·16. The popularity of the two-address computer has grown enormously since 1960, and now rivals or surpasses that of the single-address computer. At the top of the page, several typical instruction-word formats are shown for the IBM 1401 series and the Minneapolis-Honeywell 200 series of computers. All of these machines basically operate in a binary-coded-decimal system, where the memory is character addressable, which is to say that a given address in the memory contains not a computer word or field, but a single alphanumeric character.

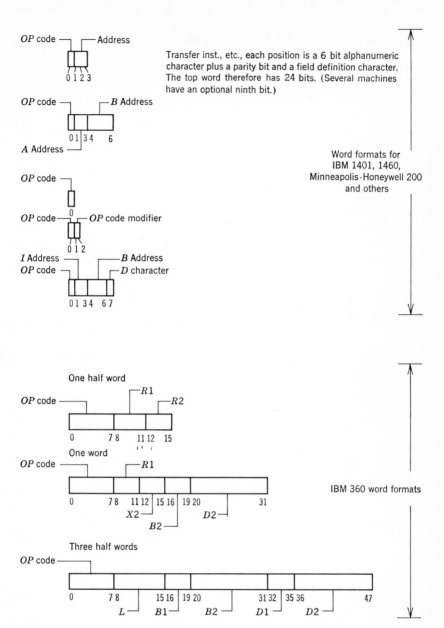

Fig. 9 · 16   Typical instruction-word formats for two-address machines.

In the IBM 1401 series of machines, a single alphanumeric character is expressed as eight binary digits, where six of the eight are used for the actual alphanumeric digit. One digit is a parity check, and the eighth binary digit indicates whether or not a given digit is the last in a computer word or field and is called an "end-of-word" bit. The Minneapolis-Honeywell 200 series also has six binary digits used as the alphanumeric character, a parity digit, and end-of-word digit which indicates the end of the computer word is a particular character. This machine also has a ninth digit called an item digit which indicates that a particular alphanumeric digit is the last alphanumeric character in an item generally containing several words.

Both the 1401 and the 200 series of machines are used a great deal in the processing of business-type data, where names, addresses, and other alphanumeric information need be stored; so a computer word may consist of a name as well as of a number, and there is a great advantage in being able to vary the length of a computer word in the system. The end-of-word digit is used to indicate the last digit in a given word, and the program instruction simply indicates the first digit in a word. Words are then read from the memory, an alphanumeric character at a time. Operands are read starting with the highest numbered location in memory at which the operand is stored, and the memory address register is decremented as each alphanumeric character is read until an end-of-word bit is read from the memory. Instruction words are read consecutively from the memory with the memory address register counting upward instead of downward. End-of-word marks or bits are used to indicate the last alphanumeric character in an instruction word or in an operand.

The operation codes in all of these machines consist of a single alphanumeric character. Since the words in the machine are of variable length, instruction words are also of variable length, although there are only five basic lengths of instruction words which are used. The simplest of these is a single alphanumeric digit which indicates a single simple operation, such as "read a card into the memory." The next most complicated instruction word consists of an OP code, such as B for branch, and an address to which the machine is to branch. In this case, one alphanumeric digit gives the OP code and three alphanumeric digits give the address to which the machine is to branch.

The more usual two-address instruction contains an OP code of one digit and two 3-digit addresses, designated the A address and the B address, making a total of eight alphanumeric characters in this type of instruction word. When these computers receive an OP code such as A indicating addition, they add the number located at the address given in the A address part to the number located at the address given in the B address part, and store this number at the location in memory given in the A address part.

There are also instruction words with only an OP-code character and an OP-code modifier, and even longer instruction words which contain an OP code, an I address, a B address, and a D character. The D character for this latter type of instruction is used to augment the number of instructions; that is, the D character is used to modify the meaning of the OP code given in the single alphanumeric character used as the basic character.

The internal operation of these machines is not too different from the single-address type of machine which was described in the section on control circuitry implementation. The primary differences arise from the binary-coded-decimal nature of the arithmetic and the fact that the memory is read from in a serial-parallel manner. However, the same basic registers are used in the control circuitry; that is, the operation-code register, the instruction counter, memory address register, and memory buffer registers are very much as previously described as well as the READ and WRITE instructions to the memory, and the fact that the machine alternates between instruction cycles and execution cycles. The primary difference in these machines is that the execution cycles are liable to require a good deal more time than instruction cycles, since two addresses in memory and hence two operands are used. Also notice that two counters must be kept operating in order to handle the alternate addressing of the two operands in the memory.

9 · 15   Examples of computer instructions

It will be instructive to examine several computer instructions from actual machines to see how they operate within the machines. The structure of the machines and organization of these machines can be deduced by examining the list of instruction words and their interpretation by the computer.

As mentioned, the Minneapolis-Honeywell 200 is a medium-size digital computer which has a two-address instruction word and a memory which is character addressable. Each character in the Minneapolis-Honeywell system consists of nine binary digits, of which six are used for the alphanumeric character. The three remaining bits consist of a parity digit, a word-mark digit, and an item-mark digit. To simplify programming, Honeywell draws a circle around those alphanumeric characters in which there is a word mark of 1 indicating the end of a word. Then, instruction words address single characters in the memory, and the machine sequences through consecutive decreasing addresses pulling out character after character from the memory and decrementing the memory address register as each character is pulled out.

Figure 9 · 17 shows a typical instruction word with the operation code A, an A address 1197, and a B address 9. This instruction word

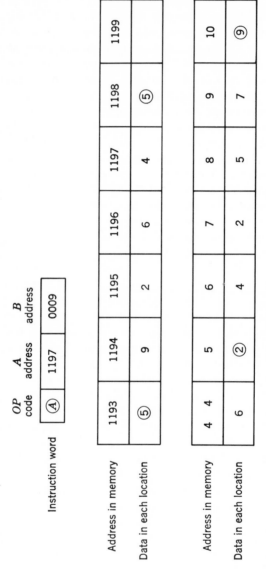

OP code | A address | B address
Instruction word | (A) | 1197 | 0009

Address in memory	1193	1194	1195	1196	1197	1198	1199
Data in each location	(5)	9	2	6	4	(5)	

Address in memory	4 4	5	6	7	8	9	10
Data in each location	6	(2)	4	2	5	7	(9)

Fig. 9·17 ADD instruction in Minneapolis-Honeywell 200.

would occupy nine character positions or addresses in the memory and would be read serially from the memory. However, the A address would be stored in one register, the B address in another register, and the OP code in the OP-code register.

The meaning of this instruction is: Add the field or number which starts at address 1197 in the memory to the field or number lying at address 9 in the memory, and place the sum of these two numbers in address 9. This particular instruction operates on binary-coded-decimal characters, and possible contents for each of the character locations in the memory are also shown in the figure. The machine will continue adding characters while decreasing both of the instruction counters until it encounters a word mark in the B-address series of characters, in which case it will terminate the addition. For instance, the character 2 at location 5 in the memory is circled, indicating that a word-mark bit is a 1 for that particular character.

The machine will first add the digit at location 9 to the digit at location 1197, so it adds 4 plus 7, places a 1 in location 9, and stores a carry digit to be added into the next pair of digits. The next digits are in locations 8 and 1196 which are 5 and 6, plus a carry of 1 from last time, so a 2 is placed in location 8 and a 1 is carried over to the addition of the next digits. These lie in 1195 and 7, respectively. The addition of these results in a 5 being placed in location 7. Then the character in 1194, which is a 9, is added to the number at location 6 giving a sum of 3 a carry, and finally we add 5 and 2 plus a carry giving 8 to be put in location 5. After the addition, the data in locations 1194 to 1197 are as when the addition was initiated, whereas the number at locations 5 through 9 in the memory now contain 83521.

This machine can also add binary numbers, in which case six of the digits at each character location are considered to comprise six digits of a binary number and are added in 2's complement fashion.

The IBM 1401 is another example of a two-address general-purpose computer. Figure 9·18 shows a typical instruction word, which is a SUBTRACT instruction, the OP code for this being an S; the A address given is 297, and the B address 164. Seven locations in memory would be used for the instruction word shown, one location for each of the alphanumeric characters. The instruction would cause the subtraction of the numerical data in the A field from the numerical data in the B field, and the storing of this dividend in the B field. It is IBM's practice to underline characters which contain word marks indicating the end of a field, and we have done this for the 6 at location 293 in memory and the 8 in location 160 in memory. The subtraction terminates when a word mark is encountered, so it will terminate when the character at 263 is subtracted from the character at 160 in the memory.

	OP code	A address	B address
Instruction word	5	297	164

Address in memory	292	293	294	295	296	297
Character at each address	4	6	5	1	4	3

Address in memory	159	160	161	162	163	164
Character at each address	5	8	3	1	8	2

	OP code	I address	B address	d character
Instruction word	B	093	167	A

↑
Indicates a branch if
"Character Equal"
Instruction

Fig. 9 · 18   IBM 1401 SUBTRACT instruction and BRANCH instruction.

The execution of this instruction word will cause 65143 to be sub-tracted from 83182 and the difference 22039 to be placed in locations 293 through 297 in the memory, replacing the 65143 which was there at the beginning of the execution of the instruction.

Another instruction word, a BRANCH - IF - CHARACTER - EQUAL instruction, is also shown in the figure. The OP code for this is B. The figure indicates an I address which is 93, a B address which is 163, and a so-called D-character A. Eight alphanumeric characters would be required to store this particular instruction word, hence it would occupy eight locations in the memory. This instruction causes the single character at the B address to be compared to the D charac-ter; and if it has the same bit configuration as the D character, the pro-gram branches to the I address. Otherwise, the program continues sequentially. The D character can be any desired character combina-tion of the six digits used for each binary-coded-decimal digit. (The presence or absence of a word mark is not considered.) For the par-ticular instruction word given, if the character located at address 167 is an A, the program will take the next instruction word starting at location 93 in the memory. If the character is not an A, the next instruction word will be pulled from the memory at the address following this particular instruction word.

The GE-635 is a single-address computer with a basic word of 36 binary digits. Floating-point numbers in the GE-635 are expressed as an 8-binary-digit exponent, and a 28-binary-digit mantissa, with the 0 through 7 digits of the word storing the exponent, and the remainder of the word the mantissa of a floating-point number. Since multiplication results in a product longer than the normal binary word, an FMP or floating-point multiply in GE-635 is executed using an accumulator-Q register, similar to that described in the multiplication algorithm in a previous section.

When the particular instruction floating-point multiply is given in the GE-635 machine, the situation is as shown in Fig. 9 · 19 where an E register contains the exponent of the multiplicand, the combined accumulator and Q register consists of a long 71-digit-number considered to be the mantissa of the multiplicand, and the word at the address in memory given in the single-address instruction contains an exponent of 8 digits plus a mantissa of 28 digits.

First, the exponent of the multiplier, which is the word read from the address given in the instruction word, is added to the exponent of the multiplicand which is stored in the E register, and this sum is stored in the E register. Then, the 28-bit mantissa of the number read from the memory is multiplied times the number stored in the combined accumulator-Q register, giving a 98-bit product plus sign, and the leading 71 bits of this product are then stored in the combined accumulator-Q register. Afterward, the product is normalized so that

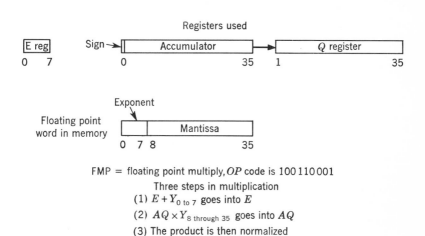

Registers used

FMP = floating point multiply, OP code is 100 110 001
Three steps in multiplication
(1) $E + Y_{0 \text{ to } 7}$ goes into E
(2) $AQ \times Y_{8 \text{ through } 35}$ goes into AQ
(3) The product is then normalized

Fig. 9 · 19   Example of GE-635 instruction.

the leading digit in the accumulator contains a signficant digit of the product. The instruction-word format of the GE-635 may be found in a previous section.

As a last example of the general-purpose computer, we will very briefly examine the IBM 360 series. In this machine the memory is organized into bytes of 8 binary digits each, and a half-word in the system is considered to be 16 binary digits or two bytes, and a word consists of four bytes or two half-words.

Instruction words come in various sizes and lengths and Fig. 9·20 shows the basic different types of instruction words and their lengths. The machine is basically a two-address machine; however, in a sense, the machine has 16 accumulators which are called *general registers*, and these are shown in Fig. 9·20. Each of these general registers consist of 32 bits and each is addressable. There are also four floating-point registers each consisting of 64 bits, and these are given the addresses 2, 4, 6, and 8, respectively. There are instructions so that one can load any of the general registers from the memory or can transfer the contents of any general register into the memory, and the same may be said for each of the floating-point registers.

In general, when we add one word to another word, we can either add one of the general registers to another general register and store the sum in one of the general registers, or add one of the general registers to a word located in the memory and store the sum in the general register or add two words in memory and store them however we please.

Further, there are floating-point instructions and fixed-point instructions, so that a floating-point word located in the memory can be multiplied times the contents of one of the floating-point registers and the product stored in one of the floating-point registers. For floating-point words the word addressed in memory will consist of 64 digits with a 7-digit characteristic and a 23-digit fraction if a short floating-point instruction is used, or of a sign digit plus a 7-digit characteristic and a 56-digit floating-point fraction or mantissa when a long floating-point word is used.

The general registers contain not only operands, but are also used to store addresses, so that many instructions form an address by adding a number in a general register to another number to form the number of the location to be used in an operand.

Let us examine several typical instruction words in this system to see how various instructions operate. The first instruction shown in the figure is an ADD instruction, the OP code for which is 1A lying in bits 0 through 7. Two operands are then designated. These operands are located in general-register 7 and general-register 9, so that the number in general-register 7 will be added to the number in

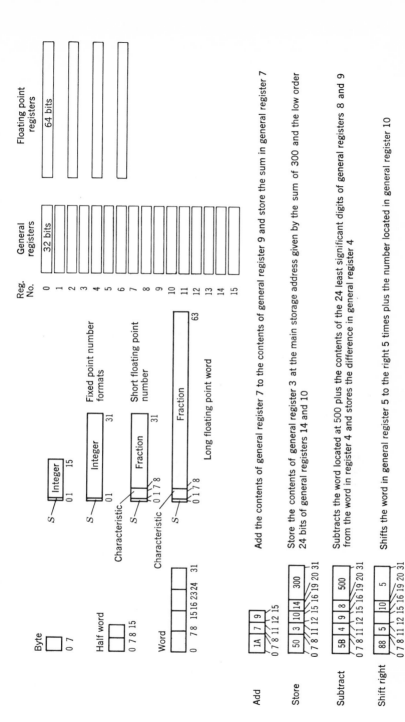

Fig. 9 · 20   Structure of IBM 360.

general-register 9 and the sum stored in general-register 7. Notice that the two addresses given in this particular type of instruction actually indicate directly the locations of the two words to be added.

The second instruction shown, which is a STORE instruction, is more complicated. Fifty is the operation code for store in this system. This operation code is followed in the instruction word by four numbers in the system. The first number, which lies in bits 8 through 11, gives the number of one general register to be used; the contents of this register are to be stored in the memory. The second set of three numbers occupies bits 12 through 31 in the instruction word and gives the address in memory where this number is to be stored. However, this address is not given directly. The address is instead formed by adding the number in general-register 10 to the number in general-register 14, and taking the 24 least significant digits of this number and adding this to the number stored in bits 20 through 31 in the instruction word, which in this case is 310. For instance, if general-register 10 contained the number 400 and if general-register 14 contained the number 200, we would add these two numbers giving 600 and add that to 310, giving the number 910, so that the word in general-register 3 would be stored in location 910 in the memory.

Subtract instructions operate somewhat similarly. The subtract instruction is indicated by the operation code 5B, and the particular type of instruction shown in the figure subtracts the number stored at an address which is determined by adding the numbers stored in general-register 9 to the number stored in general-register 8, and to this adding the number lying in bits 20 to 31 of the subtract instruction. When these three numbers are combined to form an address in the memory, the word located at that address is then subtracted from the word located in general-register 4 and the difference is stored in general-register 4.

For instance, if general-register 4 contains 300, general-register 9 contains 100, general-register 8 contains 200, and in the memory the location 800 contains the word 1000, we will form the address number 800 by adding together the number 200 lying in general-register 8 to the number 100 lying in general-register 9, and then adding this to the 500 given in bits 20 through 31 in the instruction word, giving the number 800. We then look in the memory at location 800 and find the word 1000. If this number is subtracted from 300, which lies in general-register 4, the difference -700 will be stored in general-register 4 when the instruction is completed.

As one last example of the instruction code for this machine, let us examine a shift-right instruction, the operation code for which is 88. In this case, the general register indicated by bits 8 through 11 in the instruction word is to be shifted right. The number of times the word is to be shifted is calculated by adding the number in bits 20 through 31 of the instruction word to the number in the register designated by bits 16 through 19 of the instruction word.

In the example shown, the general-register 10 is called out by bits 16 through 19, so the number stored in general-register 10 will be added to the 5 stored in bits 20 through 31 and the general-register 5 will be shifted right this many times. If, for instance, general-register 10 contains the number 7, then we would add 7 to 5 saying that the word in general-register 5 should be shifted right a total of 12 times.

We have only touched upon the large operation and instruction codes of the machines mentioned in this chapter. Present-day machines contain many instruction-word formats so that a vast artillery of operations are available to the programmer. The complexity of these instructions may seem unreasonable, but many of them are slanted toward the system programmer who prepares compilers and they are primarily useful at that level of programming.

QUESTIONS

1 A single-address, one-instruction-per-word computer has a word length of 22 binary digits. The computer can perform 32 different instructions and it has three index registers. The inner memory is a 16,000-word magnetic-core memory. Draw a diagram of the computer word, allocating space for each part of the basic instruction word (operation-code part, address part, index-register part). Do not use the sign digit (leftmost digit) of the word.

2 If the basic computer word in a machine has 24 binary digits and we have 55 different instructions, make up an instruction-word format for a single-address machine. How many different memory locations can be directly addressed by the address portion of this computer-instruction word? Make up the computer-instruction word for a double-address computer with 24 binary digits in the computer word and 55 instructions. How many different locations can now be addressed directly by a single-instruction word?

3 A three-address computer has a word length of 11 decimal digits plus sign. The computer can perform 50 different instructions and the inner memory has 1,000 words. Draw a diagram of the basic computer instruction leaving the sign bit unused.

4 Write a simple program, using the operation codes for the Raytheon 7180 computer given in Table 9 · 1, which will evaluate the polynomial $ax^2 + bx + c$, given that a, b, c and x are in memory addresses 29, 28, 27 and 25 respectively. Store the result in 30.

5 Why does the four-address instruction-word type of computer not necessarily need a program counter?

6   For the IBM 1401, how many binary digits are required to store the
following decimal numbers?
a. 749   *b.* 1,050   *c.* 24   *d.* 19,278
7   The instruction code for the DDP-24 is listed in Table 9 · 2 along with
a diagram of the basic instruction word. Write, in binary form, the
instruction word which will cause the contents of the B register to be
multiplied by the word stored at location 24 of the computer's inner
memory.
8   In the Minneapolis-Honeywell 200, how many binary digits are required to store the following decimal numbers when the alphanumeric format is used? When the binary format is used?
a. 1,924   *b.* 22   *c.* 87   *d.* 10,924
9   How many trips to memory must be made to perform an addition
instruction in a three-address type of computer?
10   In the IBM 360, how many binary digits are required to store the
following decimal numbers in BCD and in binary?
a. 20   *b.* 10,241   *c.* 984   *d.* 6
11   Tell how to modify Fig. 9 · 8 so that the BRM instruction becomes
a BRP instruction, meaning the computer transfers when the ACC
is positive, not negative.
12   Using the Booth algorithm, what is the maximum time required to
multiply two 21-bit signed numbers, assuming each has already been
positioned in the B register and the Q register? Assume it requires
0.5 μsec to shift and 1 μsec to add or subtract.
13   How many phases might you expect to find in a three-address
instruction-word type of serial computer, if it is constructed along
the lines described in the chapter?
14   What is the minimum time required to multiply two 21-bit signed
numbers assuming all other conditions are as in question 12?
15   Modify the program in Sec. 9 · 11 so that the numbers located at
memory addresses 353 through 546 are added together and stored at
address 600. Modify the program in Sec. 9 · 11 so that the numbers
located addresses 300 through 305 are multiplied together and the
product stored at address 310.
16   If we use the Booth algorithm and have a clock with a rate of 2 megacycles so that a clock pulse arrives each 0.5 μsec, and if we can add or
shift in each 0.5-μsec period, how long will be required on the average
to multiply two 20-digit binary numbers? Do not count the time required to position the numbers in the MQ or B register; count only
the time which elapses after the actual multiplication is initiated.
17   Write the numbers 62×10^4 and 26×10^6 in floating-address form
and place the exponent and mantissa sections in the computer word
for the Datatron computer as described in Sec. 9 · 12. Describe the

operations which must be performed if the numbers are to be added, and write the sum as it might be stored in the computer word.

18 Using the index instructions in Sec. 9 · 11, write a program which adds 40 numbers located in the memory starting at address 200, storing the sum in register 300.

19 If we use three binary digits in the instruction word to indicate which index register is used, or if one is to be used, how many index registers can we use in the machine?

20 If a computer has a 35-bit word, how many flip-flops must be in the step counter (see Fig. 9 · 9) in order for it to multiply and shift right or left?

21 The MQ register in Fig. 9 · 10 must be designed so that we can transfer the AC into it and so that we can shift it right when desired. Design a single stage of this register using the control signals AC INTO MQ and SHR to initiate these operations. (Most machines shift both the AC and MQ right when a SHIFT-RIGHT instruction is given.) Add these gates to those in Fig. 9 · 4.

22 Design a single stage of an accumulator and B register which will add and shift left in one operation (step) or will simply shift left in one step. Use SHL (shift left) and ASL (add and shift left) as control signals, a full adder, AND and OR gates, and SC flip-flops.

23 Make out a timing table and modify the control circuitry in Fig. 9 · 6, including the modification in Fig. 9 · 8, so that the machine has an unconditional BRANCH instruction BRA as well as a conditional BRANCH instruction BRM, generating the necessary control signals.

24 Write a program for the DDP-24 using the OP codes in Table 9 · 2, which will evaluate the expression $\dfrac{x + y^2}{z}$, assuming that X, Y, and Z are at addresses 301, 302, and 303 in the memory. Assume no scaling is necessary and store the result at address 304 in the memory.

25 Explain the RND instruction in Table 9 · 2.

26 Explain the SBM instruction in Table 9 · 2.

27 Explain the STD instruction. This is called an address-modifying instruction. Why?

28 The block diagram in Fig. 9 · 21 is of the control and arithmetic registers of the IBM 1401. The I-address register contains the address of the next instruction character to be used by the stored program. The number in this register is increased each time a character is read. The A-address register and the B-address register contain the address of the operand alphanumeric character currently being used. These registers are decreased by 1 each time a character is used. The memory address register addresses the core memory; the A and B

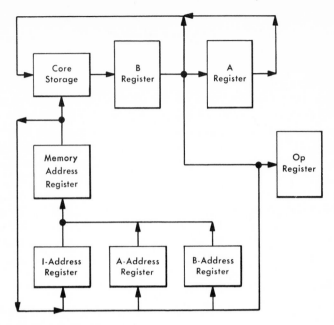

Fig. 9 · 21   Question 28.

registers are 8-bit registers which hold the characters read from memory B, always receiving what is read directly from the memory. The OP register also has 8 bits and is designed to hold the OP-code character from each instruction word. Discuss the sequencing of the operation of these registers during the SUBTRACT instruction described in Sec. 9 · 15.

29 Using the same block diagram as for the preceding instruction, describe the sequencing of these registers in the Minneapolis-Honeywell 200 during the addition instruction in Sec. 9 · 15. This machine would have 9-bit *A* and *B* and OP-code registers.

Bibliography

References for chapter 1

1   Alt, F. L.: "Electronic Digital Computers," Academic Press Inc., New York, 1958.

2   Bauer, W. F.: Advanced Computer Applications, *Proceedings of the IRE*, vol. 49, no. 1, January, 1961.

3   Berkeley, E. C., and L. Wainwright: "Computers: Their Operation and Applications," Reinhold Publishing Corporation, New York, 1956.

4   Brooks, F. P., and K. E. Iverson: "Automatic Data Processing," John Wiley & Sons, Inc., New York, 1963.

5   Engineering Research Associates: "High-speed Computing Devices," McGraw-Hill Book Company, New York, 1950.

6   Gutenmakher, L. I.: "Electronic Information-Logic Machines," Interscience Publishers, Inc., New York, 1963.

7   Ivall, T. E.: "Electronic Computers," Philosophical Library, Inc., New York, 1956.

8   Lewis, T. B.: Digital Computer Equipment for an Advanced Bombing, Navigation, and Missile Guidance Subsystem for the B-70 Air Vehicle, *Proceedings of the IRE*, vol. 49, no. 1, January, 1961.

9   Livesley, R. K.: "Digital Computers," Cambridge University Press, London, 1957.

10   Mandl, M.: "Fundamentals of Digital Computers," Prentice-Hall, Inc., Englewood Cliffs, N.J., 1958.

11   McCormick, E. M.: "Digital Computer Primer," McGraw-Hill Book Company, New York, 1959.

12   O'Neil, L. R.: "Electronic Data Processing Systems," Prentice-Hall, Inc., Englewood Cliffs, N.J., 1964.

13 Scott, N. R.: "Analog and Digital Computer Technology," McGraw-Hill Book Company, New York, 1960.
14 Stibitz, G. R., and J. A. Larrivee: "Mathematics and Computers," McGraw-Hill Book Company, New York, 1956.
15 Truxal, J. G.: Computers in Automatic Control Systems, *Proceedings of the IRE*, vol. 49, no. 1, January, 1961.
16 Ware, W. H.: "Digital Computer Technology and Design," John Wiley & Sons, Inc., New York, 1963.

References for chapter 2

1 Alt, F. L.: "Electronic Digital Computers," Academic Press Inc., New York, 1958.
2 Archard-Hays, W.: The Evolution of Programming Systems, *Proceedings of the IRE*, vol. 49, no. 1, January, 1961.
3 Arden, B. W.: "An Introduction to Digital Computing," Addison-Wesley Publishing Company, Inc., Reading, Mass., 1963.
4 Booth, K. H. V.: "Programming for an Automatic Digital Computer," Academic Press Inc., New York, 1958.
5 Burks, A. W.: The Logic of Programming Electronic Digital Computers, *Industrial Mathematics*, vol. 1, pp. 36–52, January, 1950.
6 Jeenel, J.: "Programming for Digital Computers," McGraw-Hill Book Company, New York, 1959.
7 McCracken, D. C., and W. S. Dorn: "Numerical Methods in FORTRAN Programming," John Wiley & Sons, Inc., New York, 1964.
8 McCracken, D. D.: "Digital Computer Programming," John Wiley & Sons, Inc., New York, 1957.
9 Organick, E. I.: "A FORTRAN Primer," Addison-Wesley Publishing Company, Inc., Reading, Mass., 1963.
10 Plumb, S. C.: "Introduction to FORTRAN," McGraw-Hill Book Company, New York, 1964.
11 Samuel, A. L.: Computing Bit by Bit: or Digital Computers Made Easy, *Proceedings of the IRE*, vol. 41, pp. 1223–1230, October, 1953.
12 Wilkes, M. V., et al.: "Preparation of Programs for an Electronic Digital Computer," Addison-Wesley Publishing Company, Inc., Reading, Mass., 1957.

References for chapter 3

1 Booth, A. D., and H. V. Kathleen: "Automatic Digital Calculators," Academic Press Inc., New York, 1956.
2 Caldwell, S. H.: "Switching Circuits and Logical Design," John Wiley & Sons, Inc., New York, 1958.
3 Harris, J. N.: Introduction to the Binary and Octal Numbering

Systems, *Lincoln Laboratory Technical Memoranda 24–40*, September, 1954.

4 Humphrey, W. S., Jr.: "Switching Circuits with Computer Applications," McGraw-Hill Book Company, New York, 1958.

5 Phister, M.: "Logical Design of Digital Computers," John Wiley & Sons, Inc., New York, 1958.

6 Smith, C. V. L.: "Electronic Digital Computers," McGraw-Hill Book Company, New York, 1959.

7 Stibitz, G. R., and J. A. Larrivee: "Mathematics and Computers," McGraw-Hill Book Company, New York, 1956.

References for chapter 4

1 Baker, R. H., E. J. Chatterton, and A. C. Parker: High-speed Graded-base Transistor Switching Circuits, *Lincoln Laboratory Technical Report 130*, December, 1957.

2 Booth, G. W., and T. P. Bothwell: Basic Logic Circuits for Computer Applications, *Electronics*, vol. 30, pp. 196–200, May, 1957.

3 Chu, Y.: "Digital Computer Design Fundamentals," McGraw-Hill Book Company, New York, 1962.

4 Gray, H. J.: "Digital Computer Engineering," Prentice-Hall, Inc., Englewood Cliffs, N.J., 1963.

5 Haggerty, P. E.: Integrated Circuits, *The IEEE Spectrum*, vol. 1, no. 6, June, 1964.

6 Hunter, L. P.: "Handbook of Semiconductor Electronics," McGraw-Hill Book Company, New York, 1962.

7 Hurley, R. B.: "Junction Transistor Electronics," John Wiley & Sons, Inc., New York, 1958.

8 Hurley, R. B.: "Transistor Logic Circuits," John Wiley & Sons, Inc., New York, 1961.

9 Lebow, I. L., R. H. Baker, and R. E. McMahon: The Transient Response of Transistor Switching Circuits, *Lincoln Laboratory Technical Report 27*, July, 1953.

10 Lo, A. W.: A Comprehensive View of Digital Integrated Electronic Circuits, *Proceedings of the IEEE*, vol. 52, no. 12, December, 1964.

11 Millman, J., and H. Taub: "Pulse and Digital Circuits," McGraw-Hill Book Company, New York, 1956.

12 Narud, J. A., and C. S. Meyer: Characterization of Integrated Logic Circuits, *Proceedings of the IEEE*, vol. 52, no. 12, December, 1964.

13 Olsen, K. H.: Transistor Circuitry in the Lincoln TX-2, *Proceedings of the Western Joint Computer Conference, Los Angeles*, Journal Article 656, February 26–28, 1957.

14 Phillips, A. B.: Monolithic Integrated Circuits, *The IEEE Spectrum*, vol. 1, no. 6, June, 1964.

15   Richards, R. K.: "Digital Computer Components and Circuits," D. Van Nostrand Company, Inc., Princeton, N.J., 1957.
16   Scott, N. R.: "Analog and Digital Computer Technology," McGraw-Hill Book Company, New York, 1960.
17   Sferrino, V. J., and W. G. Schmidt: One Megacycle Silicon Transistor Circuits Applicable to Airborne Digital Systems, *Lincoln Laboratory Technical Report 177*, March, 1958.
18   Shea, R. F.: "Principles of Transistor Circuits," John Wiley & Sons, Inc., New York, 1955.
19   Smith, C. V. L.: "Electronic Digital Computers," McGraw-Hill Book Company, New York, 1959.
20   Texas Instruments, Inc.: "Transistor Circuit Design," McGraw-Hill Book Company, 1963.

References for chapter 5

1   Bartee, T. C.: The Automatic Design of Logical Networks (ASTIA 207170), *Lincoln Laboratory Technical Report 191*, December, 1958.
2   Bartee, T. C., I. L. Lebow, and I. S. Reed: "Theory and Design of Digital Machines," McGraw-Hill Book Company, New York, 1962.
3   Birkhoff, G., and S. MacLane: "A Survey of Modern Algebra," The Macmillan Company, New York, 1947.
4   Boole, G.: "An Investigation of the Laws of Thought," Dover Publications, Inc., New York, 1954.
5   Brown, R. M.: Some Notes on Logical Binary Counters, *IRE Translations on Electronic Computers*, vol. EC-4, pp. 67–69, June, 1955.
6   Caldwell, S. H.: "Switching Circuits and Logical Design," John Wiley & Sons, Inc., New York, 1958.
7   Craven, T. L.: Logic and the Circuit Designer, *Electronic Engineering*, vol. 25, pp. 257–259, 1953.
8   Ginsburg, S.: "An Introduction to Mathematical Machine Theory," Addison-Wesley Publishing Company, Reading, Mass., 1962.
9   Higgonet, R. A., and R. A. Grea: "Logical Design of Electrical Circuits," McGraw-Hill Book Company, New York, 1959.
10   Humphrey, W. S., Jr.: "Switching Circuits with Computer Applications," McGraw-Hill Book Company, New York, 1958.
11   Huntington, E. V.: "Fundamental Propositions of Algebra," Galois Institute of Mathematics and Art, 1950.
12   Keister, W., et al.: "The Design of Switching Circuits," D. Van Nostrand Company, Inc., Princeton, N.J., 1951.
13   Langer, S. K.: "An Introduction to Symbolic Logic," Dover Publications, Inc., New York, 1953.
14   Marcus, M. P.: "Switching Circuits for Engineers," Prentice-Hall, Inc., Englewood Cliffs, N.J., 1962.

15 McCluskey, E. J., and T. C. Bartee: "A Survey of Switching Circuit Theory," McGraw-Hill Book Company, New York, 1962.
16 Phister, M.: "Logical Design of Digital Computers," John Wiley & Sons, Inc., New York, 1958.
17 Reed, I. S.: Symbolic Synthesis of Digital Computers (ASTIA 2230), *Lincoln Laboratory Technical Report 15*, October, 1952.
18 Richards, R. K.: "Arithmetic Operations in Digital Computers," D. Van Nostrand Company, Inc., Princeton, N.J., 1957.
19 Shannon, C. E.: A Symbolic Analysis of Relay and Switching Circuits, *Transactions of the AIEE*, vol. 57, 1938.
20 Stibitz, G. R., and J. A. Larrivee: "Mathematics and Computers," McGraw-Hill Book Company, New York, 1956.
21 Torng, H. T.: "An Introduction to the Logical Design of Switching Systems," Addison-Wesley Publishing Company, Inc., 1964.
22 Wier, M. H.: Some Direct-coupled Computer Circuits Utilizing NPN and PNP Transistors in Combination, *U.S. Government Research Reports*, vol. 26, p. 329, December, 1956.

References for chapter 6

1 Bartee, T. C., I. L. Lebow, and I. S. Reed: "Theory and Design of Digital Machines," McGraw-Hill Book Company, New York, 1962.
2 Caldwell, S. H.: "Switching Circuits and Logical Design," John Wiley & Sons, Inc., New York, 1958.
3 Dinneen, G. P., J. A. Dumanian, I. L. Lebow, I. S. Reed, and P. B. Sebring: Logical Design of CG24 (A General-purpose Computer) (ASTIA 147496), *Lincoln Laboratory Technical Report 139*, April, 1957.
4 Felker, J. H.: Arithmetic Processes for Digital Computers, *Electronics*, vol. 26, pp. 150–155, March, 1953.
5 Flores, I.: "The Logic of Computer Arithmetic," Prentice-Hall, Inc., Englewood Cliffs, N.J., 1963.
6 Frankel, S. P.: The Logical Design of a Simple General-purpose Computer, *IRE Translations on Electronic Computers*, vol. EC-6, pp. 5–14, March, 1957.
7 Freiman, C. V.: Statistical Analysis of Certain Binary Division Algorithms, *Proceedings of the IRE*, vol. 49, no. 1, January, 1961.
8 Gray, H. J., Jr.: Logical Description of Some Digital Computer Adders and Counters, *Proceedings of the IRE*, vol. 40, pp. 29–33, January, 1952.
9 Humphrey, W. S., Jr.: "Switching Circuits with Computer Applications," McGraw-Hill Book Company, New York, 1958.
10 MacSorley, O. L.: High Speed Arithmetic in Binary Computers, *Proceedings of the IRE*, vol. 49, no. 1, January, 1961.

11   Mailey, G. A., and E. J. Skiki: "Modern Digital Computers," Prentice-Hall, Inc., Englewood Cliffs, N.J., 1964.
13   Reed, I. S.: Symbolic Design of Digital Computers, *Lincoln Laboratory Technical Memorandum 23*, January, 1953.
14   Reed, I. S.: Symbolic Design Techniques Applied to a Generalized Computer (ASTIA 110009), *Lincoln Laboratory Technical Report 141*, January, 1957.
15   Richards, R. K.: "Arithmetic Operations in Digital Computers," D. Van Nostrand Company, Inc., Princeton, N.J., 1957.
16   Smith, C. V. L.: "Electronic Digital Computers," McGraw-Hill Book Company, New York, 1959.

References for chapter 7

1   Barbeau, I. A., and J. I. Aweida: IBM's 7340 Hypertape Drive, *Proceedings of the 1963 Fall Joint Computer Conference*, American Federation of Information Processing Societies.
2   Best, R. L.: Memory Units in the Lincoln TX-2, *Proceedings of the Western Joint Computer Conference, Los Angeles*, Journal Article 752, February 26–28, 1957.
3   Bittmann, E. E.: A 2mc, Magnetic Thin-Film Memory, *Proceedings of the 1964 Fall Joint Computer Conference*, American Federation of Information Processing Societies.
4   Bloom, L., et al.: Card Random Access Memory: Functions and Use, *Proceedings of the 1961 Eastern Joint Computer Conference, Washington, D.C.*
5   Brown, D. R.: Ferrites for Digital Computers, *West Coast IRE Convention, San Francisco*, Journal Article 45, August 19, 1953.
6   Carothers, J. D.: A New High Density Recording System; the IBM 1311 Disc Storage Drive with Interchangeable Disc Packs, *Proceedings of the 1963 Fall Joint Computer Conference*, American Federation of Information Processing Societies.
7   Eckert, J. P., Jr.: A Survey of Digital Computer Memory Systems, *Proceedings of the IRE*, vol. 41, pp. 1393–1406, October, 1953.
8   Forrester, J. W.: Digital Information Storage in Three Dimensions Using Magnetic Cores, *Journal of Applied Physics*, vol. 22, no. 1, pp. 44–48, January, 1951.
9   Forrester, J. W.: Random Access 3-dimension Magnetic Memory, Symposium on Digital Computers: Advanced Engineering Techniques, Argonne National Laboratory, Journal Article 71, August 4, 1953.
10   Hoagland, A. S.: Magnetic Data Recording Theory: Head Design, *AIEE Transactions, pt. I, Communications and Electronics*, vol. 75, pp. 506–512, November, 1956.

11 Hoagland, A. S.: Magnetic Drum Recording of Digital Data, *AIEE Transactions, pt. I, Communications and Electronics*, no. 14, pp. 381–385, September, 1954.

12 Ishidate, T.: Edicard Memory—A Semipermanent Storage, *Proceedings of the 1961 Eastern Joint Computer Conference, Washington, D.C.*

13 Jack, R. W., et al.: An Engineering Description of the Burroughs Disc File, *Proceedings of the 1963 Fall Joint Computer Conference*, American Federation of Information Processing Societies.

14 Lubkin, S.: An Improved Reading System for Magnetically Recorded Digital Data, *IRE Transactions on Electronic Computers*, vol. EC-3, pp. 22–25, September, 1954.

15 McGuigan, J. H.: Combined Reading and Writing on a Magnetic Drum, *Proceedings of the IRE*, vol. 41, pp. 1438–1444, October, 1953.

16 McMahon, R. E., and F. L. McNamara: Transistor Core Memory (ASTIA 110010), *Lincoln Laboratory Technical Report 133*, November, 1956.

17 Meyerhoff, A. J.: "Digital Applications of Magnetic Devices," McGraw-Hill Book Company, New York, 1960.

18 Mitchell, J. L., and K. H. Olsen: TX-0, A Transistor Computer with a 256 × 256 Memory, *Proceedings of the Eastern Joint Computer Conference, IRE-AIEE, New York*, Journal Article 659, Special Publication T-92, December 10, 1956.

19 Nordyke, H. W.: Magnetic Tape Recording Techniques and Performance, *Proceedings of the AIEE-IRE-ACM Computer Conference, New York, December, 1952*, pp. 90–95, March, 1953.

20 Papian, W. N.: A Coincident Current Magnetic Memory Cell for the Storage of Digital Information, *Proceedings of the IRE*, vol. 40, no. 4, pp. 475–478, April, 1952.

21 Papian, W. N.: Ferromagnetic and Ferroelectric Memory Devices, Northeastern University Joint Student Branch of AIEE and IRE, Journal Article 79, October 15, 1953.

22 Papian, W. N.: The MIT Magnetic-core Memory, *Proceedings of the Eastern Joint Computer Conference, ACM, AIEE, and IRE, Washington, D.C.*, Journal Article 78, December, 1953.

23 Prywes, M. S.: "Amplifier and Memory Devices with Films and Diodes," McGraw-Hill Book Company, New York, 1965.

24 Pyle, W. I.: A 10mc NDRO BIAX Memory of 1024-word, 48-bit per Word Capacity, *Proceedings of the 1964 Fall Joint Computer Conference*, American Federation of Information Processing Societies.

25 Raffel, J. I., et al.: Magnetic Film Memory Design, *Proceedings of the IRE*, vol. 49, no. 1, January, 1961.

26 Richards, R. K.: "Digital Computer Components and Circuits," D. Van Nostrand Company, Inc., Princeton, N.J., 1957.

27 Robinson, A. A., F. McAulay, A. H. Banks, and D. Hogg: Magnetic-

tape Digital Recording Equipment, *Proceedings of the Institution of Electrical Engineers*, vol. 193, pt. B, supplement 2, Convention on Digital Computer Techniques, pp. 346–353, April, 1956.

28 Sims, R. C., et al.: A Survey of Tunnel Diode Digital Techniques, *Proceedings of the IRE*, vol. 49, no. 1, January, 1961.
29 Stephen, J. H., and E. H. Cooke-Yarborough: An Interleaved-Digit Magnetic-Drum Store for a Transistor Digital Computer, *Proceedings of the Institution of Electrical Engineers*, vol. 103, pt. B, supplement 3, Convention on Digital Computer Techniques, pp. 382–389, April, 1956.
30 Wieselman, I. L., et al.: A Multiple Access Disc File, *Proceedings of the 1963 Fall Joint Computer Conference*, American Federation of Information Processing Societies.
31 Yovits, M. C.: "Large Capacity Memory Techniques for Computing Systems," The Macmillan Company, New York, 1962.

References for chapter 8

1 Carroll, J. M.: Trends in Computer Input-Output Devices, *Electronics*, September, 1956.
2 Forgie, J. W.: The Lincoln TX-2 Input-Output Systems, *Proceedings of the Western Joint Computer Conference, Los Angeles*, Journal Article 653, February 26–28, 1957.
3 Hamming, R. W.: Error Detecting and Error Correcting Codes, *Bell System Technical Journal*, vol. 29, pp. 147–160, April, 1950.
4 Hargraves, B., et al.: Processing Hardware for a Man-machine Graphical Communication System, *Proceedings of the 1964 Fall Joint Computer Conference*, American Federation of Information Processing Societies.
5 Hosken, J. C.: "Survey of Mechanical Printers," Review of Input and Output Equipment Used in Computing Systems, AIEE, March, 1953.
6 Jacks, E. L.: A Laboratory for the Study of Graphical Man-machine Communication, *Proceedings of the 1964 Fall Joint Computer Conference*, American Federation of Information Processing Societies.
7 Kleist, R. A., M. A. Lewis, and B. C. Wang: Single Capstan Tape Memory, *Proceedings of the 1963 Fall Joint Computer Conference*, American Federation of Information Processing Societies.
8 McCormick, E. M.: "Digital Computer Primer," McGraw-Hill Book Company, New York, 1959.
9 Mermelstein, P., and M. Eden: A System for Automatic Recognition of Handwritten Words, *Proceedings of the 1964 Fall Joint Computer Conference*, American Federation of Information Processing Societies.

10 Pike, J. L., and E. F. Ainsworth: Input-Output Devices for NBS Computers, *Computer Development at the NBS, NBS Circular 551,* pp. 109–118, January, 1955.

11 Richards, R. K.: "Digital Computer Components and Circuits," D. Van Nostrand Company, Inc., Princeton, N.J., 1957.

12 Susskind, A. K.: "Notes on Analog-Digital Conversion Techniques," John Wiley & Sons, Inc., New York, 1958.

References for chapter 9

1 Boutwell, E. O., Jr., and E. A. Hoskinson: The Logical Organization of the PB-440 Micro-programmable Computer, *Proceedings of the 1963 Fall Joint Computer Conference,* American Federation of Information Processing Societies.

2 Chu, Y.: "Digital Computer Design Fundamentals," McGraw-Hill Book Company, New York, 1962.

3 Clark, W. A.: The Lincoln TX-2 Computer Development, *Proceedings of the Western Joint Computer Conference, Los Angeles,* Journal Article 654, February 26–28, 1957.

4 Dinneen, G. P., J. A. Dumanian, I. L. Lebow, I. S. Reed, and P. B. Sebring: Logical Design of CG24 (A General-purpose Computer) (ASTIA 147496), *Lincoln Laboratory Technical Report 139,* April, 1957.

5 Dinneen, G. P., I. L. Lebow, and I. S. Reed: Systematic Design of CG24, *Proceedings of the Eastern Joint Computer Conference, Philadelphia,* Journal Article 1119, December 3–5, 1958.

6 Eckert, W. J., and R. Jones: "Faster, Faster," McGraw-Hill Book Company, New York, 1955.

7 Fagg, P., et al.: IBM System 360 Engineering, *Proceedings of the 1964 Fall Joint Computer Conference,* American Federation of Information Processing Societies.

8 Frankel, S. P.: The Logical Design of a Simple General Purpose Computer, *IRE Translations on Electronic Computers,* vol. EC-6, pp. 5–14, March, 1957.

9 Frankovitch, J. M., and H. P. Peterson: A Functional Description of the Lincoln TX-2 Computer, *Proceedings of the Western Joint Computer Conference, Los Angeles,* Journal Article 655, February 26–28, 1957.

10 Gerace, G. B.: Micro-program Control for Computing Systems, *IEEE Transactions on Electronic Computers,* vol. EC-12, no. 5, December, 1963.

11 Gram, C., et al.: Gier: A Danish Computer of Medium Size, *IEEE Transactions on Electronic Computers,* vol. EC-12, no. 5, December, 1963.

12 Helbig, W. A., et al.: The Logic Design of the FC-4100 Data Processing System, *Proceedings of the 1961 Eastern Joint Computer Conference*, American Federation of Information Processing Societies.

13 Lebow, I. L.: On the Structure of Digital Systems, *Lincoln Laboratory Group Report 52-1*, February, 1959.

14 Ledley, R. S.: "Digital Computer and Control Engineering," McGraw-Hill Book Company, New York, 1960.

15 Lehman, M., R. Eshed, and Z. Netter: Sabrac: A New Generation Serial Computer, *IEEE Transactions on Electronic Computers*, vol. EC-12, no. 5, December, 1963.

16 Maley, G. A., and E. J. Skiko: "Modern Digital Computers," Prentice-Hall, Inc., Englewood Cliffs, N.J., 1964.

17 Mann, M. F., R. R. Rathbone, and J. B. Bennett: Whirlwind I Operation Logic, *MIT Digital Computer Laboratory Report R-221*, May, 1954.

18 Murata, K., and K. Nakazawa: Very High Speed and Serial-parallel Computers, HITAC 50-20 and 50-20E, *Proceedings of the 1964 Fall Joint Computer Conference*, American Federation of Information Processing Societies.

19 Nechman, F. S., F. P. Brooks, Jr., and W. J. Lawless, Jr.: Developments in the Logical Organization of Computer Arithmetic and Control Units, *Proceedings of the IRE*, vol. 49, no. 1, January, 1961.

20 Phister, M.: "Logical Design of Digital Computers," John Wiley & Sons, Inc., New York, 1958.

21 Reed, I. S.: Symbolic Design of Digital Computers, *Lincoln Laboratory Technical Memorandum 23*, January, 1953.

22 Reed, I. S.: Symbolic Design Techniques Applied to a Generalized Computer (ASTIA 110009), *Lincoln Laboratory Technical Report 141*, January, 1957.

23 Reed, I. S.: Symbolic Synthesis of Digital Computers (ASTIA 2230), *Lincoln Laboratory Technical Report 15*, October, 1952.

24 Richards, R. K.: "Arithmetic Operations in Digital Computers," D. Van Nostrand Company, Inc., Princeton, N.J., 1957.

25 Schorr, H., and N. E. Wiseman: System Design of a Small, Fast Digital Computer, *IEEE Transactions on Electronic Computers*, vol. EC-12, no. 5, December, 1963.

26 Scott, N. R.: "Analog and Digital Computer Technology," McGraw-Hill Book Company, New York, 1960.

27 Smith, C. V. L.: "Electronic Digital Computers," McGraw-Hill Book Company, New York, 1959.

Answers to selected odd-numbered problems

Chapter 2   Programming

3

ADDRESS	OPERATION CODE	ADDRESS PART
1	CLA	40
2	ADD	41
3	ADD	42
4	STO	43
5	HLT	000

40 contains X
41 contains Y
42 contains Z

5

ADDRESS	OPERATION CODE	ADDRESS PART
1	CLA	40
2	MUL	40
3	MUL	40
4	STO	41
5	HLT	000

40 contains X

7

ADDRESS	OPERATION CODE	ADDRESS PART
1	CLA	30
2	SUB	31
3	BRM	7
4	CLA	30
5	STO	40
6	HLT	000
7	CLA	31
8	STO	40
9	HLT	000

30 contains X
31 contains Y

9

ADDRESS	OPERATION CODE	ADDRESS PART
1	CLA	40
2	MUL	45
3	STO	45
4	CLA	41
5	ADD	42
6	STO	41
7	BRM	1
8	HLT	000

40 contains X   42 contains 1
41 contains -8 45 contains X

11 The program is the same as the program on page 28 except that address 39 contains a 1 instead of 000 and address 40 contains −49 instead of −50.

Chapter 3   Number systems

1 *a.* 100111   *b.* 111011   *c.* 1,000,000,000   *d.* 0.011100   *e.* 0.11001
   f. 0.110011   *g.* 100,000,000.11   *h.* 10,000,001.1001
   i. 1,000,000,000,000.11101
3 *a.* 13   *b.* 27   *c.* 23   *d.* 0.6875   *e.* 0.203125   *f.* 0.21288065
   g. 59.6875   *h.* 91.203125   *i.* 22.3408203125
5 *a.* 10100.11 = 20.75   *b.* 1001010 = 74
   c. 1.1 = 1.5   *d.* 10101 = 21

7 *a.*   1 0 0 0 0 0 0   *b.*   1 1 1 1 1 1 1
       − 1 0 0 0 0 0   − 1 1 1 1 1 1
       ‾‾‾‾‾‾‾‾‾   ‾‾‾‾‾‾‾‾‾
         1 0 0 0 0 0   1 0 0 0 0 0 0

   c. 1 0 1 1 1 0 1 . 1   *d.* 1 0 1 0 1 0 0 . 0 1 0 0 1
     − 1 0 1 0 1 0 . 1 1   − 1 1 0 0 0 0 . 0 1 0 1 0
     ‾‾‾‾‾‾‾‾‾‾‾‾‾   ‾‾‾‾‾‾‾‾‾‾‾‾‾‾‾
       1 1 0 0 1 0 . 1 1   1 0 0 0 1 1 . 1 1 1 1 1

9 *a.* 100100000   *b.* 11111100   *c.* 100   *d.* 101   *e.* 10100000001.101
   f. 10.1

11   9's complement   10's complement
   a.   4563   4564
   b.   8067   8068
   c.   54.84   54.85
   d.   81.706   81.707

13   1's complement   2's complement
   a.   0100   0101
   b.   00100   00101
   c.   0100.10   0100.11
   d.   00100.10   00100.11

15   9's complement   10's complement
   a.   9 4 8   9 4 8
              7 6 5   7 6 6
            ‾‾‾‾‾‾   ‾‾‾‾‾
            1 7 1 3   7 1 4
            └──→1
            ‾‾‾‾‾
              7 1 4

	9's complement	10's complement

b.
```
      347              347
      736              737
    1 083            0 8 4
    └──→1
      0 8 4
```

c.
```
    349.5            349.5
    754.6            754.7
    104.1            104.2
        1
    104.2
```

d.
```
    412.7            412.7
    590.7            590.8
    003.4              3.5
        1
      3.5
```

17   1's complement   2's complement

a.
```
      1011             1011
      1010             1011
    1 0101            0110
    └────→1
      0110
```

b.
```
      11011            11011
      00110            00111
    1 00001            00010
    └────→1
        10
```

c.
```
    10111.1          10111.1
    01100.0          01100.1
    00011.1            100.0
         1
     100.0
```

d.
```
    11011.00         11011.00
    01100.00         01100.01
    00111.00           111.01
          1
     111.01
```

19   1,000 different numbers in each case (from 0 to 999, for instance)

21   0, 1, 2, 3, 4, 5, 6, 7, 8, 9, A, 10, 11, 12, 13, 14, 15, 16, 17, 18, 19, 1A, 20, 21, 22

Chapter 4   Basic logical circuits

1 *b.* Cutoff

3 *a.* Active

5 Active

7 No storage time delay for inverter when base goes negative because circuit goes from cutoff to either active or saturated regions. No storage time delay when emitter-follower input goes negative because transistor is in active region.

9 1 μsec

11 *a.* negative

13 -2 volts d-c

15 *b.* reverse biased

17 Lower in potential (more negative)

19 0 output line will be at -7 volts d-c
    1 output line will be at 0 volts d-c

21 CR 2

23 No

25

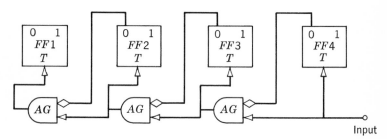

Fig. Ans. Question 25

27 0.1 msec

29 False, because not only are the base-to-emitter currents switched, but also the emitter-to-collector currents.

Chapter 5   Logical design

1 First part of question: the output signal will be a 0. Second part of the question: $c = 1$ instead of $c = 0$, in which case the output will be a 1.

3 I have listed only the values of the expressions.

a.

a	b	$ab' + a'b$
0	0	0
0	1	1
1	0	1
1	1	0

b.

a	b	c	$ab' + bc'$
0	0	0	0
0	0	1	0
0	1	0	1
0	1	1	0
1	0	0	1
1	0	1	1
1	1	0	1
1	1	1	0

c.

a	c	$ac' + ac$
0	0	0
0	1	0
1	0	1
1	1	1

d.

a	b	c	$ab'c + abc' + a'bc$
0	0	0	0
0	0	1	0
0	1	0	0
0	1	1	1
1	0	0	0
1	0	1	1
1	1	0	1
1	1	1	0

e.

a	b	c	$ab(ab'c + ab'c' + abc)$
0	0	0	0
0	0	1	0
0	1	0	0
0	1	1	0
1	0	0	1
1	0	1	1
1	1	0	1
1	1	1	0

5   a. $abc(abc' + ab'c + a'bc) = 0$; for no assignment of binary values will make this expression take the value 1.

b. $ab + ab' + a'c + a'c' = 1$; for every assignment of values will give this expression the value 1.

c. $xy + xyz + xyz' + x'yz = y$

d. $xy(x'yz + xy'z' + x'y'z') = 0$

7 The important columns in these tables are as follows.

x	y	z	$(x + y + z)$	$x'y'z'$
0	0	0	1	1
0	0	1	0	0
0	1	0	0	0
0	1	1	0	0
1	0	0	0	0
1	0	1	0	0
1	1	0	0	0
1	1	1	0	0

x	y	z	$(xyz)'$	$x' + y' + z'$
0	0	0	1	1
0	0	1	1	1
0	1	0	1	1
0	1	1	1	1
1	0	0	1	1
1	0	1	1	1
1	1	0	1	1
1	1	1	0	0

9 Theorem 13

11 $x'y'z + xyz'$

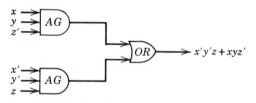

Fig. Ans. Question 11

13 $xy + xz'$

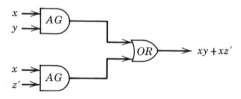

Fig. Ans. Question 13

15 $yz' + y'z$ is the sum-of-products expression and $(y + z)(y' + z')$
    is the product-of-sums expression.

Chapter 6   The arithmetic element

3   ¼ would be stored 1.0100 in the magnitude system, 1.1011 in the 1's
    complement system, and 1.1100 in the 2's complement system.
5   $s = 1$ and $c = 1$
7   The sum will overflow the register and cause an incorrect addition.
    Most machines sense for this, and either stop and turn on an "addi-
    tion overflow" light or indicate the overflow in some manner.
9   During an addition, the sign bits would indicate whether the addend
    and augend should be routed through the adder or subtracter and
    the same thing applies if the numbers are to be subtracted. If the
    sign bit follows the numbers, the decision can only be made after
    the numbers have been circulated once, necessitating an additional
    pass.
11 0.0010
13 Shift left one 1.0011 $= -¾$
    Shift right one 1.1100 $= -\frac{3}{16}$
    Shift right two 1.1110 $= -\frac{1}{16}$
15 Overflow can occur only during division, not during multiplication.
    The product of two numbers, both with magnitude less than 1, must
    be less than 1. But ¼ divided into ½ equals 2, so overflow can occur
    during division.
17 Logical addition, 0.111011
    Logical multiplication, 0.100010
    Exclusive OR, 0.011001

Chapter 7   The memory element

1   143,360 cores
    12 flip-flops for address register
    35 flip-flops for memory buffer register
3   True, because only the selected cores are to be set to the 0 state and
    the sum of the x-line and y-line currents are sufficient.
5   *a.* 1
7   160 diodes for a 5-input flip-flop 32-output line matrix.
9   180,000
11 7 bits to address a track
    6 bits to address a sector
    13 bits to address a word
13 40 μsec
15 262,500 bits per sec

Chapter 8 Input-output devices

1 23 lines not counting any final carriage return
59 holes not counting final carriage return and not counting the "seventh hole" in each line. If the seventh hole is added in for each of the 23 lines the total will be 82 holes and this will correspond to the tape formed in Fig. 8 · 1.

3 27 holes in 3 cards. Easier to correct if cards are used, for erroneous cards may simply be replaced.

5

DECIMAL	EXCESS 3 CODE	EVEN PARITY CHECK	ODD PARITY CHECK
0	0011	0	1
1	0100	1	0
2	0101	0	1
3	0110	0	1
4	0111	1	0
5	1000	1	0
6	1001	0	1
7	1010	0	1
8	1011	1	0
9	1100	0	1

7 10—One such code can be formed by adding a leading 0 to each of the 4-binary-digit Gray code groups listed on page 286 and then adding another 167 rows with the four rightmost binary digits the same as those on page 286 and with a leading 1 added to each of these code groups. (Any permutation of the columns of a Gray code will yield another Gray code.)

9 0101 gives $+2\frac{2}{3}$ volts
1010 gives $+5\frac{1}{3}$ volts
1111 gives $+8$ volts

Chapter 9 Computer organization and control

1

S	OP code	index register	address
1 digit	5 digits	2 digits	14 digits

3

decimal digits

S	OP code	1st address	2nd address	3rd address
1 binary digit	2 digits	3 digits	3 digits	3 digits

5 The address of the next instruction is stored in the instruction word.

7 Sign
   bit 1↔11 12 ↔ 15 16 17 ⟵————⟶ 23 24 ⟵————⟶ 30

   | 0 0···0 0 1 1 1 0 0 1 1 1 1 0 0 0 1 1 0 0 0 0 |

   OP · · · · · track · · · · sector
   code · · · · · bits · · · · · bits

9 4 trips for an addition instruction.

11 Change each AC_0 to AC_0', each AC_0' to AC_0, and BRM to BRP.

13 8 phases

ADDRESS	INDEX REGISTER	OP CODE	ADDRESS PART
0	01	SIR	193
1	01	CAD	353
2	00	ADD	600
3	00	STO	600
4	00	BRI	1
5	00	HLT	0

15 353 thru 546 contain the numbers to be added.
   600 is the address at which the sum is stored. This address originally must contain 0.

ADDRESS	INDEX REGISTER	OP CODE	ADDRESS PART
0	01	SIR	5
1	01	CAD	300
2	00	MUL	310
3	00	STO	310
4	01	BRI	1
5	00	HLT	0

300 thru 305 contain numbers to be multiplied.
310 contains a 1.

17 62×10^4 is 0.5662000000
   26×10^6 is 0.5826000000
   The number with the smaller exponent must be shifted right a number of times equal to the difference in the exponents, so 62000000 is shifted right twice and 2 added to the exponent giving 0.5800620000. The mantissas are then added giving 0.5826620000 or 26.62×10^6.

Index

In his autobiography, Kareem Abdul-Jabbar describes the extraordinary impact Coach Wooden's confidence has had on his life:

> I don't know why fate placed me in his hands, but I'm grateful that it did. My relationship with him has been one of the most significant of my life. He believed in what he was doing and in what we were doing together. He had faith in us as players and as people. He was about winning basketball and winning as human beings. The consummate teacher, he taught us that doing the best you are capable of is victory enough, and that you can't walk until you can crawl, that gentle but profound truth about growing up.

Just as with poise, confidence is built from within. As it grows inside you, your impact on others amplifies. The challenge for many is that the feeling of confidence is fleeting. Often, we may feel confident and poised in one context, but insecure and full of doubt in others. How, then, can we build on our moments of confidence so we may carry that level of faith and trust within us consistently, regardless of the situation?

Activate Your Confidence Instantly

Years ago, I developed an exercise that can help you do precisely that. I call it the Personal Victory exercise because it is a process that enables you to tap into your past moments of supreme confidence, terrific energy, and sublime peace of mind, so that you can transfer those feelings into the present moment. Each of us has hundreds of these personal victories stored in our memories. These are triumphs in the Wooden sense because they do not require that you have defeated others. Instead, a victory is a moment of self-satisfaction in knowing you have given the best of which you are capable.

The Personal Victory exercise combines a specific visualization process with a technique called "anchoring" developed by Richard Bandler and John Grinder, the cofounders of a communication science known as Neuro-Linguistic Programming (NLP). I learned a great deal about anchoring from one of Grinder and Bandler's prize students, Anthony Robbins. In his early years as a therapist, Robbins used anchoring as an important technique to help clients overcome severe phobias or other debilitating emotional disorders. An "anchor" is a trigger for a conditioned emotional response to some stimulus in your environment. In his best-selling book *Unlimited Power* Robbins described the process of anchoring this way: "Whenever a person is in an intense state where the mind and body are strongly involved together and a specific stimulus is consistently and simultaneously provided at the peak of the state, the stimulus and the state become neurologically linked. Then, anytime the stimulus is provided, the intense state automatically results."

Anchors appear in various forms depending on which of our five senses receives the stimulus. For instance, flashing red and blue lights in your rearview mirror are vivid examples of visual anchors that can induce some instantaneous and intense emotions. The howl of the siren on the police car is an auditory anchor. Unique anchors that combine different modalities—such as visual, auditory, and kinesthetic (the sense of touch)— tend to be more powerful triggers, especially when they are associated with particularly strong emotional states. Anchoring is a natural process that occurs constantly and unconsciously in our lives. It is also a process that can be used deliberately and effectively as a powerful tool of influence. For example, when you understand the process of anchoring, you become immediately aware of how advertisers spend billions of dollars to set anchors they hope will create compelling associations to their products.

An "anchor" is a trigger for a conditioned emotional response to some stimulus in your environment.

You can also use anchoring to influence yourself. As I write this book, I am surrounded with a variety of very special anchors. My walls are filled with photos of my wife and children, my personal vision statement, a special drawing about a favorite story I shared with my swimmers when I was a coach, and the copy of Coach Wooden's Pyramid of Success that he gave me when I first interviewed him. When I work, I often play my favorite music. As soon as I hear the first few notes, I feel my spirit rise and my creative juices begin to flow. Each of these is a very powerful anchor that I associate to intense feelings of love, respect, inspiration, and leadership.

The Personal Victory exercise, however, arose in a moment not of inspiration but of panic! The idea came to me when I was about to make a presentation that would have a major impact on my family's future.

Putting Personal Victories to the Test

Five months earlier, I had left my job as vice president at Lynden Air Freight. I had not resigned in order to accept a position with another company. Instead, I had set out to design the future I wanted, in which I could devote my professional energy to my passion for training and team development. When I announced that I was leaving my secure job to invent something brand new, many of my friends and associates thought I had jumped off the diving board without first checking to see if there was any water in the pool! But, overflowing with the unbridled enthusiasm that gushes from within when you follow your heart, I immersed myself in developing a detailed business plan for an exciting new training enterprise. My partner and I spent five months preparing the plan. We had exhausted most of our savings to pursue our dream. We were about to put it all on the line in a presentation to the owner of the company with which we were seeking to join forces.

The presentation was set to begin at 11 A.M. At 11:20 the owner still had not arrived. Suddenly the phone in the conference room rang. I felt my heart leap into my throat! It was the owner's secretary. He would be delayed until 1:30 or 2, but hoped very much that we would be able to rearrange our schedules and move ahead with the presentation at that time. I told her that we understood how packed his schedule was and would be happy to wait until he was free. As I hung up the phone I joked to my partner that without a successful presentation today, we had no schedule to worry about!

We decided to stay put and go back over our notes rather than heading off for a bite to eat. As we began to review the material we had prepared I felt a massive rush of fear sweep over me. I hadn't felt this kind of nervous stomach since my days as a competitive swimmer. I had been primed to go at 11, but now I was beginning to second-guess every point I had planned to make. I actually began to tremble with anxiety.

Finally, I decided I had to do something to relax and regain my shaken confidence. In desperation, I began to write down short descriptions of experiences in my life when I had been at my best. Beside each description, I wrote three or four words that best expressed the emotions I felt about the experiences. In twenty minutes I jotted down about fifteen of these personal victories. They ranged from moments of accomplishment in business, the classroom, and athletics, to the unparalleled love and joy I felt on my wedding day and at the birth of my children. As I wrote, my fear began to subside almost as quickly as it had risen. I started to feel strong and confident once again.

Next, I went back to each description and visualized the experience as if it were happening all over again. As I put myself back into each personal victory, I began to feel the same vivid emotions as I had in the actual experience. It was incredible!

Create Your Personal Victory Anchor

When I felt strong emotion swell within me during each personal victory visualization, I squeezed my left wrist with my right thumb and index finger, clenched both fists tightly for just a moment, and loudly exclaimed the word, yes! with my inner voice. This unique sequence of squeeze, clench, and yes! became my personal victory anchor. I repeated this same anchoring process three or four times for each personal victory. In a short time, I had fully associated my new personal victory anchor to all of the empowering emotions the original events had stirred within me.

When the owner finally arrived and I felt a twinge of panic returning, I quickly fired my personal victory anchor—squeeze, clench, yes! Instantly I felt a resurgence of confidence and strength. The presentation went beautifully. More important, I had discovered a terrific method for enhancing my ability to be at my best—by choice and not by chance. Over the years, as new victories occur, I have continued to strengthen my anchor by associating them to my squeeze, clench, yes! ritual. In this way, I use each instance when I feel great internal satisfaction about my effort and focus as a springboard to greater confidence, poise, and, ultimately, peace of mind.

The Personal Victory Exercise

Step 1   Write a brief description of five to ten of your greatest personal victories—experiences when you felt you were at your very best. Beside each description list three or four emotion-charged words that best express your feelings about the personal victory.

Step 2   Create your own personal victory anchor similar to my squeeze, clench, yes! ritual. You strengthen the anchor by making it unique and combining visual, auditory, and kinesthetic elements. For example, you could create a personal victory anchor in which you picture the sun shining brightly (visual) at the same time as you shout the word *Now!* with your inner voice (auditory) and touch the points of your index fingers together (kinesthetic).

Step 3   Go back to each personal victory description and visualize the event as if it were actually happening right now. Feel the same emotions, breathe the same, and adopt the same physiology. Fully associate to the experience! When you feel your emotions surge, fire your personal victory anchor. Repeat this at least three times for each personal victory.

Step 4   Meet with a friend and share your personal victories with this person. Before you begin, show your personal victory anchor. When your friend sees you becoming fully associated to your personal victories, he or she is to signal you to again fire your personal victory anchor. Have great fun with this! Once you've gone all the way through your list, reverse roles.

Step 5   Try firing your personal victory anchor when you're in a neutral frame of mind, and notice the emotional impact.

Step 6 Add at least one personal victory to your list each day for thirty days and repeat steps 1 through 5. Use your personal victory anchor to buoy your confidence in situations where you previously doubted yourself.

16

Secret #15:

**Competitive
Greatness**

Together we have built your own personal pyramid, block by block, into a new model that incorporates the secrets of a winning life. In this new paradigm, winning no longer requires anyone else to lose. Instead, true success is peace of mind derived from the inner knowledge that we've given our very best. Coach Wooden made sports history by leading with this unique approach. In every leadership context, from business to family to social and spiritual causes, a similar impact is created when we merge the Stairway to Self-Leadership with the Leadership Triangle into this new model I call the *relay paradigm*. In this exciting environment of enabling trust and confidence, teammates automatically elevate their spirit from willingness to eagerness, and performance soars. The relay paradigm is the collective manifestation of the 15 Secrets.

During my years as a swim coach, I marveled at the remarkable transformation I saw in virtually every young athlete who participated in relay events. Over time, I began to think of relays as superteams. It made no difference whether the swimmers were stars or beginners. Something almost magical happened when they became part of a relay. It was as if every ounce of fear that held them back when they competed on their own turned into unstoppable positive energy when they joined their teammates for a relay event.

Something almost magical happened when these young athletes became part of a relay.

As a coach, I often puzzled over this powerful relay effect. Continually in relays, the kids dramatically improved their times in comparison to the identical event in individual competition. What was it about relays that enabled them to bring out their best? These were the same kids, in the same bodies, swimming the same distances. But something very special happened to their spirit when they knew they were performing as a team. Although relays were usually held at the very end of the competition, when you would logically expect the athletes to be physically spent, the improvement rate over their individual performances was well above 90 percent! As a coach and leader, if I could somehow help them access the same thoughts and emotions in their individual events that ignited them in relays, they would truly begin to tap into their potential.

For years I struggled to discover the explanation for the relay paradigm. Finally, the year after I left coaching, an event occurred that moved me so deeply that I finally became aware of the subtle differences that combine to create this special relay effect. To this day, much of my work centers around assisting clients to instill these important relay principles into the hearts of their organizations and families, and into their own spirit.

The Race of a Decade: U.S. vs. West Germany

The event that jolted my awareness of the relay paradigm took place during the Summer Olympics of 1984. I watched the Olympic swimming competition that year with very special interest. In my final few years as a coach, several of my swimmers participated in the National and Junior National Championships. At these elite events, my kids had competed side by side with the athletes who later qualified for the Olympic Swimming Team. Consequently, my swimmers and I knew most of the Olympians and their coaches. We felt a special kinship with these wonderful young people, having shared the same pool decks and the same dreams.

That year the Olympics were held in Los Angeles. A highly partisan, pro-American crowd filled the new Olympic swimming stadium on the campus of the University of Southern California. They had come to cheer for their heroes in the red, white, and blue. America had been the preeminent force in the sport of swimming since the days of Johnny Weissmuller and Duke Kahanamoku. By 1984, however, the rest of the world was catching up. In fact, at these Los Angeles Games, the dominant athlete in swimming was not from the United States, but from West Germany.

Remember Pablo Morales' rival? Michael Gross was known as "the Albatross." Standing 6'7" tall, he had perhaps the widest "wingspan" in swimming history. His arms fully extended from the fingertip of one hand to the fingertip of the other measured more than seven feet! In the water, he was a coach's dream. He had an incredibly efficient stroke, with remarkable power that took full advantage of his great height and reach. I marveled at his smooth, slow turnover. His stroke looked almost effortless as he opened huge leads over the other elite athletes. He was in a class by himself.

Gross's best event was the 200-meter freestyle. He won the individual event by two seconds—an immense margin at the Olympic level for that distance. He shattered the world record in the process, traveling the distance in

1:47.44. No other swimmer had ever cracked the 1:49 mark. Gross would soon have the opportunity to swim the two hundred meters once more when he anchored West Germany's 800-meter freestyle relay—the event that would finally awaken my deeper understanding of the relay paradigm.

Going into 1984, the United States had never lost the 800-meter freestyle relay in Olympic competition. With the Albatross poised to anchor the West German team, however, the U.S. found itself the underdog for the first time. The Germans not only had the unmatched talent of the Albatross—they also boasted the bronze medal winner from the 200-meter freestyle, who had been narrowly edged out for the silver by American Mike Heath. The final two swimmers for the German team were also solid, world-class performers.

With the Albatross poised to anchor the West German team, the U.S. found itself the underdog for the first time.

The U.S. relay team did not boast any superstars. It was a team of fascinating and diverse personalities and talents. The fastest American swimmer in the event was Mike Heath. I called him the Avis of swimming because his career seemed to mirror the car rental company's history. For years he had competed in the shadow of the great American freestyler, Rowdy Gaines. He had been near the top in many competitions at the national and collegiate level, but had never reached number one. Finally in 1984, Heath put it all together. He won the Olympic Trials with one of the fastest times in the world. Any other year, he would likely have been a gold medalist, an Olympic star. He was handsome, talented, and at the peak of his career. But this was the year of the Albatross. Heath gave his all but was a distant second to the German superstar.

The second U.S. swimmer in the relay had one of the great swimming names of all time: Jeff Float. Had the United States not boycotted the 1980 Olympics, Float could very well have become a household name on a par with Mark Spitz or Jesse Owens. At that time he was a twenty-one-year-old USC senior who was the finest all-around swimmer in the world. He would have been a strong contender for at least four gold medals had he been allowed to compete in the Moscow Games. Instead, that dream was taken away from him. Now, at twenty-five, he was the "old man" of the team. Somehow he had mustered the drive to come back from retirement and qualify for the team. (Float was also partially deaf and was quite possibly the greatest hearing-impaired athlete in the history of this country.)

Float was a special favorite of mine because of the way he had handled the injustice of the 1980 Olympic boycott and the other obstacles that had challenged him through the years. He was a very classy human being. Instead of harboring bitterness about the past, he was ecstatic to finally be competing in the Olympics. He had competed in the individual 200-meter event, but had missed earning a medal. This relay would be his last chance.

The third member of the relay was an up-and-coming swimmer from the University of Florida named Dave Larson. He had been a surprise to make the squad because he had always turned in his top performances in short-course intercollegiate competitions swum in 25-yard pools. But international competitions such as the Olympics are held in 50-meter pools, and he had yet to break through at that level.

The final U.S. relay member was the most unlikely of all. His name was Bruce Hayes. By swimming standards he was quite short, well under six feet tall. In the pool, he was pure guts. If the Albatross's powerful and efficient stroke was a coach's dream, Hayes' choppy, high RPM technique was a coach's nightmare. I called him the Thrasher, because instead of gliding effortlessly through the water, he willed himself along, bouncing and thrashing his way to an Olympic berth. As an ex-coach, I had phenomenal respect and admiration for this young man. No one had expected him to qualify for this relay team. His best events were the 400 and 1500 meters. Through pure heart and amazing determination he had made it.

Gambling on an Unusual Strategy

The stage was set for a historic relay event. On paper, West Germany appeared to have a decided edge. Seven of the eight swimmers from the two teams were within 1.3 seconds of one another. The eighth, the mighty

Albatross, was a full two seconds faster than his closest rival. That put him more than three seconds faster than our slowest swimmer, Bruce Hayes, alias the Thrasher.

Typically, most coaches employ a time-tested strategy for relays by positioning their fastest swimmer as the "anchor." This means the strongest swimmer swims the fourth and final leg of the relay. With Michael Gross poised for the anchor leg, West Germany looked truly formidable.

The second fastest swimmer generally swims in the lead-off spot. The strategy is aimed at firing up the middle two swimmers by putting them in a strong position for their relay legs. They get caught up in the emotion and often turn in extraordinary performances. Once again, West Germany was perfectly suited for this solid relay strategy. They looked to be in a power position heading into the middle legs of the relay with Thomas Fahrner, the bronze medal swimmer, leading off.

The United States, however, did not have the personnel for the standard game plan. The team simply did not appear to have an anchor who could match up to the Albatross. All four Americans had lifetime best times that were within about 1.1 seconds of one another. The coaches decided to scrap the normal strategy and go with a tactic called "runaway." This meant they would lead off with the fastest swimmer, followed by the second fastest, followed by the third fastest, and anchored by—you guessed it—the Thrasher. The thinking was that their best chance would be to build a huge lead and hang on!

Later, after the race, Bruce Hayes joked about the nightmares he had had before the Olympics. In Hayes' dreams, Gross stepped up onto the starting blocks and looked down on him with a confident smile, knowing the American lead going into the anchor leg was too little to hold him off. Then, in his dream, the Thrasher watched helplessly as the Albatross swooped right by him, leaving him in his wake. He never told his teammates about the dream. Instead he implored them, "Give me a four-second lead, and he won't catch me. Just give me those four seconds!"

When the event was ready to begin, the Germans were determined to end the U.S. dynasty in the 800-meter freestyle relay, and the Americans were equally determined to give the performances of their lives and keep the record intact. As the lead-off swimmers pierced the water it was a rematch of the race for the silver medal. By one hundred meters, Mike Heath and the German bronze medal winner, Fahrner, had already pulled away from the rest of the field. They were locked in a classic battle, stroke for stroke, churning for home. The U.S. hoped Heath could improve on the half-second margin he had built over his rival in the individual 200 meters. As he drove for the wall, Heath found one last burst from deep within and opened nearly a full second over his great German rival. Both had improved over their individual performances. *Something very special happens when you are part of a relay.*

As the second swimmers on each team dove into the water, the stadium crowd was already on its feet. An epic contest was taking shape. The U.S. and West German teams were more than four body lengths ahead of the third-place team and were pulling away. From the

Americans' perspective, so far, so good! The runaway strategy looked like it just might work.

But as the teams reached the midpoint of the race with two swimmers each remaining, the U.S. lead had dwindled to a little over a half second. West Germany's weakest swimmer had obliterated his previous best time by well over a second and a half. Again, every swimmer had posted a personal record. Relay magic was alive, but the American strategy now seemed in dire jeopardy with the great Albatross waiting in the wings.

The third leg was a real dogfight. Previous best times meant nothing now. Each swimmer exploded toward home with every ounce of energy and emotion. With only one pool length remaining before the anchor showdown between the Albatross and the Thrasher, the U.S. had again opened a slight lead. This was to be the last fifty meters in Jeff Float's swimming career. Always a phenomenal finisher, he somehow found the special reserve of a true champion. Head down and muscles pumping to the breaking point, he accelerated into the wall, having built the U.S. lead back up to 1.5 seconds. It was a heroic effort. Yet it did not appear to be nearly enough of a lead to hold off the Albatross.

Neck and Neck: the Albatross and the Thrasher

On the dive alone, Gross immediately cut Hayes' lead in half. He was already at Hayes' waist as he powered into his first arm stroke. By the first turn at fifty meters he had pulled practically even. The Thrasher was churning like a maniac. Head bobbing and arms flailing, he turned over twice for every stroke the Albatross took. It seemed to no avail as they turned at one hundred meters. The Albatross had now overtaken him and was beginning to pull away. Bruce Hayes' nightmare was coming true.

But something magical happens in a relay. On the third fifty meters, Hayes edged close to the lane line, right next to the Albatross. He began drafting with him, gaining momentum by latching on to Gross's great wake. The crowd was now in an utter frenzy. Miraculously, Hayes was staying close, hanging on with everything he had, only half a body length behind.

Something magical happens in a relay.

As they made the final turn for home with fifty meters to go, the roar of the crowd was deafening. Something magnificent was occurring. Incredibly, Hayes began to close the gap. Thrashing now like never before, he inched closer and closer. Would there be enough pool? Could he catch him? They were flying, drawing from each other a level of energy they never knew they possessed.

With ten meters to go they were dead even. They took a final breath and drove at the wall, summoning every drop of desire left in them. Together they lunged at the finish. It was too close to call. They whirled and looked up at the scoreboard clock. It was a new world record: U.S.A. 7:15.69; West Germany 7:15.73. Bruce Hayes had touched out the Albatross by four one-hundredths of a second!

As I sat there overcome with excitement, tears of pure joy and inspiration flowed down my cheeks. I was struck by what I had just seen. The Albatross, in defeat, had swum over one and a half seconds faster than his own world record. At a time when no other human had broken the 1:49 mark for 200 meters, I had just watched Michael Gross cover the distance in 1:45.9!

Only then did I realize what Bruce Hayes had accomplished. Going into the race with a best time of 1:50.4, he discovered within himself a level of competitive greatness he had never dreamed possible. He had swum his anchor leg in 1:47.3. The indomitable spirit of the relay had filled the Thrasher's heart and driven him to one of the greatest pressure performances in the history of the sport. It would take eight years before another American would swim as fast.

How to Bring the Spirit of the Relay Paradigm to Life

As I replayed that amazing scene over and over in my mind, I finally began to understand the principles at the heart of the relay paradigm. After years of searching for them, I was startled at their simplicity. The differences in attitude and belief between the Bruce Hayes who made history in that astonishing relay performance and the Bruce Hayes who finished fourth in the individual 200 meters at the United States Olympic Trials appear very subtle on the surface. Yet the magnitude of the change these differences inspire is immense. The shifts in attitude and belief are not confined to Olympic athletes. They are available to every person, on every team, at every moment. Great leaders can foster these special attitudes and beliefs within their organizations just as parents can build them into their families. All of us can choose to live in the spirit of the relay paradigm and unleash our true competitive greatness by making the commitment to adopt these principles as our own.

First and foremost, we must decide to create a higher level of certainty about our responsibility to our team than ever before. When Bruce Hayes swam in the individual 200 meters, he was determined to do well. He wanted to do his best for himself, his coaches, his parents, and his country. But when he dueled the Albatross in the Olympic relay, *he absolutely refused to let his teammates down*. It was no longer a matter of not wanting to disappoint his teammates. He absolutely refused! With every fiber of his body, mind, and spirit he cut off all possibility of failure. Deep within himself he found complete and utter certainty that whatever his team needed he would deliver.

This complete certainty about coming through, this absolute commitment to be responsible for your contribution to your team, does not ensure you will always win. Whether it's an athletic contest, your business, or raising your family, you cannot control others' performances. It simply means that you will tap into the hidden reservoir of your true potential that is unleashed only when you transform ego into "we go!" It means that you will no longer view obstacles as obstructions, but will use them as catapults to soar to the next level.

All of us can choose to live in the spirit of the relay paradigm and unleash our true competitive greatness by making the commitment to adopt these principles as our own.

As the Albatross and the Thrasher hurtled, stroke for stroke, down those last fifty meters, they drew from one another the very best they had to give. In a very real sense, each became his rival's most important teammate. Without the Albatross giving his greatest effort, the Thrasher would not have discovered what he was truly capable of. Without the Thrasher beside him, mounting the supreme challenge, the Albatross would never have swum so fast. Rather than sapping energy from one another, each gained new strength from his competitor.

With a shift to the relay paradigm, you no longer fear your competition. Filled with absolute certainty that you will come through for your team, you have accepted total responsibility for your contribution and performance.

You view your competitors not as threats, but instead as catalysts to help you bring out even more of your talent, energy, and determination. You do not want them to falter, because the greater their effort and concentration, the more energy and resolve you will derive from the challenge.

The third and final fundamental principle of the relay paradigm is the most important of all, for it fuels the fire of absolute certainty and inspires the transformation from feared competitor to supreme catalyst. It is at the very heart of every great team. Anthony Robbins expressed this principle very powerfully when he said, "Human beings will do more for a team than they will ever do by themselves." We are at our very best when we are devoted to a purpose that reaches beyond ourselves.

View your competitors not as threats, but instead as catalysts to help you bring out even more of your talent, energy, and determination.

When athletes participate in relays, they immediately feel that they are competing for much more than themselves. They are united in energy and focus. They know they are being counted on, and feel equally eager to count on their teammates. Most important, these feelings are proactive and based on trust, not contingent upon what happens as the event unfolds. The decision to completely devote themselves to the team is made before the event takes place. Every member of the team eagerly accepts ownership of the common cause. One of the most amazing paradoxes of human beings is that only through unselfishness can we discover our true selves. When we commit ourselves unselfishly to a cause that truly impacts others, we gain a freedom of spirit and action that bursts through previous self-imposed limits.

Coach Wooden defined competitive greatness as the ability to be at our best when our best is needed. When we combine the principles of the Stairway to Self-Leadership with those of the Leadership Triangle, the competitive greatness that is innately within each of us is unleashed. The relay paradigm emerges as our new leadership model, and we begin to view our efforts as valuable contributions to special relay teams such as our businesses, schools, and families. These teams, in turn, unite us in a global relay we all share called humanity. We recognize that we can choose to let go of antagonism and decide instead to view our competitors as cooperative catalysts, assisting us to draw forth our ultimate effort by giving theirs. With this decision we shift our focus from a short-term desire to defeat others to a long-term commitment to give our very best so that everyone may continually grow and feel successful. The relay paradigm shatters the misconception that success is by nature limited and scarce, and replaces it with the empowering belief that success is abundant and is constantly replenishing because *we human beings are far more connected than separate.* In this connection is the special magic of the relay paradigm. Never was this more vividly revealed to me than by the unforgettable story of a young woman named Annette.

Meeting Heavy Challenges with Resolute Courage

I met Annette when my business partner and I presented a two-day team-building seminar to a company that manufactures and markets highly specialized cardiac care equipment. The event was a reward for the company's sales team and held at a beautiful ski resort in Vermont.

After flying into Logan Field in Boston, we joined the team for the two-and-a-half-hour bus trip to the ski resort. It was a perfect opportunity to meet the participants and learn more about them before the seminar. As I settled into my seat I was greeted with the friendly smile of a young woman who was obviously very pregnant. She introduced herself as Annette, and we experienced an instantaneous, warm connection. My wife and I had welcomed our youngest daughter, Jenna, into the world only three weeks before, so I was still glowing with the unmatched joy of the new love in our lives. Annette was in the final two months of her pregnancy.

I noticed immediately that she was exceptionally fit for a woman who was seven months pregnant. I asked if she had been exercising regularly, and she explained that she was a serious long-distance runner. She had kept running right up through her second trimester. Only in the last month or so before this trip had she slowed down to brisk walks. When I asked her what she liked best about running, she replied that the discipline and concentration running demanded had helped her get through a very tough time over the past few years.

Her answer piqued my curiosity, so I asked if she would feel comfortable telling me what had made this such a challenging period in her life. I told her that it might help me make the seminar more meaningful for her and her teammates. She smiled and said, "Sure. I'd like to tell you about it." For the next two hours I sat spellbound as she shared her amazing story with me.

Three years earlier, she and her husband had been living their dreams. They were deeply in love and cherished every precious moment together. Professionally, they were each flourishing in careers they truly enjoyed. As a young executive on the fast track in the Pepsi Cola organization, he had risen rapidly through the corporate ranks and earned tremendous respect throughout the company as one of its finest young leaders. Annette, a highly energetic and nurturing person, reveled in the responsibility and fast pace of her work as an intensive care nurse.

Outside of work they were heavily involved in their church and enjoyed a rich and rewarding social life with family and friends. They had purchased a beautiful new home and had begun talking about starting a family.

Overnight, their world came crashing down. Without warning, Annette's husband was struck with a rare disease of the nervous system that plunged him deep into a coma. The doctors held little hope that he would ever come out of it.

But from the instant she rushed to the hospital and saw her husband lying unconscious in the intensive care ward, Annette was convinced that he would revive. It was more than a feeling of hope. She was completely certain. For the next twenty days she stayed by his side around the clock. She prayed beside him, read to him, talked with him, and never let go of her vision of him awakening and holding her close. Others tried to protect her from disappointment and prepare her for the worst. But no one could dissuade her from her belief that he would regain consciousness and that they would once again enjoy the wonderful life they had created together.

No one could dissuade her from her belief that she and her husband would once again enjoy the wonderful life they had created together.

Then, as unexpectedly as it had come, the coma lifted. She was there, as always, beside him when his eyes opened. She squeezed his hand tightly, as if refusing to ever let him go again now that he had returned to her. As his vision cleared, he saw the tears of joy that welled up in her eyes. It was a moment of indescribable love and happiness.

For several days he seemed to grow stronger and stronger. The doctors were encouraged but cautious. Annette and her husband could hardly wait to return home and dive back into their lives.

Then, in an instant, the floor dropped out from under them once again. He suffered a grand mal epileptic seizure, a sudden and terrifying episode of neurological disarray. The violent convulsions left him unconscious and utterly exhausted.

The Burden of Uncertainty

From that day forward, Annette and her husband lived in constant fear. The seizures continued to plague their every moment. Not a month went by without at least one grand mal episode. There was no pattern to their onset, no way to predict when the next attack would hit. The one certainty that tormented their lives was that the seizures would return.

He could no longer work because the seizures left him completely incapacitated. His company treated him extraordinarily well, providing him with generous disability income and leaving the door open should he fully recover. But, like an eagle without wings, his spirit was shattered. Accustomed to soaring, he had to learn to be content to walk.

For Annette, the stress from the relentless seizures proved almost unbearable. Unlike the empowering vision of his revival from the coma that had bolstered her spirit and solidified her positive belief, she could not let go of the nightmare of the seizures. Even when her husband gradually came to accept his new lifestyle and to feel genuinely grateful to be alive, Annette held onto a deep sense of sadness and loss. She could not understand why her incredibly bright and energetic husband had been stricken by this insidious disease. A deeply religious person, she frequently prayed for strength and guidance. Still, she often found herself feeling helpless and alone. With each new seizure her hope faded further. She tried her best to appear upbeat and vibrant, but inside she had begun to resign herself to a life of acquiescence rather than one of passion.

With their income sharply reduced, she made the painful decision to give up nursing for a potentially more lucrative medical sales opportunity. It had been a struggle at first, but through pure determination and effort she had started to make some real progress. Then, just when her sales commissions began to approach the salary she had earned as a nurse, she became pregnant.

The pregnancy came as a total shock to everyone. The doctors had explained to Annette and her husband early in his battle with the seizures that the odds of their conceiving a child were extremely minute because of the medication he took for his epilepsy and the devastation the seizures wreaked on his system. With such constant trepidation about his health, the thought of starting a family had all but disappeared. When he and Annette discovered she was pregnant, they called their baby the "miracle child."

Now, as the pregnancy moved into the final trimester, Annette felt as if she were on an emotional roller coaster, excited and hopeful about the birth one moment, then terribly anxious and worried about making ends meet the next. It was tough enough taking care of her husband while shouldering the bulk of their financial responsibilities. She wondered how she could possibly be a good mother with so many other important roles to play, then chided herself for her lapse of faith.

Just as we pulled into the resort, Annette finished telling me her story. I thanked her for her courage and honesty and told her that she was in the right place at the right time, because the seminar would be all about breaking through our greatest barriers as individuals and teams. She had already demonstrated great leadership so often during the turmoil of the past three years. Now, more than ever, her very best was needed. Somehow, I hoped that this event would help her rediscover the supreme poise and confidence that had carried her through the days when her husband lay comatose in the hospital.

Break Through with New Beliefs

The next day Annette was right in the thick of the action as we guided the group through a series of exercises and stories designed to draw them closer and closer together as a team. They were a marvelous group, wonderfully animated and eager to express their thoughts and feelings openly.

We ended the day with an incredible experience I learned from Anthony Robbins called the Board Breaking

Metaphor, where we taught participants in about an hour to break through a one-inch-thick pine board, karate style. It typically takes many months in a martial arts class before students even attempt this, but by focusing our instruction first on the key beliefs most necessary to break through before we even discuss the physical strategies, we are able to dramatically accelerate the process.

Board breaking provides a wonderful vehicle for helping people experience the amazing impact that belief has on performance. It is also an event that truly captures the unmatched emotion and almost magical synergy of a relay team.

As we prepare our students for breakthroughs, three beliefs stand out as the most critical to adopt if they are to accomplish their goal. First is the belief that success is not determined by whether or not you break the board, but simply by giving your best. You cannot be certain the board will break. But you can be completely certain that you will give your maximum effort with each attempt. It is the very same belief that guided Coach Wooden through-out his life and that gives the ultimate direction to leg-endary leadership.

We achieve our goals by focusing on what we want, not on what we don't want.

Second is the core belief that we achieve our goals by focusing on what we want, not on what we don't want. I have watched hundreds of participants fail to break their boards on their first or second attempts because at the last moment as they moved to strike, they shifted their eyes directly to the board. It didn't matter how strong they were or how hard they hit it. When they focused on the board it became as thick as the Great Wall of China. As soon as they adjusted their vision, however, and looked beyond the board to the other side of their barrier, they broke through almost effortlessly.

The third key belief is about the enabling power of human connection. When it is time to break the boards, we gather the team in a close circle around the instructor, who holds the board for each participant. Tremendous energy fills the room. One by one, the participants make the decision that they are ready to break through. As each individual steps into the center with the instructor, the team cheers wildly, chanting the board breaker's name and sending him or her incredible support. Everyone is completely present for the teammate in the center. In every board breaking session I have ever conducted, participants have commented that they felt certain that more than they alone broke the board. The total support of teammates filled them with a whole new level of positive spirit and belief. This is the third key belief: the *whole team* breaks through every board.

Just before we gather in our board breaking circle, participants give the board meaning by using it as a metaphor for a specific limit or fear that is somehow holding them back in their lives. They draw a picture or write a word or phrase on the front of their boards to represent what they want to break through. Perhaps they are petrified of public speaking, or unable to commit fully to a relationship. They may feel shackled by a physical challenge like an addiction to cigarettes or alcohol from which they deeply want to break free. Whatever they perceive is limiting them from true fulfillment, they represent on the front of the board. As soon as this is complete, we ask them to flip the boards over and describe on the other side what awaits them when they break through this limit or fear. This is the side they are going for.

Shattering the Last Barrier with the Power of the Team

When Annette received these instructions she didn't hesitate a moment. On the front of her board she spelled the word *seizures* in big, bold letters. On the reverse side she wrote, "Freedom, Peace, and Happiness."

Finally we joined together in our circle and began the board breaking. The support and spirit in the room was amazing as participant after participant stepped forward. Each breakthrough was celebrated with huge cheers and joyous group hugs. If anyone had harbored any doubts about the positive impact we have on one another when we join together as a genuine relay team, those doubts vanished now. It was crystal clear that when one person broke through, everyone broke through with them. Finally, only Annette remained.

As she stepped into the circle I understood the immensity of the obstacle she had represented. This was no longer a one-inch board, but a barrier of seemingly insurmountable proportions that blocked out virtually every last glint of hope. Although she was physically strong enough to break through three boards easily, she could not bring herself to focus on what she wanted. All she could see were the seizures.

She must have tried twenty times to break through that board, to no avail. Yet she refused to quit. The team rallied closer and closer around her, unwilling to give up as long as she persisted. I used every coaching technique I knew to help her shift her focus beyond the seizures to the freedom, peace, and happiness that awaited her on the other side. But still she could not take her eyes off the board.

Finally, one of her teammates stepped between us and wrapped her arms around Annette. She whispered a few quiet words of encouragement and hugged her once more. In that moment of extraordinary leadership and connection, she helped Annette rediscover the power of positive expectation. When Annette turned back to me, her eyes stared straight ahead into mine for the first time. I knew the board was history. In one last explosive effort she split the pine as if it were paper!

Instantly, the entire team swallowed her up in a magnificent embrace of love and connection. Tears of absolute joy flowed everywhere. No one wanted to leave. We stayed together for quite some time, soaking in the experience of special connection.

Annette's teammate helped her rediscover the power of positive expectation.

The next morning Annette excitedly explained a powerful realization that had occurred to her during the night. Throughout her husband's battle with the seizures she had felt utterly helpless and completely alone. She could only respond to the attacks, but did not see any way she could actively help her husband heal. But as she replayed the events of the night before over and over again in her mind, she remembered how much her team-mates' encouragement and support had lifted her and kept her from giving up. When her friend stepped into the circle and whispered to her, suddenly she realized that in a very real sense, everyone in the room had eager-ly accepted co-ownership of her challenge. She was no longer alone. Although she was the one who physically broke the board, they were completely with her in mind, body, and spirit. They sought no credit, wishing only that she feel their support and deep faith in her. Somehow she knew that she had broken through as much for her hus-band and her teammates as for herself.

When she woke up that morning she recognized for the first time that the seizures were as much hers as her husband's. Her constant fear and expectation blocked out any opportunity for her to focus on his recovery rather than his disease. Suddenly she believed that with her faith in God and the deep connection she felt with her husband, she could somehow make a difference. She could stop looking at him as a patient and instead see the soul mate she had chosen to spend the rest of her life with. She had rediscovered that in their combined power as a team, practically anything was possible.

Four months later I received a letter from Annette. Two miracles had transformed her life since her breakthrough at Killington. She had given birth to a beautiful, healthy baby boy who brought incredible new love and meaning to both her and her husband's lives. It was as if their hearts had somehow grown magically overnight.

What's more, in the last three months her husband had suffered no more seizures! No one knew why they had stopped, or if they would return. But to Annette and her husband, they now looked at the present moment as a fresh beginning. Whatever happened, they felt absolute certainty that together they could meet any challenge and grow stronger from it. They had discovered their true competitive greatness and the peace of mind that comes from knowing that when their best was called for, they were prepared.

Competitive greatness is a natural result of *enthusiastically and industriously* using the fifteen secrets that take us beyond success. As we climb to the top of the Stairway of Self-Leadership, we gain the *self-control, condition,* and *poise* to allow our true selves to flourish. Regardless of the situation, we will be ourselves. This is the essence of leadership by example, the internal manifestation of winning leadership. We let go of the need to win or hunger to control or impress others, and instead focus on the self-satisfaction and peace of mind that grow within us when we know in our own hearts that we have given our finest effort.

> **They had discovered the peace of mind that comes from knowing that when their best was called for, they were prepared.**

We have learned that as important as self-leadership is, only when we bring others into our lives can we discover our ultimate strength. The *confidence* we find at the apex of the Leadership Triangle enables us to become consistent, positive Pygmalions because it is as strong for others as it is for ourselves. With a foundation of *friendship, loyalty,* and *cooperation,* we constantly seek to bring out the finest in our teammates and *enthusiastically* enjoy the process of sparking great synergy. We become servant leaders when we move beyond the need to compare and look instead for creative ways to help others unlock their true potential. Thus, our *intent* extends beyond ourselves, to make a positive difference for someone else. We eagerly sacrifice the desire for personal glory, for the welfare of all. Inspired by this unselfish *team spirit,* we are *alert* for opportunities to both learn and give because we know a great leader is as much a student as a teacher. This openness frees us to use our *initiative* and constantly improve our effectiveness as leaders through the five master *skills* of winning leadership: flexibility, enabling questioning, visualization, letting go, and expressing ourselves with dimension. With patience, faith, and determination to remain truly present for ourselves and others, we are rewarded with the peace of mind that is at the heart of a winning life.

**Only when we bring others
into our lives
can we discover
our ultimate strength.**

The fifteen secrets provide us with something very special: a practical blueprint to guide us as we build outstanding leadership. Now more than ever, it is essential that each of us recognizes that we are all leaders. In 1988 as he received the Nobel Peace Prize, the Dalai Lama characterized our global family as "the pivotal generation." The decisions we make each day are becoming increasingly critical to the preservation of our environment and to the opportunity for our children to live in a world of peace, vitality, and harmony. Perhaps no decision is more important than applying yourself conscientiously to developing the leadership qualities represented by each of the fifteen secrets. With this pivotal choice you accept personal responsibility for making a genuine difference in the world.

The path to becoming a winning leader—fostering the relay paradigm in every team of which you are a part, from your family to your business to humanity—is not always easy. Obstacles and impediments will often challenge your resolve and occasionally demand resiliency. But the simple decision to be a leader sets you in motion and provides the opportunity for valuable feedback along the way. As you receive this input, the fifteen secrets can serve you as extremely valuable tools with which you can instill the relay paradigm in yourself and your teammates. Use these secrets to help you focus specifically on the areas most pertinent to your present needs and to reinforce important steps you have already taken in your leadership development.

Now . . . It's Up to You!

My greatest goal for this book is that you consistently apply the principles and skills of the fifteen secrets in your life. This requires more than just being interested in these ideas. It means you must commit to living them. With each step you take, you will experience the sublime reward of knowing you've given your best. And, if you persevere like the starfish thrower, others will be compelled to join you.

So how do you make this book more than an enjoyable reading experience? Use it as a transformation springboard to a new level of leadership, team building, and energy in your life and your business. Here is a simple ten-step action plan to help you get started now using the fifteen secrets as you bring the relay paradigm to life.

The Relay Paradigm Ten-Step Action Plan

Step 1   Write a *personal dedication statement* devoting your purpose and mission to a team that extends beyond yourself. This is a powerful way to create a compelling vision of your own relay team. As you write, remember the story of Pablo Morales and the profound inspiration and strength he derived from his dedication to his mother. In a very real sense, this book is a tangible result of my own personal dedication statement, which continues to inspire me each and every moment:

> Through openness and appreciation of new ideas I will live with genuine peace of mind. I seek to understand, to learn, and above all to care, rather than to have to be right. I will have great fun by continually creating and growing. As I move forward in life centered on these fundamental principles, I will both exude and inspire gentleness of spirit. I will constantly give and will happily and gratefully receive. In this way I will bring people together. I will express my

unceasing love and devotion to Carole, Kelsey, and Jenna by being truly present with them whenever they seek my presence. I will fuel my alignment with my mission by living at an extraordinary level of energy. Most important, I will be true to myself. This will enable me to lead by example without seeking credit. My reward for commitment to the principles of my mission will be a joy for life that will make a positive difference for my family and my fellow man.

Once you've written your personal dedication statement, post it where you will see it daily or keep it with you for inspiration in the same way Coach Wooden carries his seven-point creed. This could become the single most important key to unleashing more of your true potential than you ever thought possible.

Step 2   Use the Team Possibility Workshop format (described in chapter 5) to organize your family or work team into a community-service project action team. Perform the project within the next ninety days. Remember the three simple steps you can use to transform slow, burdensome sessions into energized and effective meetings: brainstorming, prioritization, and action commitments.

Step 3   One of the best ways to learn is to teach. Within the next two weeks, share in detail with at least two friends or business associates the principles and ideas you gathered from this book. As you discuss each of the fifteen secrets add your own stories, analogies, and personal experiences to further enrich your understanding and application of *Beyond Success* principles.

Step 4   Identify at least three situations in which you see that subgrouping is detracting from your business or family by separating rather than connecting. Write down a specific action plan to break through to a new level of cooperation for each of the three situations. You will be using your initiative as a "starfish thrower" in a very important way.

Situation 1   _____

Situation 2   _____

Situation 3   _____

Step 5   Identify at least three situations in which you have blamed others or have created a habit of blame. These can be as minor as becoming irritated at other drivers in traffic. Include at least one situation in which you blame a person you deeply care about. Become a blame buster by shifting from blame to positive win-win solutions.

Situation   Solution

1. _____   _____

2. _____   _____

3. _____   _____

Step 6 Energy and enthusiasm are unbelievably powerful. Speak to at least ten people in the next ten days with passion and enthusiasm about a leadership principle or skill you are committed to mastering.

Step 7 Choose the single most important person in your life to be more *present* with over the next thirty days. When you are together, devote your full attention to this individual—letting go of the need for approval or control. Simply be present in body, mind, and spirit. Make this your top priority.

Step 8 Select five people with whom you sincerely want to build a successful business or personal team. Over the next thirty days, spend at least ten minutes twice a week being completely present with them, offering support, brain-storming, surprising them, planning together, or just listening.

Step 9 Once each week, set aside a fifteen-minute block of *alertness activating time* for uninterrupted observation of others. You will gain new insights about your teammates that will enable you to serve them and connect with them better than ever before.

Step 10 Identify an individual or team to whom you are committed to becoming a truly positive Pygmalion. Write down five specific actions you will take in the next thirty days to carry out this commitment. Your heightened belief in others will magnetically pull them in the direction of your expectations.

The person or team to whom I commit to being a Pygmalion:

_____

My five specific actions:

Action 1 _____

Action 2 _____

Action 3 _____

Action 4 _____

Action 5 _____

With each of these ten steps you will strengthen the foundation of your personal Pyramid of Success so that you can continue to build on it throughout your life. The key is to focus on what you want and to realize that the magic ingredient of complete success is a complete effort. Coach Wooden, Mahatma Gandhi, the Kaufman family, and Jackie Robinson all personify this simple yet inspiring truth. Their unparalleled achievements are indisputable proof that by concentrating on elements of performance that you can control—your enthusiasm, cooperation, loyalty, friendship, industriousness, intentness, initiative, alertness, self-control, team spirit, skill, condition, poise, and confidence—you can achieve true competitive greatness and elevate yourself beyond success. I will always remember the answer Coach Wooden gave when I asked how he had compiled such an amazing winning percentage without ever once talking with his players about winning and losing. With a twinkle in his eye he smiled and said, "When you leave perfection to God and strive instead to be your best, the score has a funny way of coming out the way you want it to most of the time!"

Like the quiet Frenchman Elzea Bufiér who created a flourishing forest from utter desolation, each day you plant seeds for the future. Yours are the seeds of hope, peace, love, and caring. Not all will sprout. But bit by bit, you too can create a miracle. As Coach Wooden says,

"Learn as if you were to live forever; live as if you were to die tomorrow." You are important. In every precious moment, remember there is an incredible Allison factor within you and your team—ready to shine.

May the wind be always at your back.

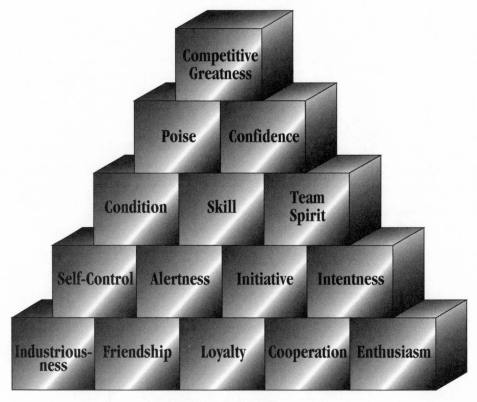

The Pyramid of Success

About the Author

As the founder of CLASS (Coaching, Leadership, and Synergy Services) Brian D. Biro is, above all, a team builder dedicated to assisting organizations in developing the remarkable leadership potential of people already working together. Believing that each of us has special qualities and capabilities that we have yet to fully apply, he acts as a dynamic catalyst for unleashing these hidden talents.

Since his graduation from Stanford University in 1976, Mr. Biro has concentrated his professional efforts on learning the secrets to extraordinary team synergy. As a United States Swimming coach who built a small private team into one of the largest in America, he helped guide young men and women to top berths both at the United States National Championships and U.S. Junior Nationals. Upon earning his master's degree in business administration from UCLA, he was recruited into the transportation industry in the Pacific Northwest where, as vice president of performance planning, he used the principles he now teaches in seminars across the nation to help engineer a dramatic turnaround that resulted in 300 percent growth in only three years. Later he joined forces with internationally renowned speaker and author Anthony Robbins to head Robbins' training and development franchise division. During that time, he also spearheaded a new division targeted specifically to Fortune 100 clients such as Digital Equipment Corporation, Martin Marietta Energy Systems, Southwestern Bell, AT&T, and GTE. His extensive consulting work with Cell Tech has helped the network marketing company become the unquestioned leader in its field, growing over 300 percent in its thirteenth year of business.

His principles of quality coaching, leadership, and team synergy plus a dynamic on-stage personality have earned Mr. Biro a reputation for warmth, enthusiasm, inspiration, and sincere commitment to making important contributions to every organization and individual he serves.

He lives in Hamilton, Montana, with his wife, Carole, and their daughters, Kelsey and Jenna.

If you're committed to living
Beyond Success, you'll want to take
advantage of these powerful resources
from Brian D. Biro . . .

Share the 15 Secrets with others:
***Beyond Success* is the perfect gift!**

Beyond Success: The 15 Secrets of a Winning Life! is that most rare of gifts—one with value to last a lifetime. When you give *Beyond Success* to family, friends, or business associates, you help them discover and expand the special qualities within them. If you found new clarity, inspiration, and understanding in this book, think of how you'll feel to share these gifts with others. Like Pygmalion, when you accept the responsibility to enrich others' lives, you can't help but enrich your own. Stock up now for birthdays, holidays, or just to show how much you care.

For Brian D. Biro products,
please visit your local bookstore,
or you may call 1-800-618-0551.

Beyond Success on Audiocassette

If you loved *Beyond Success: The 15 Secrets of a Winning Life!* as a book, just wait until you hear it on audiocassette! Now you can listen to Brian D. Biro as he personally shares the 15 Secrets with you via the magic of audiocassette. Every time you listen to these life-changing tapes you'll discover something new that is just what you're looking for to bring greater balance, love, and confidence to your life. Brian is one of America's great storytellers and teachers, sure to delight and inspire you. Purchase volumes individually or you can buy the complete unabridged book on audiocassette.

Code 3001: **Beyond Success** (unabridged book on audiocassettes)

Code 3011: **Volume 1:** Pygmalion, Vision, and Character

Code 3012: **Volume 2:** Enthusiasm, Industriousness, Friendship, Cooperation, and Loyalty

Code 3013: **Volume 3:** Self-Control, Alertness, Initiative, and Intentness

Code 3014: **Volume 4:** Condition, Skill, and Team Spirit

Code 3015: **Volume 5:** Poise, Confidence, and Competitive Greatness

Another audio from the author of Beyond Success!

"Four Changing Paradigms for a New Millennium"

Announcing a brand new audiocassette from Brian D. Biro introducing an exciting opportunity for greater health, hope, and freedom. All of us would soar to new heights if we felt more energy, mental clarity, and possibility each and every day. There are ways to bring these into our lives more fully. Part of the puzzle is better nutrition. Part is unceasing, unconditional love. And all of it begins with the decision to take action.

Enjoy this powerful audiocassette and know that there is always the opportunity for greater health, hope, and freedom for you and those you love.

Code 3010:   "Four Changing Paradigms for a New Millennium"

A picture really is worth 1,000 words!

Video Tapes from *Beyond Success* Author Brian D. Biro

Enjoy one of today's most inspiring, heartwarming, and dynamic speakers right in your own living room with the "Triumphs of Transformation" videos. You'll find yourself bursting with new vitality and belief as Brian D. Biro shares his stories of transformation, love, and discovery. There is unlimited potential within each of us to make a lasting difference for ourselves and others. The "Triumphs of Transformation" videos are treasures to enjoy again and again. Order today and remember to share the Triumphs as a special gift with those you love.

Purchase volumes individually or as a two-volume video set!

Code 4001: **"Triumphs of Transformation" video set**
(both volumes)

Code 4010: **Volume 1:** The Allison Factor—Awakening the Pygmalion Spirit

Code 4011: **Volume 2:** Intervention

Special Reports from Brian D. Biro

These information-packed special reports provide valuable insights and solutions to challenges facing you every day at home, at work, and within yourself. These reports will help you become the communicator, the coach, and the champion you truly are. Purchase reports individually or all four as one package.

Code 2001:   **Special Reports package** (all four reports)

Code 2010:   **Special Report 1:** Meetings that Work!
Save time and build momentum with the Team Possibility Meeting Method.

Code 2011:   **Special Report 2:** Brian's interview with the Wizard of Westwood, Coach John Wooden.
An unmatched guide to quality coaching.

Code 2012:   **Special Report 3:** The Magic of Enabling Questions. Outstanding leadership is more about questions than answers. Learn how to bring out the best in yourself and others through questions that ignite resourcefulness, creativity, and understanding.

Code 2013:   **Special Report 4:** Communicating in Times of Stress. How do you help others feel supported and strengthened during difficult times? What are the key ingredients in communication that enable you to replace uncertainty and doubt with renewed faith and confidence? In this Special Report you will learn simple, clear, and effective communication strategies to transform crises into opportunities.

Unparalleled Team-Building Events: Seminars from Brian D. Biro

Lasting success today and in the future will be determined by the level of communication, support, and synergy you build into your organization's spirit. Coach John Wooden, the UCLA basketball legend once said,

> *"The difference between good teams and great teams can best be summed up by the difference between two words:* willing *and* eager. *On good or average teams the players, coaches, and support crew are 'willing' to help each other. But willing means they'll do it reluctantly without full enthusiasm. On great teams, everyone is completely united in their eagerness to do whatever it takes to support one another."*

There is simply nothing more important to the growth and future of your business than developing greater passion and understanding of team, and the ability to communicate effectively, compassionately, and vibrantly as leaders. Carl Lewis, the great Olympic track and field athlete, expressed the kind of winning mind-set you are looking to instill in your team when he said, "I love being depended on and I love depending on my teammates." This is the tremendously empowering message of Brian's seminars—programs that will help transform your organization from a group of talented but separate individuals into a cohesive, connected, and synergized team.